discovering
science

Continuity and change

9

Photos on title page   The peppered moth (*Biston betularia*). Top left: the typical form and the *carbonaria* form seen against the bark of a tree from a rural area. Bottom right: the typical form and the *carbonaria* form seen against the bark of a tree from an industrialized area. The relative abundances of the two forms have varied with changes in levels of atmospheric pollution

The Open University, Walton Hall, Milton Keynes MK7 6AA

First published 1998

Written, edited, designed and typeset by the Open University.

Printed and bound in the United Kingdom by Jarrold Book Printing, Norfolk, England.

ISBN 0 7492 8195 2

This text forms part of an Open University course, S103 *Discovering Science*. The complete list of texts that make up this course can be found on the back cover. Details of this and other Open University courses can be obtained from the Course Reservations and Sales Office, PO Box 724, The Open University, Milton Keynes MK7 6ZS, United Kingdom: tel. (00 44) 1908 653231.

For availability of this or other course components, contact Open University Worldwide Ltd, The Berrill Building, Walton Hall, Milton Keynes MK1 6AA, United Kingdom: tel. (00 44) 1908 858585, fax (00 44) 1908 858787, e-mail ouwenq@open.ac.uk. Alternatively, much useful course information can be obtained from the Open University's website http://www.open.ac.uk

s103block9i1.1

Contents

Introduction

The most striking thing about the living world is its sheer diversity (a concept introduced in Block 4). Among the 30 million or so different species there is great variation in size, form, life cycle and habitat. For example, an adult blue whale of about 1 000 tonnes (10^9 g) is around 10^{21} times more massive than a bacterium, at a mere 10^{-12} g. The difference in form between a bacterium, a whale and an oak tree requires little comment, and likewise the asexual reproduction of bacteria, which can double their number every 30 minutes or so, is obviously different from the reproduction of mammals, such as ourselves, that produce one or a few offspring by a sexual process involving months of gestation and years of maturation. And, as far as habitat is concerned, whether you look at the South Pole, or deep-ocean hydrothermal smokers with temperatures of around 300 °C, or suburban Britain, living organisms can usually be found. Few, if any, environments have proven too hostile for some species or other to colonize. Given such diversity, one inevitable question is: 'what do different species have in common?'

A relatively simple answer is that living organisms have three things in common — they share the three attributes of life (Block 4, Section 2): (a) they are composed of cells, each of which carries out *metabolism*; (b) they *grow*; and (c) they are capable of *reproduction*. All living organisms are made up of cells, whether a single cell as in the case of, say, most bacteria and most protoctists, or around 10^{14} cells which is typical of plants and animals, such as oak trees and humans. Furthermore, all living organisms have a shared history to some degree or other, that is, some ancestry in common. This concept of shared ancestry is of fundamental importance to the principles of inheritance and a central tenet of the theory of evolution. All living organisms derive, ultimately, from a single primitive ancestor that arose out of the pre-biotic (literally 'before life') phase of the Earth's history, some 4 billion years ago. In other words, although species *change* they are *continuously* linked through their relatedness. Thus, if we are to understand what unites living organisms, we must examine in more detail the shared features — cells and ancestry — and this is what Block 9 sets out to do.

In Sections 2–7, we look at *cell biology*. In particular, we begin by asking: 'what features of cells are central to life?' This leads us into cell *biochemistry*, the molecular components and chemical reactions characteristic of living cells. Then, in Sections 8 and 9, we focus on how information is passed down from generation to generation; this is the province of *genetics*. Sections 10–12 look at the molecules involved in inheritance, an area often termed *molecular genetics*. In Sections 13 and 14, we move on to consider longer-term ancestry, and the forces that have shaped, and continue to shape, the living world — the study of *evolution* (introduced in Block 4, Sections 9–11). The block ends with a brief Section 15, in which we review the various levels of explanation (Block 4, Section 12) and their interrelationships in the study of living organisms.

By following the path outlined above, we will be moving through different levels of biological explanation. We begin with *small molecules* and look at how these are built into *polymers* that both form the structures of each *cell* and carry out the vital functions within the cell. The largest of these polymers is DNA, which carries information in units called genes. *Whole living organisms*, whether oak trees, humans or bacteria, pass to their offspring copies of their genes, and these carry the information and specification for building cells, and thus more living organisms, from materials in the environment. So we will be examining the genes, which link generations through their continuity. Finally, we return to evolution — genetic change over time — which acts on *populations of organisms* and which shapes species.

This block emphasizes a very important skill: the ability to relate knowledge and concepts both within and between the different sections of the block and with other blocks of the course. In addition, you will be asked to produce summaries, which will be useful both for assessing your progress and for revision purposes. You will also make critical assessments of your writing, plan a long account on a particular scientific topic and work with the mathematics of probability and chance.

Activity 1.1   *Quantifying mortality factors in the holly leaf miner: Part 2*

During your study of this block you should complete the practical work, introduced in Block 4, Activity 8.1, on the holly leaf miner, which by late June will have completed its life cycle. This practical work, and the biology behind it, is supported by a CD-ROM activity. Now would be a good time to plan when to do this work. ◀

2 Cells

The cell is the basic unit of all living organisms. Yet there is a very wide range of cell types, so the cell exemplifies unity within diversity. This section begins by considering the structure of cells, building on what you know already from Block 4. We then look at cell diversity, and discuss how the structure of cells is related to their function. Finally, we examine an hypothesis that provides a unifying concept to account for the evolutionary relationships of all types of cell.

Activity 2.1 Revision: cells and classification of organisms

This activity will enable you to revise the major concepts and key terms introduced in Block 4, on which this section builds. It also gives hints on revision. ◀

2.1 Cell structure

Cells have many components in common, and we will explore these by examining three basic cell types: animal cells, plant cells and prokaryote cells. A comparison of these three types of cell will also reveal differences between them.

Look at Figure 2.1, which shows views through a microscope of two 'slices', or *sections*, of material taken from different parts of the body of a mammal. Note that both are made up of many cells but also have areas without cells. If you were to examine material from other parts of an animal, say from bone, brain or muscle, you would see that these too are composed of cells.

○ What features are common to the cells in both Figures 2.1a and b?

○ Each cell contains a round or ovoid, dark object (the nucleus), and is bounded by a cell membrane. Outside the nucleus, but contained within the cell membrane, is the cytoplasm.

We have now identified several key features which typify a eukaryote cell: each has an outer, boundary cell membrane, which encloses grainy cytoplasm and the nucleus. In photographs such as those in Figure 2.1 there is not much more detail that can be discerned. These photographs have been taken using a light microscope and are called *light micrographs*. In order to see greater detail we need to examine *electron micrographs*, i.e. photographs taken with an electron microscope, which can enlarge images to a much greater magnification, as described in Box 2.1, *Microscopy*.

Box 2.1 Microscopy

Virtually all cells are too small to be seen by the unaided eye. Therefore, in order to visualize cells and examine their external form and internal details, they have to be enlarged, or magnified, using microscopes. There are two principal types of microscopy, which differ in the ways that images are viewed: light microscopy and electron microscopy.

In light microscopy, an object to be examined is illuminated by placing it in a beam of light. The beam of light passes through the object and then through a series of lenses, which magnify the object. The beam of light then reaches the eye of the observer; the magnified image is viewed directly by the eye. Using this technique, certain living cells can be examined: those of unicellular

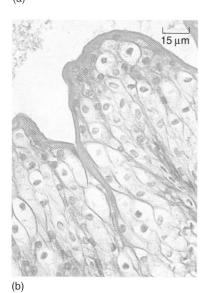

(a)

(b)

Figure 2.1 Sections of cells from (a) a kidney and (b) a ureter (the tube through which urine passes from the kidney to the bladder); both are from a mammal. Note that the colours are not the natural colours of the cells shown, but result from the treatment of the cells with coloured stains.

organisms or those from very thin sections of multicellular organisms. Whatever the source of the material, it has to be thin enough for light to pass through it. So, for example, you cannot examine the cells in your finger or from a large piece of a plant leaf by simply placing the finger or leaf under the microscope, because light cannot travel through such material.

Most cells in their natural state are almost invisible under a light microscope. More detail can be seen by staining the cells with dyes, although this treatment immobilizes and kills them. For example, a thin slice, a section, can be cut from a plant leaf or a part of an animal, and this section can be treated with dyes that preferentially stain particular parts or features of the cell. The cells shown in Figure 2.1 are from thin sections that have been treated with a stain that specifically adds colour to cell nuclei. Only the large-scale structure of cells (i.e. their size and shape) can be observed in living cells examined by light

microscopy, which can enlarge, or magnify, an image up to 1 500 times.

To study the detail of individual features within cells, greater magnification is needed, and this is achieved using electron microscopy. Objects can be enlarged up to a million times by an electron microscope — nearly 700 times greater than the maximum possible with a light microscope. Unfortunately, because of the need to dry and stain the material for examination by electron microscopy, only dead cells can be observed. In an electron microscope, instead of shining a beam of light through an object, a beam of electrons is fired at it, and the electrons that are transmitted through the section, or reflected off its surface, are collected and viewed on a screen. Figure 2.2a is a photograph of an electron microscope image (an *electron micrograph*) showing a section of an animal cell and parts of other cells that surround it. Compare this with Figure 2.1 and you will appreciate how much more detail can be seen using electron microscopy; surface features of cells as well as internal structures can be identified.

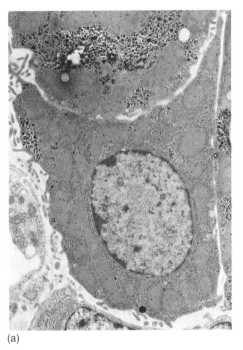

(a)

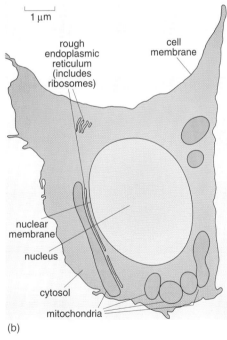

1 µm

rough endoplasmic reticulum (includes ribosomes)

cell membrane

nuclear membrane

nucleus

cytosol

mitochondria

(b)

Figure 2.2   (a) An electron micrograph of part of a section of chick (*Gallus domesticus*) liver. One complete cell can be seen in the middle of the picture and parts of the adjacent cells are also visible. (b) A drawing of the cell shown in (a) with the key features identified.

Figure 2.2b is a drawing of the same cell as that in Figure 2.2a, and highlights the key features. It is important to realize that this shows just one section through a cell, so all that we are seeing is a two-dimensional slice of a three-dimensional object. We will look at each of the key features of this cell in turn.

The cell is bounded by a cell membrane, which, as you can see from Figure 2.2b, can be folded and convoluted. The most prominent feature of the cell is the central nucleus, which contains the DNA, the genetic material. The nucleus, like the cell itself, is bounded by a membrane, the *nuclear membrane*. The presence of a nucleus means that this is a eukaryote cell (Block 4, Section 3).

The nucleus is the largest of several membrane-bound cell components, called **organelles**. Outside the nucleus other organelles can be seen. The most prominent of these are the **mitochondria** (pronounced 'my-toe-kon-dree-a'; singular mitochondrion). These vary in size and shape, being either spherical or sausage-shaped, but in Figure 2.2 they are shown in section and appear mainly as circles. Not only do mitochondria have an outer membrane, but they also have a highly convoluted internal membrane. The mitochondrion is often described as the 'power-house of the cell'; this is because it is within this organelle that energy is transferred to a form that can be used by the cell, as will be described in Section 5.

Another structure composed of membranes is identified in Figure 2.2b, namely **rough endoplasmic reticulum**. This is membrane material organized into sack-like or sheet-like structures. Rough endoplasmic reticulum has a granular appearance because of the attachment to its surface of many small, roughly spherical particles; these are known as **ribosomes** (pronounced 'rye-bo-zome-s'). It is on the ribosomes that protein synthesis takes place. You will learn about this process in Section 11.

Membranes are key features of cell organelles and serve as partitions between different regions of the cell; thus a cell can be viewed as a series of separate but linked compartments. The partitioning enables some cell functions to be restricted to particular parts of the cell, as will be revealed when we examine cell metabolism in Sections 5 and 6. You have met two examples of cell compartmentation already: energy metabolism within the mitochondria and protein synthesis on the ribosomes attached to the rough endoplasmic reticulum.

Another cell component is the *cytoplasm*. This is all the material outside the nucleus and contained within the cell membrane, so includes all the organelles, internal membranes and ribosomes. The gel-like liquid that remains when rough endoplasmic reticulum, mitochondria and all other subcellular structures have been removed is termed the **cytosol** (Figure 2.2b).

The scale bar in Figure 2.2b represents a length of 1 μm (10^{-6} m).

○ What is the horizontal diameter of the nucleus shown in Figure 2.2a? Give your answer in both micrometres and metres.

○ The nucleus is about three times wider than the scale bar, so it is about 3 μm, i.e. 3×10^{-6} m, in diameter.

So far, we have described the principal features of a typical animal cell. We will now consider a plant cell, shown in Figure 2.3.

○ What features are common to both the animal cell in Figure 2.2 and the plant cell in Figure 2.3?

○ Cell membrane, cytosol, nucleus, and nuclear membrane. (Rough endoplasmic reticulum and mitochondria are also present in plant cells, but are not visible in Figure 2.3.)

Having identified the similarities between an animal and a plant cell, let us now contrast the two types of cell.

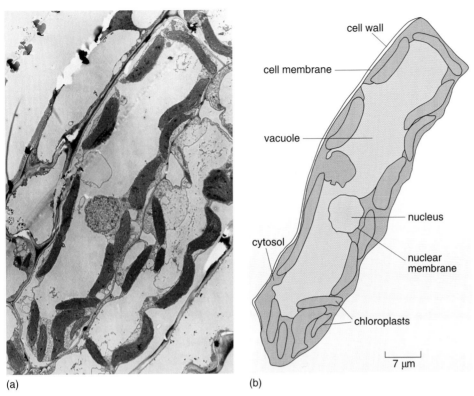

(a)   (b)

Figure 2.3   (a) Electron micrograph of a section of part of a maize (*Zea mays*) leaf. (b) A drawing of the one of the cells shown in (a) with the key features identified.

⬤   Which of the features labelled on the drawing of the plant cell (Figure 2.3b) are absent from the animal cell in Figure 2.2?

◯   Cell wall, chloroplasts and vacuole.

These three features are found in most plant cells. The rigid **cell wall** occurs just outside the cell membrane. It is made of fibres of cellulose (described in Section 3) held together by a glue-like substance, and helps to maintain the shape of the cell. The **chloroplasts** are organelles which, like mitochondria, are bounded by a membrane, but also have complex internal membranes. These are the organelles where photosynthesis occurs, a process which is discussed in Section 6. Finally, occupying most of the cell volume, there is a **vacuole** filled with a watery solution and bounded by a membrane. The large vacuole helps to maintain the shape of the cell; it also acts as a store for water, other small molecules and ions, as well as waste products. Vacuoles can also occur in animal cells, but here they are generally small.

The two types of cell we have considered so far are both eukaryote cells. Our third basic cell type is the prokaryote cell shown in Figure 2.4.

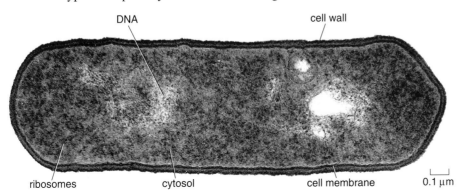

Figure 2.4   An electron micrograph of a section through a prokaryote cell, the bacterium *Bacillus subtilis*.

○ What is the main feature that distinguishes the prokaryote cell (Figure 2.4) from the eukaryote cells shown in Figures 2.2 and 2.3?

○ The prokaryote cell lacks a nucleus.

The prokaryote cell also lacks membrane-bound organelles such as mitochondria and chloroplasts. So, inside the cell membrane there are no clearly defined structures. Ribosomes are present in the cytosol, and are not associated with rough endoplasmic reticulum.

○ How long is the cell shown in Figure 2.4?

○ About 2.4 µm.

Prokaryote cells are generally smaller than eukaryote ones. In the examples we have chosen, the prokaryote cell is even smaller than the animal cell nucleus.

○ What feature is common to the prokaryote cell (Figure 2.4) and the plant cell (Figure 2.3), but absent from the animal cell (Figure 2.2)?

○ A cell wall; both the plant cell and the prokaryote cell are bounded by a cell wall, but the animal cell is not.

As in plant cells, cell walls help to maintain the rigid shapes of prokaryote cells, in contrast to animal cells which can readily change their shape.

Question 2.1   (a) Summarize and compare the basic features of animal cells, plant cells and prokaryote cells, by completing Table 2.1. For each of the cell features listed, indicate with a tick or cross whether it is present or absent in each of the three cell types.

Table 2.1   Comparison of three basic cell types.

Cell feature	Cell type		
	animal	plant	prokaryote
cell membrane			
cell wall			
chloroplasts			
cytoplasm			
cytosol			
mitochondria			
nucleus			
nuclear membrane			
organelles			
ribosomes			
rough endoplasmic reticulum			
large vacuole			

(b) Which of the three cell types, animal, plant or prokaryote, has the largest number of the cell features listed in Table 2.1? ◄

Question 2.2   List six eukaryote cell features that are composed of, or are bounded by, membranes. ◄

2.2 Cell diversity

Cells come in an immense variety of sizes and shapes. So, having looked at the features that cells have in common, we move on to consider how diverse they are. We explore diversity across the range of living organisms, in order of increasing complexity. We will start with prokaryote cells (members of the domain Bacteria) and will then look in turn at examples from the four kingdoms of the domain Eukarya: Protoctista, Fungi, Plantae and Animalia (Block 4, Section 4.3). What is important here is the diversity of cell form, and the relationship between form and function in multicellular organisms. You are not expected to memorize the various cell features illustrated in Figures 2.6–2.9.

Before we look at true cells, a brief consideration of *viruses* is appropriate. Viruses cause many diseases of plants and animals. For example, the tobacco mosaic virus produces brown blotches on the leaves of tobacco plants and the pox virus causes cowpox in cattle. Viral damage to crop plants can result in loss of yield and the effects of viral disease on livestock can also have serious economic consequences. Familiar viral diseases of humans in the Western world include the common cold, influenza, mumps and AIDS (acquired immunodeficiency syndrome).

Each virus particle consists of genetic material contained within a protein coat. Viruses are not free-living because they are incapable of independent reproduction or replication, and can reproduce only when inside a host cell. Outside of their host cells, viruses are inert, capable of neither reproduction nor metabolism. Viruses are therefore not cells. These parasitic particles are small, significantly smaller than the smallest known cells (see Figure 2.5).

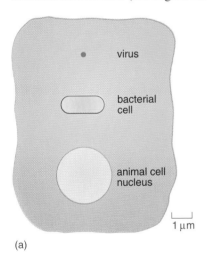

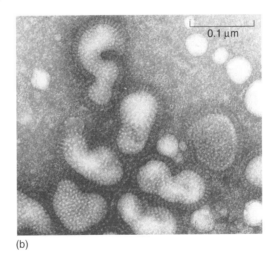

Figure 2.5 Virus size and structure. (a) The size of a typical virus particle compared with a typical animal cell and its nucleus, and a typical bacterial cell. (b) An electron micrograph of influenza virus particles.

(a)

(b)

Having dismissed viruses as non-cellular, we move on to prokaryotes, that is, bacteria. Most bacteria are unicellular and usually spherical or rod-shaped (such as the one illustrated in Figure 2.4).

We will now consider members of the much more diverse eukaryote domain, beginning with protoctists. Cell diversity within protoctists is illustrated in Figure 2.6. The vast majority of organisms in this kingdom are unicellular (although some do have multicellular stages within their life cycle). Many of these can move and hence are described as *motile*. Some protoctist cells, such as that shown in Figure 2.6a, are covered in numerous small, hair-like structures termed cilia (pronounced 'silly-a'; singular, cilium). Others have one, or two, whip-like projections known as flagella

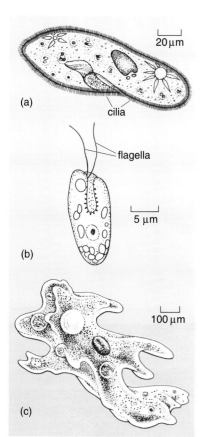

Figure 2.6   A sample of
protoctists showing the range of
cell shapes. (a) *Paramecium* sp. (b)
Chilomonas sp. (c) *Amoeba* sp.
(For these organisms the species
has not been defined, hence the
genus name is followed by 'sp.',
the abbreviation for 'species'.)

(pronounced 'fla-jell-a'; singular, flagellum), which are longer than cilia; a unicellular
protoctist with two flagella is shown in Figure 2.6b. This contrasts with the protoctist
shown in Figure 2.6c, which moves by pushing out projections of cytoplasm. This
capacity to change shape illustrates that some protoctist cells do not have cell walls.
(In fact, this is true for the majority of protoctists.)

Cells of fungi are illustrated in Figure 2.7. A relatively small number of fungi are
unicellular, such as the bakers' or brewers' yeast shown in Figure 2.7a. These cells
can exist on their own, and as they grow and divide (by a process called *budding*) the
new cells either remain loosely attached or become separated. Most fungi, though, are
multicellular organisms, as shown in Figure 2.7b. In these fungi, different cell types
with different functions occur in the same organism, i.e. the cells are *specialized*
(Block 4, Section 3.4). Most fungi consist of long thin filaments comprising large
numbers of cells linked together. Most of the smaller cells shown in Figure 2.7b are
reproductive structures, which will separate off, be dispersed, and begin their separate
life cycles. A characteristic feature of the cells of most fungi is that, like prokaryote
and plant cells, they have rigid cell walls.

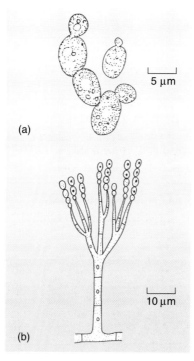

Figure 2.7   Cell shapes and organization found
in fungi. (a) A budding yeast (bakers' or brewers'
yeast, *Saccharomyces cerevisiae*). (b) A
filamentous fungus (*Penicillium* sp., which makes
the antibiotic penicillin).

Members of the plant kingdom are principally complex, multicellular organisms. An
individual plant contains a wide range of specialized cells, a few examples of which
are illustrated in the section through a leaf shown in Figure 2.8. Two main cell types
can be seen. The cells in the outer layers of the leaf (top and bottom of the section)
are different from the cells inside the leaf. These outer cells have thickened cell walls;
in fact they have a waterproof outer coating which prevents water loss from the plant.
The cells on the inside of the leaf contain chloroplasts and carry out photosynthesis.
The two main cell types shown in Figure 2.8, therefore, have different roles, or
functions. In contrast to the cells that make up leaves, the cells in plant stems are
extremely long and narrow, which accords with their principal function, which is the
transport of materials, such as water, ions and sugars, through the stem.

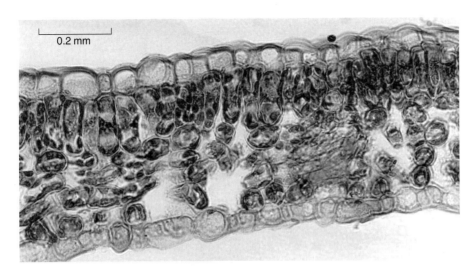

Figure 2.8 Section through a leaf of beech (*Fagus sylvatica*) showing a range of cell shapes and organization.

Finally, in our review of cell diversity, we look at specialized cells of animals, a few of which are shown in Figure 2.9 — sufficient to give you an idea of the diversity found in these organisms. Figure 2.9a shows red blood cells; these have the very regular appearance of concave disks. Their primary function is to transport oxygen around the body via the bloodstream. In contrast, muscle cells (Figure 2.9b) do not exist singly, but like the liver cells in Figure 2.2, are part of a continuous structure made up of many cells of the same type, called a *tissue*. Muscle cells are long and thin, and since they can contract, the actions of these cells bring about movement. The cells in Figure 2.9c are from the lining of the windpipe, or trachea. The cilia on their surface move mucus up into the throat, thus preventing inhaled particles, which become trapped in the mucus, from reaching the lungs. Finally, Figure 2.9d shows two types of cell of markedly different shape and size: many spermatozoa on the surface of an ovum. Each spermatozoon is a single cell with a flagellum which enables it to swim and so make contact with the ovum (also a single cell). Note that the structure of each specialized type of cell is closely related to the function it carries out.

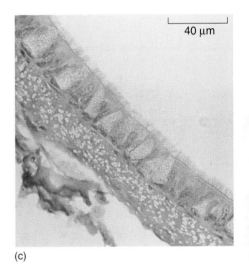

(c)

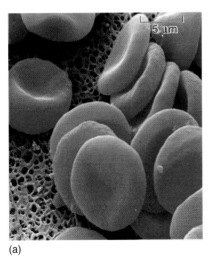

(a)

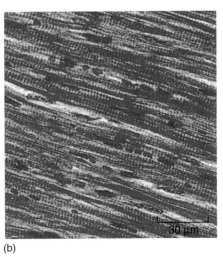

(b)

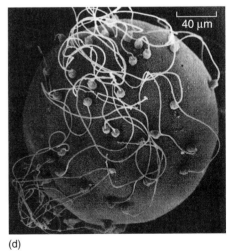

(d)

Figure 2.9 Some of the range of cell shapes and cell organization found in animals. (a) Human (*Homo sapiens*) red blood cells. (b) A section of heart muscle cells from a rat (*Rattus norvegicus*). (c) A section of the layer of ciliated cells lining the trachea (windpipe) of *R. norvegicus*. (d) A number of spermatozoa, each with a single flagellum, on the surface of an ovum from a mollusc (*Mya* sp.).

Figure 2.9 emphasizes a key message of this section: cells come in a diverse range of sizes and shapes. However, all the types of cell illustrated have the same basic features that we elaborated in Section 2.1: there is unity within diversity. This unity of structure, at the level of organelles and other intracellular structures, is also found in the molecules that make up cells, as you will discover in Section 3.

The other key point of this section is that the various cell types found in multicellular organisms, a selection of which are shown in Figures 2.8 and 2.9, are said to be specialized; they each carry out particular functions. In contrast, in the case of unicellular organisms all the functions of the organism are carried out inside the single cell.

Question 2.3   Examine Figure 2.10, which shows a unicellular organism, and then answer the following questions.

(a) Is this a prokaryote or a eukaryote cell? Justify your answer.

(b) Identify the structures labelled A, giving a reason for your answer. (You will find it helpful to compare these features with those illustrated in Figure 2.2.)

(c) Is this organism an animal, a bacterium, a fungus, a plant or a protoctist? Again, you should justify your answer. (This is not an easy question, so do not worry if you cannot come to a definite conclusion.)◄

Figure 2.10   An electron micrograph of a unicellular organism, for use with Question 2.3.

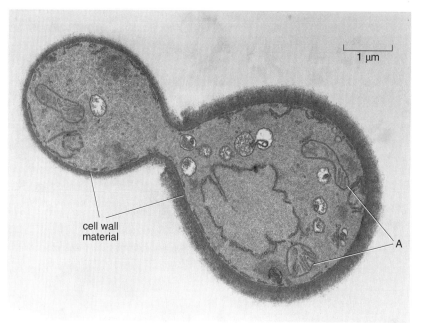

2.3   The origin of eukaryotes: endosymbiosis

Even though there is a wide diversity of cell types, they all fall into two principal groups: prokaryote or eukaryote. In this section we will examine a hypothesis, proposed in the 1970s by the American biologist Lynn Margulis (Figure 2.11), which provides a unifying concept to account for the evolutionary relationships of cells of all domains and kingdoms.

It is believed that the earliest eukaryote cells had only a nucleus, but no other organelles, and that mitochondria and chloroplasts were acquired later, by an interesting route. Margulis proposed that both types of organelle were originally free-living bacteria, which were engulfed by eukaryote 'host' cells. The association between the host cell and its bacterial 'lodgers' must have been mutually beneficial (with each partner performing a useful function for the other) and eventually the bacterial partners must have become completely integrated into and dependent upon the host cell. A useful term which describes this process is *endosymbiosis* ('endo-' meaning inside and 'symbiosis' meaning living together). The so-called **endosymbiotic hypothesis** provides a plausible explanation for the evolutionary origin of modern-day eukaryote cells.

Figure 2.12 shows the proposed pathway for the evolution of eukaryote cells from a universal ancestor. This ancestor gave rise to three different cellular lines (1–3) which represent the three domains. There are two different prokaryote domains: the Bacteria (1) and the Archaea (2). The third major evolutionary line, or Eukarya domain, arising from the univeral ancestor was the nuclear line (3), which gave rise to a primitive eukaryote cell, i.e. one with a nucleus (event 4). Event 5 was the evolution of a relationship between a primitive eukaryote cell and a non-photosynthetic bacterium (a primitive mitochondrion), giving a cell with a nucleus and a mitochondrion. From here protoctists (6), animals (7) and fungi (8) evolved.

Another major evolutionary route (9) involved a relationship between a relatively primitive eukaryote cell (containing a nucleus and a mitochondrion), and a photosynthetic bacterium (a primitive chloroplast). This is the origin of a photosynthetic eukaryote cell, from which further evolution (10) gave rise to plants.

Figure 2.11 Lynn Margulis, working at the University of Massachusetts, USA, suggested in 1970 that mitochondria and chloroplasts originally evolved as separate organisms — bacteria — which then merged with their host cells. Both these organelles have two important attributes that support Margulis' endosymbiotic hypothesis: they reproduce by dividing and they contain DNA. The hypothesis has since become widely accepted by the scientific community. Margulis is currently working on a controversial theory that sperm tails in humans and other animals evolved from another kind of bacterium (called a spirochaete).

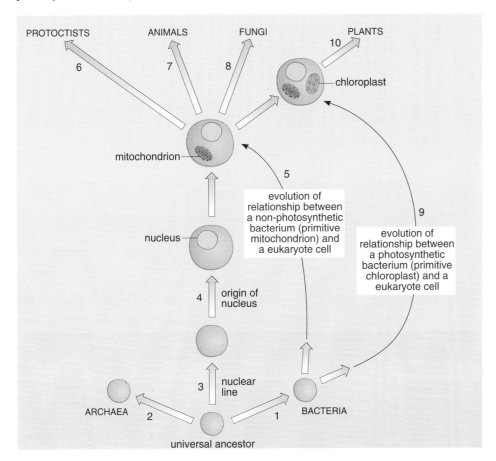

Figure 2.12 The origin of eukaryote cells as accounted for by the endosymbiotic hypothesis.

There are many endosymbiotic relationships known to exist today; for example, unicellular green plants live inside the cells of coral (an animal). Evidence supporting the endosymbiotic hypothesis for the evolution of eukaryotes is the fact that mitochondria and chloroplasts still retain traces of their free-living ancestry in the form of genetic material (DNA) and ribosomes, both of which are similar to those found in modern bacteria; in addition, both mitochondria and chloroplasts reproduce by dividing.

2.4 Summary of Section 2

All living organisms are composed of one or more cells, and are either prokaryotes or eukaryotes. Viruses are not cells but can reproduce inside a host cell.

Membrane-bound cell structures — chloroplasts, mitochondria and nuclei — are called organelles.

Prokaryote cells differs from eukaryote cells in that they lack organelles, so chloroplasts, mitochondria and nuclei are absent. Prokaryote cells are bounded by cell walls.

A eukaryote cell has a number of characteristic features, the most important of which are: a cell membrane, cytosol, mitochondria, a nucleus, nuclear membrane, and ribosomes, present on rough endoplasmic reticulum. In addition to these features, a plant cell has a cell wall, chloroplasts and a large fluid-filled vacuole.

Cells of living organisms exhibit a wide diversity of form, within which there is unity of structure in terms of the basic cell features. Multicellular organisms are composed of different types of specialized cells, and the structure of each is related to its function.

The endosymbiotic hypothesis accounts for the evolutionary origin of eukaryote cells; it is believed that the nucleus, mitochondrion and chloroplast had independent origins, but came together through symbiotic associations.

The chemistry of life: introducing biological molecules

3

If similarities in cell structure are impressive, similarities in cell chemistry and biochemistry are even more so. This underlying 'chemical unity' is hardly surprising, given the evolutionary relationships between cells as proposed by the endosymbiotic hypothesis (Section 2.3). All the groups of organisms shown in Figure 2.12 are organized cellular assemblages of similar chemicals: they comprise both soluble and insoluble, organic and inorganic molecules and ions.

The description of cells in Section 2 was based mainly on observations of dead cellular material. But it is important to remember that living cells are complex 'molecular factories', with many different processes going on at once. So at a given moment, a fully functional cell may be replicating its genetic material (DNA) between cell divisions (Block 4, Section 3), building large molecules, taking in small molecules and ions from outside the cell membrane, breaking down complex molecules and creating new cell parts. Such activities require energy (which is released inside the cell, largely from sugars) and, directly or indirectly, involve metabolism — the sets of chemical reactions that take place inside cells.

Since before the beginning of the 20th century, organic chemists have been assiduously isolating and identifying the great range of molecules found inside cells. In more recent years, with the rapid growth of biochemistry, more and more information about cell metabolism has been revealed.

⬤ Bearing in mind that biochemical research is expensive, what reasons would you suggest, from general knowledge, for large resources being made available for this kind of work?

◯ Biochemical knowledge lies at the heart of modern medicine and agriculture, and vast international industries depend on continuing research in biochemistry.

A living cell is composed of a restricted set of elements, four of which, carbon, hydrogen, nitrogen and oxygen, make up nearly 99% of its dry mass. This composition differs markedly from the average composition of the Earth's crust and is evidence of a distinctive type of chemistry associated with life. Sections 3–7 look at this special chemistry, beginning here in Section 3 with a description of the types of molecules found in living organisms — both within cells and in the surrounding extracellular space. As you saw in Section 2, structures have functions in the living world, and so this section also answers the question: how do the structures of molecules relate to their biological functions? Sections 4–7 then consider how cells make molecules, and where they get their energy from, for this and for all the other activities that occur in living organisms.

Activity 3.1   Revision: chemical compounds

This activity will help you to recall some of the organic molecules that you met in Block 8, as well as the types of reactions in which they are involved. Again it will help you with the task of revising, by giving you more hints on how to do this. ◀

3.1 The substances of life

What are cells made of? This section gives an overview of the molecules found in cells. By far the greatest contributor to cell mass is water — as you learnt in Block 1, and as shown here in Table 3.1. Apart from water, nearly all of the molecules in a cell are compounds of carbon. As described in Block 8, carbon is outstanding among all the elements for its ability to form very large molecules in which carbon atoms are linked by strong covalent bonds to each other and to hydrogen, oxygen, nitrogen and phosphorus atoms.

As can be seen from Table 3.1, apart from water, proteins are the compounds present in mammalian cells in the largest proportion, followed by lipids (fatty substances) and polysaccharides. Nucleic acids are present in smaller proportions; you have already met one of these — DNA — (in Block 4) as the genetic material. Proteins, polysaccharides and nucleic acids are all **biopolymers**, that is, polymers synthesized by living organisms from small-molecule 'building blocks', or monomers (Block 8, Section 15.3). Although lipids share some of the features of biopolymers, they are not generally regarded as such, for most exist as large aggregates of individual, relatively small, lipid molecules. All the biopolymers and lipids are synthesized inside the cell itself. Some biopolymers, such as the major components of wood and bone — which are extracellular, having been secreted by cells — are so tough that they last long after the cells that made them have died. The small proportion of organic molecules that remains free in solution inside the cell includes amino acids and sugars. Only about 1% of body cell mass comprises inorganic ions, e.g. calcium, sodium, potassium, magnesium, chloride and bicarbonate ions.

Table 3.1 Chemical composition of a typical mammalian cell.

Compound	Mass/% of total
water	70
proteins	18
lipids (fatty substances)	5
polysaccharides (made of sugars)	2
nucleic acids	1
small organic molecules	3
inorganic ions	1

A comparison between Table 3.1 and a table of nutritional information on, say, a packet of breakfast cereal or a packet of ham, reveals remarkable similarities. These food products also contain proteins, lipids (fats) and polysaccharides (listed on food packets as 'carbohydrates', which also includes sugars). The food we eat — cereals, such as maize, wheat or oats, fruit, vegetables and meat — was once living material, and this similarity emphasizes the uniformity between the chemical components of all organisms.

Most of the remainder of Section 3 is concerned with the biopolymers, with a final subsection on lipids. So by the end of the section you may have a better understanding of the chemical components of both living cells and the food you eat.

3.2 Biopolymers

You have already met a variety of 'industrial' polymers (e.g. polythene and nylon) in Block 8, Section 15. In the subsequent section of Block 8 an important class of biopolymers was introduced, namely proteins (Box 16.1). Polysaccharides and nucleic acids, as we have already said, are also biopolymers, and they have a number of features in common with proteins. Each biopolymer is made by linking together large numbers of monomers by covalent bonds. The monomer units are different in each class of biopolymer: they are amino acids in proteins, nucleotides in nucleic acids and sugars (commonly glucose) in polysaccharides. Even though there is a limited repertoire of these monomer units, as we shall see, each biopolymer within a class can have unique properties. In this section we explore some general properties of biopolymers, in particular the functional groups of the monomer units and the bonds that link these units together.

Any number from a few hundred to several thousand monomers can be linked together in a single biopolymer chain. Consequently, biopolymers are enormously large molecules — often called *macromolecules*, where 'macro' simply means large. The relative molecular mass of a biopolymer may run into thousands or even millions, compared to only 18 for water (H_2O) and 180 for a simple sugar like glucose ($C_6H_{12}O_6$). For a long time, scientists thought that macromolecules were too large to operate simply through the laws of physics and chemistry, and postulated that they contained a special 'life force'. But it eventually became clear that macromolecules have the same functional groups as small molecules and it is these functional groups, rather than any 'life force', that largely governs their behaviour.

○ In Block 8, Section 15.3, polymers were likened to long trains, formed by coupling together large numbers of railway carriages. The 'couplings' that monomers have are functional groups that allow them to form covalent bonds to other monomers. How many such groups must each monomer have for polymerization to take place?

○ Each monomer needs at least *two* functional groups for polymerization.

Biopolymers are formed by *condensation* reactions, in which the functional groups from two separate monomers react with one another, eliminating a molecule of water and forming a covalent bond (Block 8, Section 15.3.1).

Question 3.1   Figure 3.1 shows the formulae of two amino acids. Draw the formula of the molecule produced in the condensation reaction between the carboxylic acid group (COOH) of amino acid 1 and the amino (NH_2) group of amino acid 2. ◀

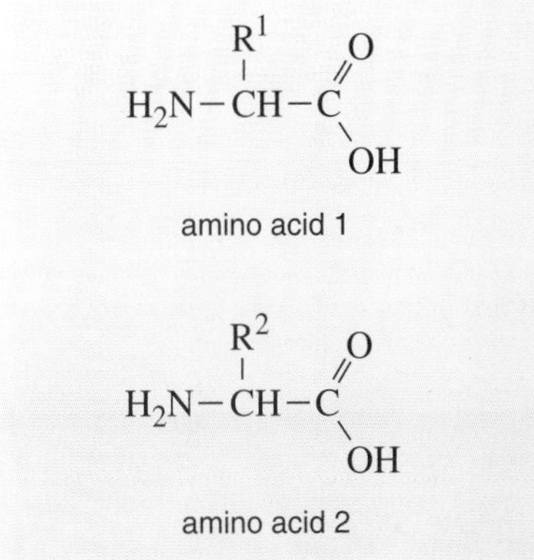

Biopolymers can be readily broken down into monomers again, by breaking the covalent bonds between them. This is accomplished by *hydrolysis* ('splitting with water'; Block 8, Box 16.2), which is the reverse of condensation. For example, in the hydrolysis of the molecule shown as the answer to Question 3.1, the OH part of a water molecule becomes attached to one monomer (amino acid 1) and the H atom to the other (amino acid 2).

A particular biopolymer assumes a specific shape in the watery environment of the cytosol, and to understand how this happens we need to look further at the functional groups that may be found in monomers. Here we are concerned with functional groups still available for reaction once the monomers are part of the biopolymer chain. In other words we are interested in the *functional groups that are not involved in the linking of the monomers to one another*. These can be divided into two types, the **hydrophilic** (water-loving) and the **hydrophobic** (water-fearing). Hydrophobic interactions were introduced in Block 8, Section 16.2.2, and we look again at these interactions in more detail later in the present section. Hydrophilic groups, such as amino (NH_2) and alcohol (OH), can interact freely with water, forming hydrogen bonds with individual water molecules. A biopolymer in the cell automatically bends or folds up so that the hydrophobic groups become tucked away towards the interior of the molecule, out of contact of the water. Here they interact with one another, thereby strengthening the three-dimensional shape of the polymer molecule. The hydrophilic groups are exposed on the surface of the molecule, forming hydrogen bonds with individual water molecules, further stabilizing the structure. This is shown in Figure 3.2 for a protein, the first of the biopolymer types discussed below.

Having discussed some of the properties that biopolymers have in common, we look at the structure and function of each of the different types of biopolymer in turn.

amino acid 1

amino acid 2

Figure 3.1   Formulae of two amino acids, for use with Question 3.1.

Figure 3.2 A molecule of biopolymer (in this case a globular protein) folding in water.

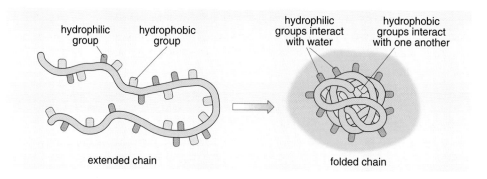

3.3 Proteins

Although nutritional information on food packets lists 'protein' as if it were a single substance, it is in fact a whole *class* of substances and there are hundreds of thousands of different protein molecules in living organisms. All life is based on proteins. As Table 3.1 showed, proteins are the major organic constituents of cells. To see *why* proteins are so important, we need to recall some of the points introduced in Section 2.2 about the structural differences between cell types. Although cells of a multicellular organism have many features in common, there are also characteristic structural and hence functional differences between the different types; in the course of development, cells become specialized for carrying out only *some* of the whole range of functions required for the survival and reproduction of the whole organism.

These similarities and differences between cells stem from differences in the proteins they contain. Figure 2.9 showed a selection of different, specialized animal cells. These cells contain some proteins common to all cell types, for example those in the mitochondria, but they each contain some proteins that are specific to that cell type. Such proteins determine the specialized functions of that cell and hence whether it is part of the blood system or muscle or liver tissue, for example.

There may be tens of thousands of different types of proteins in any organism. Each different protein has its own specialist job to do and each type of protein has its own unique structure.

3.3.1 Fibrous and globular proteins

Figure 3.3 Structure of collagen, a fibrous protein. A collagen molecule is a triple helix: three polymer chains (which themselves are helical) coiled around each other and held together by weak, non-covalent bonds.

Proteins are remarkably versatile with respect to the structures that they form. However, as you saw in Box 16.1 of Block 8, they fall into one of two classes: *fibrous* and *globular*. The **fibrous proteins** are usually very elongated, with roughly linear structures in which two, or three, almost identical polymer chains wind round one another like the strands of a rope, to form a spiral, or *helix*.

All fibrous proteins are made within cells but many are then secreted outside the cell into the extracellular space, where the individual molecules come together into double or triple helices. Most animal tissues are composed not only of cells but also of extracellular space, which is filled with a network of macromolecules permeated by fluid. This network is called the *extracellular matrix* and is made up of a variety of proteins and polysaccharides. The matrix plays a very important role because it determines many of the physical properties of the tissue. One of the most abundant fibrous proteins in the extracellular matrix of vertebrates (such as humans) is *collagen* (Figure 3.3), which accounts for 25% of all body protein. Collagen has great tensile strength and is found particularly in the skin and tendons of vertebrates.

Hair and fingernail protein, or *keratin*, is formed from hundreds of closely packed pairs of intertwined helices. *Myosin*, which consists mainly of fibrous protein, is present in enormous quantities in muscle cells, and hence is a major component of meat (which is mostly muscle).

Individual molecules of these fibrous proteins are extremely thin and long. For example, the collagen triple helix molecule is 1.5 nm wide (1 nanometre = 10^{-9} m), and hundreds of micrometres in length. However, the molecules are always packed side by side into small groups — up to 200 triple helices — to form fibrils, as shown in Figure 3.4a and b. Fibrils are then bundled together to make larger structures called fibres (Figure 3.4c), and the fibres in turn may be bundled together into yet larger aggregates. So fibrous proteins are mostly used in large numbers to build up body structure. The controlled aggregation of hundreds of parallel fibrous molecules ultimately produces something very strong and tough, such as the skin or the tendons of vertebrates mentioned above. Hence fibrous proteins are important for providing support.

Figure 3.4 A collagen molecule (a), up to 200 of which are packed together to form fibrils (b), which themselves pack together to form fibres (c).

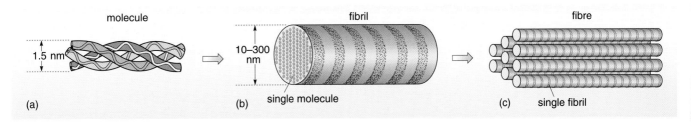

molecule

1.5 nm

fibril

10–300 nm

single molecule

fibre

single fibril

(a) (b) (c)

In contrast to the fibrous proteins, the **globular proteins** are compact and roughly spherical in shape. This shape is achieved by the polymer chain winding round and round itself, rather like a ball of string, as shown in Figure 3.5 for *myoglobin*, the oxygen-binding protein found in muscle. Globular proteins usually have more specialized roles than fibrous proteins. Most importantly, they rely for their activity on specialized 'pockets' built into the protein surface. These specialized pockets, or *binding sites*, are precisely shaped so that each provides an exact fit with one particular type of molecule. (This concept was introduced in Block 8, Section 16.2.)

Figure 3.5 Structure of myoglobin, a globular protein that is present in muscle and is responsible for binding oxygen. The black dots (some of which are numbered) are amino acid monomers. The blue 'folded sausage' shows the higher-order structure (see text) and the red disc is the oxygen-binding group.

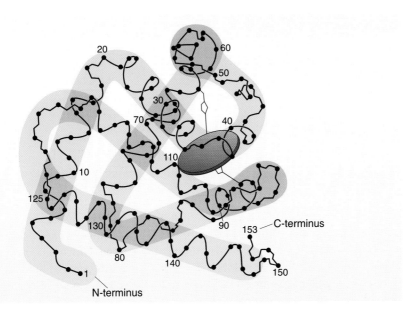

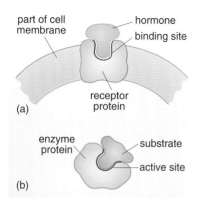

(a)

(b)

Figure 3.6 Specific binding sites (a) on the surface of a receptor protein within the cell membrane, and (b) on an enzyme protein. The binding site of an enzyme is called the active site.

The binding of a globular protein to a specific molecule serves a number of different functions. For instance, for a particular *receptor* protein which forms part of the cell membrane, the molecule with which it has an exact fit is the hormone (Block 8, Section 16.2.2), or other molecule, that it recognizes. A receptor protein can receive messages from specific hormones only if it has a binding site that the hormone fits into exactly, as shown in Figure 3.6a. In insects, for example, female sex hormones can stimulate a male of the same species even if he is a mile downwind — because he has receptor proteins on the cells of his antennae that have specific binding sites for that particular hormone molecule. Humans are not sexually aroused by insect sex hormones because they lack the right receptor proteins! In *enzyme* proteins, which are biological catalysts (such as trypsin and cyclo-oxygenase discussed in Section 16 of Block 8), the specific binding site is known as the **active site**, and its shape determines the molecule that it can bind (the substrate) and the reaction it catalyses (Figure 3.6b).

To explore this subject of protein binding sites with which specific molecules interact, we look at another type of globular protein, the *antibodies*. Antibody proteins are produced by certain types of white blood cells, which are part of the body's immune system. They are produced in response to attack from viruses and bacteria, for example, and can be induced by immunization against specific diseases. For instance, the polio vaccine stimulates white blood cells to make antibodies against the polio virus. Antibodies are very large globular proteins, and in this case, each has a binding site that exactly matches part of the surface structure of a polio virus, as illustrated in Figure 3.7. By 'locking' the virus onto its surface as shown, the antibody effectively prevents the virus from entering cells and reproducing. (The virus is then destroyed by further processes in the blood.) Having once met and overcome the polio virus, the body can rapidly respond to any future polio infection by rapidly synthesizing more of this same polio virus antibody. However, to be similarly prepared against, say, tetanus (caused in this case by a bacterial infection), the body must be immunized specifically against the tetanus bacterium. The important point here is that the body becomes immune to *specific* diseases only by producing antibody protein with a *specific binding site*, one that precisely fits the surface structure of the invading organism. Such binding specificity is found in *all* globular proteins.

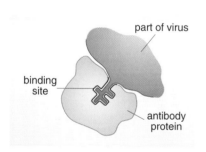

Figure 3.7 A specific binding site for a virus on an antibody protein molecule.

The precise shape of the binding site is unique to each type of globular protein and confers on it a unique specificity which is the basis of its precise biological function.

3.3.2 Primary and higher-order structure of proteins

Having introduced some proteins with very different structures and therefore very different functions, we now explore how these structures are built up and look at the structural features that proteins have in common. To do this, we will consider myoglobin, the protein that is shown in Figure 3.5.

Muscles need a plentiful supply of oxygen while they are working to produce movement. (The reasons for this will become clear in Sections 4 and 5.) Myoglobin is one kind of oxygen-storage protein, and is largely responsible for the red colour of meat. This protein is found in many muscles, including those of humans, but is particularly abundant in the muscles of diving mammals, such as whales and seals. While the animal is breathing in air, oxygen is taken up from the bloodstream by the muscles, and concentrated by binding to myoglobin. The myoglobin releases oxygen while the animal is under water, when the blood does not contain enough oxygen to meet the muscles' demands.

In Figure 3.5 the myoglobin molecule is represented as a long, contorted, blue 'sausage'. The string of black dots within the blue sausage represents the chain of amino acid monomers. The amino acids are linked together by *condensation* reactions between amino (NH_2) and carboxylic acid (COOH) functional groups, and as you saw in the answer to Question 3.1, the result of each condensation reaction is an amide bond, known in biology as a **peptide bond** (Figure 3.19). There is always a free amino group at one end (conventionally drawn as the 'left-hand' end of the chain) and a free carboxylic acid group at the other, 'right-hand' end; these ends are known respectively as the *N-terminus* and the *C-terminus* of the protein chain.

There are around 20 different types of naturally occurring amino acids. The structure shown in the margin is the general formula of an amino acid, and the different types differ in the *R group* they contain.

$$H_2N-CH-C\underset{OH}{\overset{O}{\diagup\!\!\!\backslash}}$$
with R above the CH.

Table 3.2 gives the full and abbreviated names and formulae of six amino acids. However, there are many thousands of different proteins, each with a particular biological function, and it is clear that there must be an enormous variety of structures. How can this be, given that they are all polymers of only 20 different amino acid monomers? The answer is that when several hundred of the 20 different types link up to form a protein chain, there is a huge number of possible *sequences*. Some amino acids may not be used at all in a protein whereas others may occur many times. Every different protein is unique because it has its own unique sequence of amino acids along its length.

Table 3.2   Six amino acids commonly found in proteins. (You do not need to memorize the structures given in this table.)

Name and pronunciation	Standard abbreviation	Formula of R group	Name and pronunciation	Standard abbreviation	Formula of R group
glycine ('gly-seen')	Gly	H	alanine ('alla-neen')	Ala	CH_3
phenylalanine ('fee-nile-alla-neen')	Phe	(benzene ring)—CH_2	aspartate ('ass-part-ate')	Asp	$O{=}C{-}O^-$ over CH_2
lysine ('lie-seen')	Lys	$\overset{+}{N}H_3$—$(CH_2)_4$	serine ('seer-een')	Ser	OH—CH_2

The structure of a protein can be partially described by listing its entire sequence of amino acids, reading from N-terminus to C-terminus (from left to right). This analysis would be rather like taking the black chain of amino acids of myoglobin (Figure 3.5), stretching it out across the page and writing the name of each amino acid above each of the black dots. This sequence of amino acids is known as the **primary structure** of the protein.

Chains of amino acids are often called *polypeptides*. Biochemists use the terms 'protein' and 'polypeptide' rather loosely and interchangeably. Here too both terms are used. When a protein is synthesized in a cell, the linear polypeptide chain folds as it is produced. The biological activity of this newly-formed molecule depends on its *three-dimensional*, folded structure, and when considering a polypeptide chain as a three-dimensional structure it is generally referred to as a protein.

The primary structure of myoglobin appears to give no clues about the overall shape of the protein, nor whether it has any specific binding sites. Yet, amazingly, there is enough information in the primary structure alone for it to fold spontaneously into a particular three-dimensional shape, called its **higher-order structure**. All polypeptide chains with the same amino acid sequence fold in the same way, provided the conditions are the same. So every molecule of myoglobin finishes up with the same convoluted higher-order structure outlined by the blue sausage in Figure 3.5. Thus primary structure determines higher-order structure.

This general rule that primary structure determines higher-order structure is true for all proteins (and indeed for all biopolymers), but is particularly important for globular proteins, such as enzymes and antibodies — and indeed any protein that depends on having a surface binding site that exactly fits the molecule(s) with which it interacts. The surface geometry of a protein is even more irregular than it appears in Figure 3.5; it is pitted with crevices and depressions and covered with protuberances, all of exact shape and size. Every pit and protuberance occurs in just the same position on *every* molecule of that particular protein. As we discussed above, this precise shape, or higher-order structure, determines the specificity of biological activity, or function, of the protein molecule.

We can summarize the important relationships between primary structure, higher-order structure and biological function of proteins in the following way:

> Primary structure determines higher-order structure which determines biological activity.

Question 3.2   Give an example of a protein molecule that can intertwine with two similar molecules to form a triple helix. What is the biological function of this protein? ◀

Question 3.3   The higher-order structure of protein X in humans has a binding site into which the hormone adrenalin fits exactly.

(a) What is the most likely biological function of protein X?

(b) Suppose that certain individuals produce a protein X that has a small change from the normal amino acid sequence. Is this change likely to affect the response of their cells to adrenalin? ◀

3.3.3 The importance of weak bonds

What exactly is the link between primary and higher-order structure? Why does a protein with a particular primary structure always have the same three-dimensional shape? The answer lies in the *weak, non-covalent bonds* that hold the polymer chain together in a particular shape. In the schematic model of myoglobin (Figure 3.5), for example, you can see a relatively straight stretch of the molecule (amino acids 125–150) lying on top of the rest of the protein, which is folded. This straight section does not flap about because it is held down by weak bonds that tether it to the underlying lengths of folded protein. Similarly there are weak bonds holding all the other lengths of polymer chain in place. *The strength of these weak bonds is very much less than the strength of covalent bonds*; but if there are enough of them, weak bonds can stabilize a particular folding pattern very effectively.

○ Look at the generalized formula for an amino acid, shown on page 25. How many functional groups does it have? Which of them are still available for reaction, once the amino acid is polymerized to form a polypeptide chain?

○ An amino acid has three functional groups: COOH, NH_2 and R. When the amino acid is part of a polypeptide chain, only the R group is available for reaction.

The biological activity of a protein depends critically on the shape of the whole molecule which in turn depends crucially on its *R groups*, of which there are 20 different ones — a different R group for each kind of amino acid. These R groups protrude from the polypeptide chain. Look at the formula of the R group for each of the six amino acids listed in Table 3.2. What is significant here is the range of different chemical structures, and hence properties, of the amino acid R groups. For example, in glycine, R is a single, unreactive hydrogen atom; some R groups are hydrophobic (e.g. the CH_3 group of alanine); some are large and bulky as well as being hydrophobic (e.g. in phenylalanine); some are charged (e.g. the negatively charged aspartate R group and the positively charged lysine R group) and others are hydrophilic (e.g. the OH in the CH_2OH group of serine).

The higher-order structure of a globular protein is held together by weak bonds between different R groups of the folded chain. This requires the two R groups to be compatible (i.e. they must have the right chemical structures for a weak bond to form between them). There are R groups all along the polypeptide chain, and this will fold to bring together as many weak-bonding pairs as possible, so that an exact and highly specific higher-order protein structure always results.

Different proteins have different primary structures (different combinations of monomers in a different order) so there are different opportunities for weak bonding. The same is true for the other types of biopolymer. To understand this effect we need to look more closely at the nature of weak bonds. You have already met two types of weak bond — *hydrophobic interactions* and *hydrogen bonds* (Section 3.2). In Figure 3.2. *all* the hydrophilic groups are on the surface of the folded molecule. However, this is an oversimplification. When a biopolymer folds in water, many of the hydrophilic groups will find themselves in the interior of the molecule, away from the surrounding water, and instead of interacting with water molecules will form weak interactions with each other. The weak bonds that result from such interactions are hydrogen bonds and *ionic interactions*. The three types of weak bonds are illustrated in Figure 3.8.

Figure 3.8   Weak bonding in biopolymers. The zigzag bars represent polymer chains. (a) A hydrophobic interaction formed between two hydrophobic groups, such as the hydrocarbon chains shown here. (b) A hydrogen bond, which is formed when two electronegative atoms (here O and N) share an H atom between them. (c) An ionic interaction, which is due to the attraction between oppositely charged groups, here a positively charged ammonium group and a negatively charged carboxylate group.

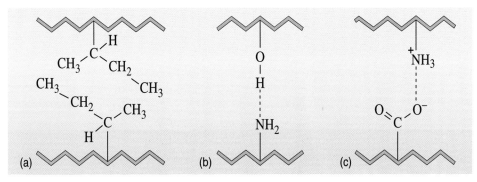

Activity 3.2   Revision: weak bonds

In this activity you will revise what you learnt in Block 8 about hydrophobic interactions, hydrogen bonds and ionic interactions, and then apply it to protein structure. ◀

Having seen where the three types of weak bond are likely to be formed, we return to the link between the structure of a globular protein and its function. The important point is that *proteins tend to fold up in a way that maximizes opportunities for weak bonding*. If all molecules of a particular protein fold in this way, they all finish up with the same shape, the same higher-order structure.

Weak bonds also play a significant role in fibrous proteins, such as collagen and keratin, which consist of several intertwined helices. For example, a collagen molecule is strengthened by hydrogen bonds that run between its three helices, at right angles to the polypeptide chains. Newly formed collagen is fairly deformable, but over the years the hydrogen bonds between the helices are supplemented by much stronger, covalent bonds, thereby making the collagen fibres much tougher. This change is one reason why skin loses its suppleness with age.

So the key to understanding the relationship between structure and function of proteins is weak bonding. Weak bonding also plays an important role in polysaccharides, which we look at in the next section.

Question 3.4   Which of the following statements are true?

(a) All proteins yield amino acids when they are hydrolysed.

(b) A molecule of any protein contains all 20 of the common amino acids.

(c) A polypeptide chain containing 100 amino acid monomer units has 100 peptide bonds. ◀

Activity 3.3   From amino acid sequence to functional protein

This activity will help you consolidate your understanding of protein structure. ◀

3.4   Polysaccharides

The second important group of biopolymers that we will consider are the **polysaccharides** (pronounced 'polly-sack-a-rides', literally 'many sugars'). The monomers of which polysaccharides are composed are known collectively as **monosaccharides** (*mono* means 'one'), each of which is a type of sugar molecule. **Sugars** are water-soluble, sweet-tasting compounds, molecules of which contain a number of OH (alcohol) groups, usually known in biology as *hydroxyl* groups. Sugars are particularly important in biology because they provide energy. The most familiar monosaccharide sugar is glucose[W], and a well-known *disaccharide* (*di* means 'two') is sucrose, or table sugar. The term *carbohydrate*, commonly used on food packaging, encompasses both polysaccharides and sugars.

Figure 3.9 shows that glucose molecules have a ring structure. The ring carbon atoms have been omitted from the structural formula drawn here; this is a common convention and makes the structure look less cluttered. Here the hexagonal ring is viewed in perspective. The numbers 1–6 in blue denote the carbon atoms, referred to as C-1, C-2, etc. Five of the carbon atoms (C-1 to C-5) and one oxygen atom form the ring; C-1 to C-4 each have an OH group and a hydrogen atom attached, and C-5 has a CH_2OH group and a hydrogen atom attached.

As in Block 8, a superscript 'W' indicates molecules that you can examine using WebLab.

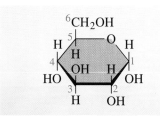

Figure 3.9   The structural formula of the monosaccharide glucose. The ring carbon atoms (C-1 to C-5) are not shown. (You do not need to remember this structure.)

● Count the number of carbon, hydrogen and oxygen atoms; then write out the molecular formula of glucose.

○ You should find your totals match the molecular formula $C_6H_{12}O_6$.

Figure 3.10 shows the formula of another common monosaccharide, *fructose* (often called 'fruit sugar' because of its presence in ripe fruit). Although both glucose and fructose have the same molecular formula, $C_6H_{12}O_6$, you can see that there are differences between them; for example, the fructose ring has one carbon atom fewer. The disaccharide sucrose is made up of one molecule of glucose and one of fructose.

In contrast to sugars, polysaccharides are usually insoluble. The commonest are energy-storage substances (starch in plants and glycogen in animals) and support molecules (cellulose in plant cell walls). All three of these polysaccharides are polymers of glucose, and we will examine the structure of each of them below.

● By analogy with proteins, suggest how monosaccharide monomers are joined together to form polysaccharides — and conversely, how polysaccharides can be converted back to the monosaccharides from which they were formed.

○ Monosaccharides are joined together by *covalent* bonds formed during sequential condensation reactions; polysaccharides are broken down again into monosaccharides by *hydrolysis*.

Figure 3.11 shows the reaction between two glucose molecules, specifically between the OH group on C-4 of one glucose molecule and C-1 of the other. This is a condensation reaction; a molecule of water is produced and a **glycosidic linkage** is formed between the glucose monomers. This process is similar to the condensation reaction between two amino acids to form a peptide bond.

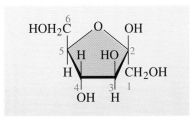

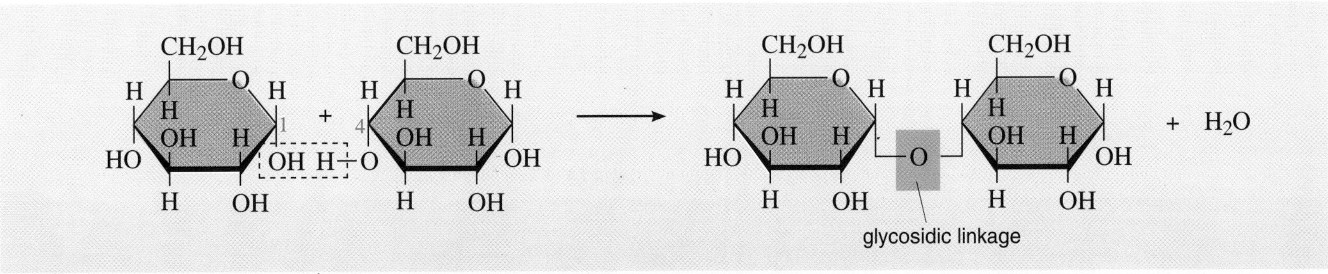

Figure 3.10 Structural formula of the monosaccharide fructose. Again the ring carbon atoms (C-2 to C-5) have been omitted. (You do not need to remember this structure.)

Figure 3.11 Formation of a glycosidic linkage between two glucose molecules. (Note that the bonds from the O atom to C-1 and C-4 in the glycosidic linkage are not actually bent!)

glycosidic linkage

Figure 3.12 shows the simplified structure of two glucose polymers; each oval represents a glucose monomer, and the lines between them denote the glycosidic linkages. *Cellulose*[W] (Figure 3.12a) is a typical fibrous polysaccharide, with extended unbranched chains, each at least 500 momomers long. The chains can pack side by side to give a very tough fibre which, like the fibres in fibrous proteins, is strengthened by many weak bonds between adjacent overlapping chains. Try breaking a thread of cotton — which is almost pure cellulose — and you can test this fibrous strength for yourself. Cellulose is the most abundant organic macromolecule on Earth. This is because it is the major component of the extracellular matrix that forms the rigid supporting framework of the cell walls in all plants (shown in Figure 2.3).

Another polysaccharide composed solely of glucose is *amylopectin* (Figure 3.12b), which is the main component of the familiar food material, *starch*. Individual molecules of amylopectin vary in size, the larger ones consisting of over 2 000 monomers. However, here the glucose monomers are not all linked between C-1 and C-4; there are occasional branch points where there are also links between C-1 and C-6. A consequence of this branching is that adjacent glucose chains cannot get close enough to reinforce one another by parallel stacking as in cellulose, and this means that starch could not function as a support material. However, its open bush-like structure is ideal for packing into a small space whilst still allowing room for the enzymes that release the glucose monomers to provide energy. This shape is therefore very appropriate for an energy storage polysaccharide. In fact, starch is the major fuel reserve of plants. It is commonly stored in chloroplasts in the cells of leaves and stems of all green plants, and is also present in large quantities in other organelles of non-photosynthesizing cells, particularly in below-ground parts of the plant; for example, the cells that make up potatoes contain a large proportion of starch. The major glucose storage molecule in most animals is the polysaccharide *glycogen*^W which is contained in granules in the cytosol of liver and muscle cells. Like amylopectin, glycogen has a branched structure and the molecules can vary in size, the larger ones consisting of more than 20 000 glucose monomers.

Figure 3.12 Simplified diagram of two polymers of glucose. (a) Cellulose. (b) Amylopectin, the main component of starch. The abbreviations '(1 → 4)' and '(1 → 6)' identify the carbon atoms involved in the glycosidic linkages: C-1 to C-4 and C-1 to C-6 respectively.

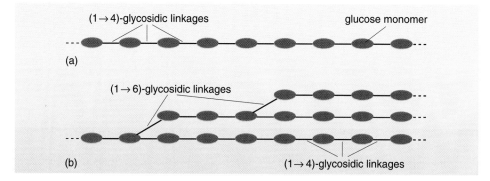

Thus we have seen that, like proteins, the molecular structure of polysaccharides — and hence their physical and chemical properties — are closely related to their biological role. The same is true for nucleic acids, the subject of the next section.

Question 3.5   Which of the following statements are true and which are false?

(a) Two water molecules are formed when a trisaccharide ('tri' denotes three) is formed from its constituent monosaccharides.

(b) Collagen is the principal polysaccharide of plant cell walls, and consists of fructose monomers.

(c) Sucrose, when hydrolysed to its constituent parts, yields equal numbers of fructose and glucose monomers.

(d) Starch is the main energy-storage polysaccharide of animals. ◀

3.5   Nucleic acids

The most abundant *nucleic acid* is DNA. In eukaryotes, DNA molecules, together with proteins, are organized into distinct chromosomes, which are present in the cell nucleus (Block 4, Section 3). In prokaryotes the DNA is present in the cytosol and is not associated with proteins.

Like proteins and polysaccharides, nucleic acids are condensation polymers. In this case the monomers are called *nucleotides*, and these are linked together into chains, which can be hydrolysed back to their constituent nucleotide monomers. As you will learn in Section 10, nucleic acids also rely on weak bonding for their higher-order structure. The biological importance of nucleic acids depends on their nucleotide *sequence*. This acts as a 'code', with different sequences representing different 'messages', and hence nucleic acids are often referred to as 'informational macromolecules'. The sequence of nucleotides within DNA *is* the genetic message. The structure of DNA and how it conveys this message is the subject of Sections 10 and 11.

Question 3.6   List the key structural similarities of the three types of biopolymer that have been discussed: proteins, polysaccharides and nucleic acids. ◄

3.6   Lipids

Lipids are the fatty components of living organisms, and include (amongst others) all the substances you might already think of as fats or oils. They are the major components of margarine, cooking oil, butter, and the white fat associated with meat. All of these lipids originated from animals or plants, which gives a hint of how widespread and important these compounds are in living things. The terms 'fat' and 'oil' simply describe whether a lipid is solid (a fat) or liquid (an oil) at room temperature.

As mentioned earlier, lipids are *not* biopolymers; their average molecular mass is very much smaller than that of proteins, polysaccharides or nucleic acids. Chemically, lipids are a rather varied group of compounds, but with one outstanding property in common: all lipids 'fear water', that is, they are hydrophobic. So they tend to separate from water and from all water-soluble, hydrophilic compounds, and to group themselves together as large hydrophobic aggregates (Block 8, Box 16.3).

⬤   What type of weak bonding holds the molecules in lipid aggregates together?

◯   Hydrophobic interactions.

This contrasts with the structure of biopolymers, in which individual monomers are held together by strong, *covalent* bonds, rather than *just* by weak, hydrophobic interactions. Because of the weak bonding between the molecules, lipids tend to be *fluid* aggregates that can easily change shape, rather than tough and even rigid like some of the biopolymers. To demonstrate this readiness to change shape, try pressing with your thumb on a packet of butter at room temperature; it dents. A material like this with a certain amount of fluidity can be extremely useful in certain situations — as you will see shortly.

The large proportion of hydrophobic groups is the most basic chemical characteristic of lipids, and underpins the crude definition of a lipid as a substance insoluble in water and soluble in hydrophobic solvents, such as chloroform. The simplest lipids are the fats and oils, collectively called *triacylglycerols* (pronounced 'try-ay-sile-gliss-er-rols'), which serve mainly as energy storage compounds. Being insoluble in water is extremely useful when it comes to forming a barrier that separates one cell from another, as in the case of *phospholipids*, which make up cellular membranes. We will now consider both of these types of lipid in more detail.

3.6.1   Triacylglycerols

Triacylglycerols[W] are the commonest lipids in living organisms. They are esters of long-chain carboxylic acids, called **fatty acids**, and an alcohol called **glycerol**. A fatty acid molecule has two distinct parts: a long hydrocarbon chain and a carboxylic acid group. Recall from Block 8 (Section 14.4) that an ester is formed by a condensation reaction between the OH of an alcohol (R—OH) and the COOH of a carboxylic acid (R—COOH), where R is the hydrocarbon chain (CH_3—CH_2—CH_2— etc.).

To remind yourself of this reaction, write out the condensation reaction between acetic acid (CH_3—COOH) and methanol (CH_3—OH).

$$CH_3-\overset{\overset{\textstyle O}{\|}}{C}-OH \ + \ CH_3-OH \longrightarrow CH_3-\overset{\overset{\textstyle O}{\|}}{C}-O-CH_3 \ + \ H_2O$$

acetic acid   methanol   methyl acetate
(carboxylic acid)   (alcohol)   (ester)

The formation of a molecule of triacylglycerol from fatty acids and glycerol is shown in Figure 3.13. Since glycerol has three OH groups it can form three ester bonds, one with each of the carboxylic acid groups at the ends of three fatty acid molecules. The hydrocarbon chains of the three fatty acids are represented in Figure 3.13 as R^1, R^2 and R^3. One of the ways in which naturally occurring fatty acids differ is in the length of the hydrocarbon chain. The name 'triacylglycerol', which is often abbreviated to **TAG**, is derived from its constituent parts: *tri* means three, fatty acids are *acyl* groups, plus *glycerol*. Figure 3.14 is a simplified representation of a triacylglycerol molecule, showing the glycerol 'core' and the long, hydrophobic, hydrocarbon 'tails' of the three fatty acids.

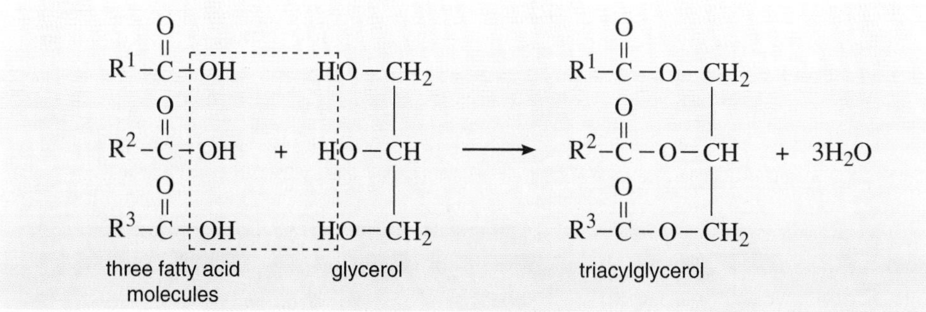

Figure 3.13 The formation of a molecule of triacylglycerol from three fatty acid molecules and one molecule of glycerol. All naturally occurring triacylglycerols contain two or three different kinds of fatty acid.

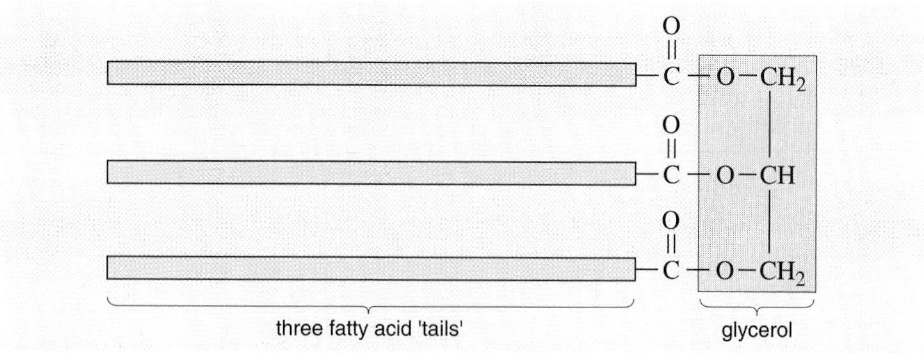

Figure 3.14 Pictorial representation of a triacylglycerol molecule showing the central 'core' (glycerol) and the three long hydrophobic fatty acid 'tails'.

The structure of two common fatty acids is shown in Figure 3.15. Note that here they are shown as the corresponding carboxylate ions because this is the form in which fatty acids are present in the cell. As well as the variability in chain length, fatty acids also differ according to whether they are *saturated* or *unsaturated*. For example, palmitate is a saturated fatty acid, whereas linoleate is an unsaturated fatty acid (Figure 3.15).

$$CH_3-CH_2-CH_2-CH_2-CH_2-CH_2-CH_2-CH_2-CH_2-CH_2-CH_2-CH_2-CH_2-CH_2-CH_2-C\begin{smallmatrix}O\\\|\\\diagdown\\O^-\end{smallmatrix}$$

$$CH_3-(CH_2)_{14}-COO^-$$

palmitate

$$CH_3-CH_2-CH_2-CH_2-CH_2-CH=CH-CH_2-CH=CH-CH_2-CH_2-CH_2-CH_2-CH_2-CH_2-CH_2-C\begin{smallmatrix}O\\\|\\\diagdown\\O^-\end{smallmatrix}$$

$$CH_3-(CH_2)_4-CH=CH-CH_2-CH=CH-(CH_2)_7-COO^-$$

linoleate

○ By comparing the formula of palmitate with that of linoleate in Figure 3.15, can you see what difference there is in the structure of saturated and an unsaturated fatty acid?

○ A saturated fatty acid has no double bonds (C=C) in the hydrocarbon chain; in contrast, an unsaturated fatty acid does have double bonds (generally two or three).

Figure 3.15 The full (upper) and abbreviated (lower) structures of two common fatty acids. Here we have shown the corresponding carboxylate ions, i.e. palmitate and linoleate — the form in which they are present in the cell.

TAGs are described as 'saturated' or 'unsaturated', depending on the types of fatty acid they contain. The proportions of each are usually listed on food packaging under the general heading of 'fats'.

In both animals and plants, TAGs are used mainly for energy storage. In animals, TAGs are stored in a specialized tissue called *adipose tissue*, commonly called simply 'fat'. Under the microscope, the individual adipose tissue cells can be seen, with the fat itself stored as a globule inside a vacuole in the cytosol; the size of the globules of stored fat is much larger in a well-fed animal than in one that is starving. Many people living in Western societies have a much greater proportion of fat than most wild animals; even a fairly thin human, for example, has a layer of adipose tissue immediately below the skin over certain parts of the body such as the thighs, upper arms and belly. In certain plants, one of the main TAG stores is the seeds, whence we obtain, for example, olive oil, maize (corn) oil and groundnut oil. These stores of TAGs, like polysaccharide energy stores, can be readily mobilized, and then broken down to provide energy (see Section 5).

3.6.2 Phospholipids

Phospholipids[W], like TAGs, are long-chain fatty acid esters of glycerol, but one of the glycerol OH groups is esterified by a phosphorus-containing group with a negative charge (instead of a third fatty acid group), as shown in Figure 3.16.

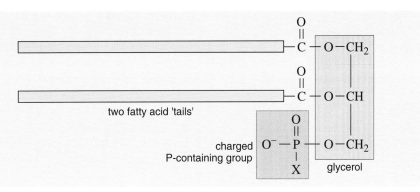

Figure 3.16 Pictorial representation of a phospholipid. The 'X' group may have a positive charge, adding to the hydrophilic nature of this part of the molecule. (Compare this figure with Figure 3.14.)

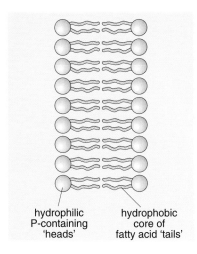

hydrophilic
P-containing
'heads'

hydrophobic
core of
fatty acid 'tails'

Figure 3.17 A phospholipid bilayer.

Charged groups are extremely hydrophilic, which accounts for the major difference in properties between phospholipids and TAGs. As in TAGs, the fatty acid hydrocarbon chains in phospholipids may be very long, with at least 14 CH_2 groups (sometimes 24 or more), making them strongly hydrophobic.

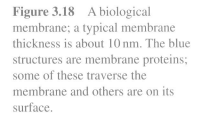

Describe how phospholipid molecules might aggregate together in a strongly hydrophilic watery environment.

The hydrophilic phosphate-containing groups will be on the *outside* of the aggregate, in contact with water molecules, while the hydrophobic chains will avoid water, coming together and interacting with one another on the *inside* of the aggregate.

When there are large numbers of phospholipid molecules, the result is a double-layered structure, a *phospholipid bilayer*. As shown in Figure 3.17, this arrangement brings the phosphate-containing 'heads' of the phospholipids into contact with water, while the fatty acid 'tails' are concealed in the interior, held together by hydrophobic interactions, so forming a hydrophobic 'core'.

3.6.3 Biological membranes

Biological membranes are composed of both phospholipids *and* proteins. However, it is the phospholipids that give membranes their unique sheet-like, bilayered structure and many of their functional properties. The phospholipid bilayer of a cell membrane (shown in Figure 3.18) is a very effective barrier, preventing hydrophilic molecules from passing freely into or out of the cell. Membranes also define the boundaries of organelles, as described in Section 2, restricting various cellular functions to particular compartments of the cell. The movement of substances (such as glucose) across membranes is controlled by special *transport* proteins which are embedded in the phospholipid bilayer, as shown in Figure 3.18. *Receptor* proteins are also found embedded in membranes (Figure 3.6a).

Figure 3.18 A biological membrane; a typical membrane thickness is about 10 nm. The blue structures are membrane proteins; some of these traverse the membrane and others are on its surface.

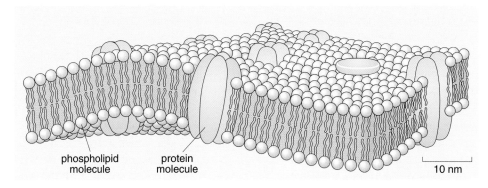

phospholipid
molecule

protein
molecule

10 nm

All the cells described in Section 2 contain all the biological polymer types we have discussed in the present section (proteins, polysaccharides, nucleic acids) and lipid aggregates. Thus the unity of structure observed at the level of cells and organelles occurs also at the molecular level. In Section 4, we will explore this molecular unity further, when we look at the chemical reactions that go on inside cells.

Question 3.7 Most cooking fats (e.g. lard) are almost pure TAGs, which melt to form a clear liquid. But beef suet is whole adipose tissue (i.e. a collection of fat-storage cells) taken from around the kidneys of cattle and shredded to form a granular material. Extracting the lipids from beef suet yields two contrasting kinds, L-1 and

L-2. When L-1 is hydrolysed to its component parts, each molecule yields one molecule of linoleate, one molecule of palmitate, a molecule of glycerol, and a phosphate ion. Hydrolysis of each molecule of L-2 yields three molecules of various fatty acids, but mostly palmitate, and one glycerol molecule.

(a) Name the lipid category to which each of L-1 and L-2 belong.

(b) In which subcellular structures might you expect to find L-1 and L-2 respectively?

(c) In a short sentence, describe the different biological roles of L-1 and L-2.

(d) What structural characteristic that is shared by molecules of both L-1 and L-2 is essential for the roles of both? ◄

Question 3.8   Which of the small molecules (i)–(vi) below are likely to be among the starting material(s) for the synthesis of each of the three storage compounds: (a) myoglobin, (b) TAGs and (c) glycogen?

(i) Glucose; (ii) alanine; (iii) glycerol; (iv) fructose; (v) lysine; (vi) palmitate. ◄

Question 3.9   Which type(s) of biopolymer or lipid provide each of the following functions in cells?

(a) Support; (b) energy storage; (c) catalytic activity; (d) carry genetic information; (e) cell compartmentation. ◄

3.7   Summary of Section 3

Proteins, polysaccharides and nucleic acids are condensation biopolymers, in which the monomer units are amino acids, monosaccharides and nucleotides, respectively. The monomer units are linked together by covalent bonds.

The primary structure of a biopolymer describes the type of monomers and the order in which they are linked. The primary structure of a biopolymer determines its higher-order structure (its shape) which in turn determines its biological activity.

Weak bonds (hydrophobic interactions, hydrogen bonds and ionic interactions) are crucial for the maintenance of the biologically active structure of proteins, polysaccharides, nucleic acids and lipids.

These relationships between primary structure, higher-order structure and biological function are particularly obvious in proteins. The unique primary structure of a protein results from its amino acid sequence. Variations in the number and sequences of amino acids in these chains give rise to a wide diversity of proteins. There are two general types of protein: fibrous proteins, such as collagen, which are long, thin structural molecules; and globular proteins, such as enzymes, antibodies and receptor proteins, which are roughly spherical in shape. The relationship between structure and function is very precise, especially in globular proteins, where the specific higher-order structure provides a binding site (called the active site in enzymes) specific for molecules with which the protein interacts.

Polysaccharides serve as energy-storage molecules in animals (glycogen) and plants (starch) or support molecules, particularly in plants (cellulose).

Nucleic acids are informational molecules.

Lipids are not biopolymers but occur as large molecular aggregates. This group includes fats and oils, collectively termed triacylglycerols (TAGs). A TAG molecule is formed by esterification of a glycerol molecule by three long-chain fatty acid molecules. TAGs serve as energy stores in animals and in the seeds of some plants. The phospholipids contain two fatty acid chains and also a hydrophilic phosphorus-containing group, and in water form a bilayered structure with the hydrophobic fatty acid chains on the inside and the hydrophilic groups on the ouside. Biological membranes are made up of a phospholipid bilayer with proteins embedded in it or attached to its surface.

Activity 3.4 Viewing biological molecules using WebLab

WebLab, the molecular modelling package you used in Block 8, has a special facility for examining large protein molecules. In this activity you will view various proteins using WebLab to explore their three-dimensional structure. ◀

Basic principles of metabolism

Metabolism is the sum total of the chemical processes that take place in living cells. It was introduced in Block 4, and we look at it in greater detail in Sections 4–7 of this block. The basic principles of metabolism are the same in all living cells, and in this section we examine these unifying principles, which underpin the processes described in Sections 5–7.

Metabolism involves series of chemical transformations of the hundreds of different substances needed for life. Each reaction is controlled by catalytic proteins called enzymes (Block 8, Section 16.2), and in the present section we will explore in detail the activity of enzymes. Some enzymes can work only in partnership with smaller molecules known as *coenzymes*, which are also described here. Finally, we consider the energy transformations that go on in metabolism — how some reactions liberate energy and others require energy.

4.1 Building up and breaking down: biosynthesis and catabolism

You will remember from Section 2 that cells contain within them many small structures — the organelles. You may be surprised to learn that organelles and other subcellular structures, and even cells themselves, are not permanent. They are constantly being destroyed and rebuilt. At the molecular level too, the biopolymers are constantly being broken down and reassembled from their monomers. Thus metabolism can be divided into two distinct but related parts — building, or *biosynthesis*, and breaking down, or *catabolism*. We look at the relationship between these two processes here.

Biosynthesis (also called *anabolism*) is the process of building small organic molecules and then combining them, as described in Section 3, into the complex molecules that make up the cell. Although the bulk of these complex molecules are proteins, polysaccharides or lipids, biosynthesis also produces numerous specialized substances, such as lignin (the material that makes the wood of trees hard) and pigments (for example, those that produce the brilliant colours of flower petals, the green pigment chlorophyll in chloroplasts, and the red pigment haemoglobin in blood). An important feature of all biosynthetic processes is that they *require energy*.

Catabolism describes the breakdown of complex organic molecules, such as polysaccharides, lipids and proteins, into smaller organic molecules, which may then be degraded further to inorganic end-products. The only catabolism we shall consider in detail is that of glucose. This is one of the major *energy-releasing* processes in the cell. The breakdown of sugar releases energy, which can be used to do work in other processes in the cell, such as the biosynthesis of biopolymers.

The interplay of biosynthesis and catabolism may be appreciated by reading Box 4.1, *An analogy for building and breaking down molecules*.

Box 4.1 An analogy for building and breaking down molecules

Figure 4.1 is a cartoon depicting the building of a house, and serves as an analogy for building a molecule, i.e. biosynthesis.

○ Look at Figure 4.1 and try to identify two distinct requirements for building the house successfully.

○ It is plain that materials, such as bricks and cement, are required. As you may have inferred from the sweat on each builder's brow, the expenditure of energy is essential too.

These two requirements are effectively the same inside cells. Thus:

(a) The raw materials for biosynthesis (i.e. small inorganic compounds in the case of plants, and small organic molecules for animals) come from the environment, that is, outside the organism. In this analogy, the builders' bricks represent the raw materials and the house-building represents biosynthesis.

(b) The energy expended by a sweating builder comes ultimately from the Sun, as does the energy of all living organisms. However, since the builder is not a green plant he cannot use solar energy directly by photosynthesis, but like all heterotrophic organisms he gets it from the food he eats. As mentioned above, the catabolism of sugars in food is one of the major energy-releasing processes in the cell.

A house being demolished serves as an analogy for the catabolism of molecules. This process releases energy (gravitational and kinetic) and raw materials, some of which (the bricks) can be recycled. In the cell, the breakdown of sugars, for example, releases energy and partial breakdown products, or *intermediates*.

Figure 4.1   The process of building a house.

Biosynthesis and catabolism happen in both *maintenance* (replacing worn-out, damaged molecules) and *growth*. Growth is an obvious process, as in the change from an elephant zygote to an adult elephant, or from a geranium cutting to a mature geranium plant. Maintenance is a rather imperceptible process, which is akin to growth in that it involves the synthesis of new cell chemicals, and often new cells as well. Both processes — growth and maintenance — involve a balance between the biosynthesis and catabolism of biological molecules.

This breaking down and replacement is referred to as **turnover**, and the actual rate of turnover varies from substance to substance and cell type to cell type. Blood proteins, for example, are replaced within a few weeks or days, depending on the particular protein. Other body components are turned over more slowly; for example, the proteins in the living core of teeth and the collagen in skin may take many months or even years to be replaced completely. The fact is that turnover of protein, and indeed of all other compounds in the body, occurs continuously. Thus the fabric of which you, as you read this page, are composed is, atom by atom, substantially different from that of the person of your name who existed when you started studying *Discovering Science*.

○ What is the name of the process by which organic carbon compounds such as sugars, polysaccharides and triacylglycerols (TAGs) are broken down to carbon dioxide and water with the release of energy?

○ The process is called respiration (Block 4, Section 2.3).

A key feature of both biosynthesis and catabolism is that they take place in stages. Each substance is made or broken down by an orderly sequence of linked chemical reactions called a **metabolic pathway**. Thus, there are biosynthetic pathways for building (synthesizing) compounds and catabolic pathways for breaking them down. An example of a much simplified catabolic pathway is shown on the left in Figure 4.2. Here glucose is being broken down, via a number of stages. The final breakdown products are carbon dioxide and water (shown at the bottom left of the figure). During this series of chemical reactions, numerous partial breakdown products, called **intermediates** — such as A, B, Q and R — are formed. The cell uses these intermediates by putting them together again in different ways to form different molecules. In this way, the early products of a catabolic pathway, such as intermediate B, may participate in a biosynthetic pathway (Figure 4.2, right). Here the intermediate B from one pathway is being combined with another intermediate, Y, from a different pathway, to form a new compound Y–B. Because of the links between different pathways, the routes of catabolism and biosynthesis are all interconnected, forming a complex network of chemical reactions inside the cell.

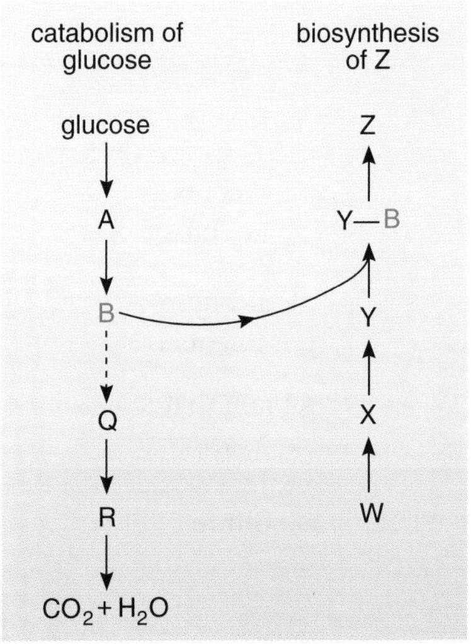

We now consider the raw materials of metabolism, which are transformed by means of metabolic pathways. We deal with the release of energy and its utilization in the cell later in this section.

Figure 4.2 Two metabolic pathways: a catabolic pathway involving the breakdown of glucose to carbon dioxide and water, and a biosynthetic pathway that produces substance Z. Note that intermediates from one pathway can be used in other pathways.

4.2   The raw materials for metabolism

The results of metabolism can be seen all around us in the way living organisms transform raw materials into different substances. An enormous oak tree grows from a very tiny acorn. The raw materials for tree building are largely invisible, being very simple molecules present in the air (carbon dioxide), and in the soil (water and dissolved inorganic ions). Only autotrophs (plants and some prokaryotes) can utilize these simple raw materials, because only they have the necessary cellular equipment. In addition to sugars and polysaccharides, autotrophs make all the other organic molecules they require, including amino acids and fatty acids. In contrast, heterotrophs make use of the more complex molecules formed by autotrophs; the products of the metabolism of plants are the starting point for the metabolism of animals.

The tissues of animals such as ourselves are constantly being replaced from raw materials in food; as the poet Walter de la Mare put it, 'whatever Miss T. eats turns into Miss T.'. Less poetically, we can say that 'cows convert grass into meat and milk'. In order to use the molecules in food and transform them into cellular substances, the food molecules — mainly biopolymers and TAGs — have to be broken down into small molecules by means of digestion. The process of digestion in humans is described in Box 4.2, *Digestion and distribution of nutrients*.

Box 4.2 Digestion and distribution of nutrients

Animals obtain their raw materials by digesting the complex molecules eaten as food, as shown in Figure 4.3. Large multicellular animals have specialized organs in which this occurs, such as the gut in humans. Apart from mechanical processes, such as chewing and churning around in the stomach and intestine, digestion is largely a matter of hydrolysis. As you saw in Section 3, hydrolysis is the reversal of the condensation reactions by which small organic molecules were linked together in the first place. There are specific *digestive* enzymes in the gut that hydrolyse the components of food: lipids (fats) are hydrolysed to fatty acids and glycerol, polysaccharides to sugars, and proteins to amino acids. Some examples of digestive enzymes are: *amylase* in saliva, which hydrolyses starch; *pepsin* in the stomach and *trypsin* in the intestine, both of which hydrolyse proteins; and *lipases* in the intestine, which hydrolyse lipids.

The small organic molecules resulting from digestion then have to reach individual cells. This is a very important step. In large multicellular animals, such as humans, there are specialized transport systems, like the blood, which carry nutrients from the gut to within a few micrometres of the cell membrane. The cell membrane is selectively permeable (Block 4, Section 3.1) and the transfer of molecules across it — the final stage of getting the molecules into the cell — requires specific membrane transport proteins (Section 3.6.3) and the expenditure of energy. When the products of digestion are inside the cell, their metabolism can begin. The steps from digestion to metabolism are summarized in Figure 4.3.

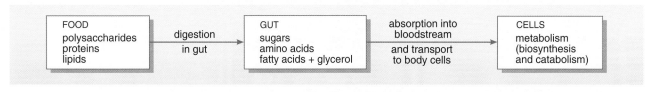

Figure 4.3   The steps from digestion of food to metabolism in cells.

Inside the cell the small organic molecules can take part in metabolism. The metabolic pathways in all living organisms involve organic chemicals with the same functional groups as the molecules you met in Block 8. Yet there are subtle differences between chemical transformations in the cell and those in non-biological material. The cell can perform highly complex chemical transformations at the moderate temperature inside the body — about 37 °C for humans — and around neutral pH. How is this done? Two essential and unique aspects of chemical transformations in living organisms make this possible.

- They are catalysed by enzymes, which speed up reactions that would otherwise be too slow to sustain life.

- They take place in small steps, each step requiring or releasing only a small amount of energy.

To understand the importance of these features in living organisms, think of some glucose on a spoon. Without some assistance this will not break down to release energy stored in it. It can be 'encouraged' to break down, outside the body, by setting fire to it. It then combines with oxygen from the air in a process that releases *large amounts of energy all at once in the form of heat.* Clearly the breaking down, or catabolism, of glucose to release energy inside the cells of living organisms must be quite a different process. The same overall reaction takes place inside cells but in a series of many small steps which make up the catabolic pathway (part of which is illustrated on the left of Figure 4.2). Each step is speeded up (catalysed) by a different enzyme and, in some of the steps, *small amounts of energy are released.* Much of this energy is *not lost as heat*, and can be used for body processes.

We will now look in turn at these two features of metabolism: the role of enzymes and the handling of energy in small amounts.

Activity 4.1   Revision: reaction rates, and oxidation and reduction

The purpose of this activity is to revise information about enzymes, and about two contrasting types of chemical reactions, oxidation and reduction, which you met in Block 8. An understanding of these concepts is essential for your study of Section 4. ◀

4.3   Enzymes

Enzymes are effective in exceedingly small amounts; even a few nanograms (10^{-9} g) can make a spectacular difference to the rate of a reaction. This can be demonstrated in the laboratory using hydrogen peroxide (H_2O_2), which breaks down according to the following equation:

$$2H_2O_2 \longrightarrow 2H_2O + O_2 \qquad\qquad (4.1)$$

Normally, a solution of hydrogen peroxide is fairly stable, breaking down only slowly. But if a tiny drop of blood — which contains the enzyme *catalase* — is added, the reaction speeds up at least a million times, the solution fizzing vigorously due to the large quantities of oxygen produced. In the video sequence 'Features of reactions' (Activity 6.1 in Block 8) you saw the catalytic effect of raw liver on the decomposition of hydrogen peroxide; this was due to the catalase present in the liver cells. What these demonstrations show is that enzymes are very powerful catalysts. In fact, they can speed up reaction rates to the levels necessary for life.

Hydrogen peroxide is a toxic substance, so its breakdown into harmless molecules by catalase serves a protective function in the body. Different enzymes in cells catalyse different reactions, either biosynthetic or catabolic ones. The great majority of enzymes occur inside the cells of an organism. Some, however, are secreted by cells into the surrounding medium; for example, digestive enzymes are secreted into the gut (Box 4.2). Whatever the process, every reaction in metabolism is catalysed by an enzyme. There is a different enzyme for every single step (reaction) in the many multi-step chemical interconversions that take place in the cell. This means that any living organism is capable of making literally hundreds of different enzymes. Most enzymes have names that relate to the reaction they catalyse and end in *-ase*; for example, cellul*ase* hydrolyses cellulose. However, a few enzymes that were discovered a long time ago have arbitrary names, such as the digestive enzymes trypsin and pepsin.

4.3.1   Enzyme specificity

All enzymes are globular proteins. One of the most distinctive features of enzyme catalysis is *specificity*, the ability of the enzyme to interact specifically with one particular molecule (or type of molecule) and to catalyse one particular reaction (or type of reaction).

○ What structural features of globular proteins account for enzyme specificity?

○ Each protein has a different amino acid sequence (primary structure) and therefore folds into a different three-dimensional shape (higher-order structure) which determines its biological activity. The higher-order structure includes a binding site — called the active site in enzymes — which has a different shape in each enzyme, so that only one specific molecule, or type of molecule, will fit it.

A molecule that binds to the enzyme active site and undergoes a chemical reaction there is known as the **substrate** of that enzyme. For example, the substrate of trypsin is the protein being digested.

○ What is the substrate of the enzyme catalase, which was referred to above?

○ Hydrogen peroxide.

Many enzymes require such an exact fit between enzyme and substrate that even small structural changes in the substrate will not be tolerated. A good example of this is the enzyme hexokinase, which catalyses the first reaction of glucose catabolism. Only glucose, out of the vast collection of other small molecules in the cell, fits precisely enough to bind effectively to the active site of the hexokinase molecule. Because of this specificity, the presence (or absence) of a particular enzyme determines which one of several possible reactions actually occurs in the cell. Consequently, enzymes play an essential role in the organization and control of metabolism.

Enzyme specificity is of crucial importance in the organization and control of metabolism.

Question 4.1   Which of the following statements about enzymes are true?
(a) Amylase is a protein.
(b) Without enzymes, life as we know it would not exist.
(c) All globular proteins are enzymes.
(d) Most enzymes catalyse a specific chemical reaction. ◄

4.3.2   How do enzymes work?

The catalase example shows that enzyme-catalysed reaction rates may be many times higher than those of uncatalysed reactions. Nevertheless, it is important to remember that, however miraculous their effects may seem, enzymes still obey the ordinary laws of physics and chemistry. Like other catalysts that operate in non-biological systems, enzymes are subject to the following restrictions:

1   They cannot catalyse a reaction that would not otherwise take place. They can only speed up reactions that are already happening. (It may *seem* as if the reaction does not start until the enzyme is added, but this is only because the uncatalysed reaction is extremely slow.)

2   They cannot change the equilibrium position of a reaction (see Block 8, Sections 8 and 10).

3   They are not used up during a reaction; they are reused over and over again. Therefore just a few molecules of enzyme can catalyse the conversion of a large number of substrate molecules.

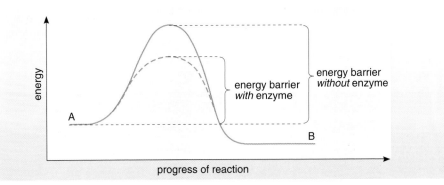

You know from Block 8, Section 10, that catalysts work by lowering the energy barrier for a chemical reaction. Figure 4.4 compares the energy change of an uncatalysed reaction with that of the same reaction catalysed by an enzyme.

How do enzymes achieve their great powers of catalysis? The key feature is the binding of the substrate to the enzyme to form an **enzyme–substrate complex (ES** for short). The substrate does this by forming weak bonds with groups at the active site, as shown in Figure 4.5. Here the substrate molecule fits into a three-dimensional cavity on the enzyme surface, and this provides the ideal environment for the reaction to take place. It is ideal because the parts of the substrate to be chemically changed are placed next to parts of the enzyme protein able to catalyse this change. This fit is crucial to the whole catalytic reaction. Only if the substrate fits absolutely correctly — like a key fitting into a lock — will the parts to be chemically modified be correctly aligned. Binding of substrate to enzyme (to form the ES complex) greatly reduces the energy barrier of the reaction. In many cases, this is related to the distortion of bonds in the substrate which occurs on binding (compare Figures 4.6a and b). These bonds, now under strain, are more readily broken, so the reaction is facilitated. After the reaction has taken place, the product(s) are then released from the active site (Figure 4.6c). Thus the analogy with the key in the lock is rather limited — because the key (substrate) does not become distorted by being inserted into the lock (enzyme), and then emerge either in pieces or with a different shape (as product(s))!

The enzyme is then free to bind again with more substrate. The whole process can be summed up in the general equation:

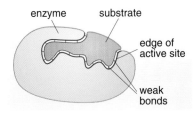

Figure 4.5 Enzyme action: binding of substrate to the enzyme.

$$E \; + \; S \; \rightleftharpoons \; ES \; \rightleftharpoons \; E \; + \; P$$

enzyme   substrate   enzyme–substrate   enzyme   product(s)
                        complex

4.4 Coenzymes

Some enzymes do their catalytic work without help from other substances. Others require assistance from one or another kind of ion, for example, hexokinase requires magnesium ions, Mg^{2+}. Still other enzymes require the help of small organic molecules called **coenzymes**.

Coenzymes are so called because they work in cooperation with enzymes and can be used many times over. Since they bind to the active site of the enzyme alongside the substrate, a more appropriate name might be 'cosubstrate'. But because coenzymes

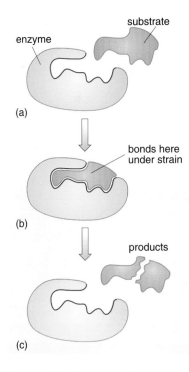

Figure 4.6 Enzyme action: catalysing a reaction. Note here the distortion of the substrate in (b) and its breakdown into products, which then leave the active site (c).

are continuously recycled, they are not substrates in the true sense. Coenzymes play a vital role in enzyme-catalysed reactions as you will see in the example below.

4.4.1 Coenzymes as group transfer molecules

Many enzyme-catalysed reactions involve the removal of (usually two) hydrogen atoms from the substrate molecule, a process called **dehydrogenation**. To understand the part played by coenzymes in metabolism we will look at one particular reaction, the transfer of two hydrogen atoms (which we represent as 2H) by a coenzyme called **NAD** (short for nicotinamide adenine dinucleotide — but you only need to remember the abbreviated name).

○ In which types of chemical reaction would you expect NAD to take part, if its role is to transfer hydrogen atoms?

○ Oxidation and reduction reactions, since these involve the removal and addition of hydrogen, respectively (see Activity 4.1).

As you will see in Section 5, one particular carbon compound accumulates in muscles when they are worked hard, i.e. when exercised vigorously. This compound is called lactic acid, or *lactate**, and it has to be removed from muscles so that they can go on working efficiently. There is a specific enzyme, *lactate dehydrogenase* (LDH), which catalyses the oxidation of lactate to *pyruvate*.

LDH is inactive on its own. To catalyse the dehydrogenation (hydrogen removal) reaction it requires the coenzyme NAD, as well as the substrate lactate — hence the idea of a 'cosubstrate' mentioned earlier. The active site of LDH, which binds both lactate and NAD, is shown in Figure 4.7. The NAD molecule collects two hydrogen atoms from lactate and is reduced to NAD.2H in the process, as shown in the figure. The equation for this reaction is:

$$\overset{\text{LDH}}{C_3H_6O_3 + NAD \rightleftharpoons C_3H_4O_3 + NAD.2H} \qquad (4.2)$$

$$\text{lactate} \qquad\qquad\qquad \text{pyruvate}$$

(Notice that this is a *reversible* reaction. In fact, many enzyme-catalysed reactions can proceed in both directions like the LDH-catalysed reaction here.)

Figure 4.7 The coenzyme NAD binds to the enzyme lactate dehydrogenase, and is reduced to NAD.2H by collecting two hydrogen atoms from the substrate, lactate, which is thereby converted to pyruvate.

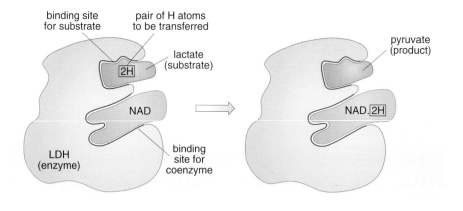

* Remember that organic acids are present in the cell as the corresponding negative ion (Section 3.6.1). For this reason we refer to 'lactate' rather than 'lactic acid'.

The reduced coenzyme, NAD.2H, can then take part in another reaction, in which the hydrogen atoms are removed and it is thereby converted back to NAD; the coenzyme is thus recycled. Coenzymes are often called *group transfer molecules*, because they 'shuttle' back and forth between reactions, picking up groups of atoms and then passing them on. This continual recycling of coenzymes explains why they need only be present in extremely small quantities in the cell.

There are just a few different coenzymes, each of which functions in a particular type of reaction. Thus one coenzyme can serve many different enzymes, provided these all catalyse the same type of reaction — oxidation or reduction in the case of NAD. Four of the coenzymes are listed in Table 4.1.

Table 4.1   Some coenzymes: their roles in group transfer and the vitamins from which they are derived.

Coenzyme	Full name	Group transferred	Vitamin source
NAD	nicotinamide adenine dinucleotide	2H	niacin (a B vitamin)
FAD	flavin adenine dinucleotide	2H	riboflavin (vitamin B_2)
CoA	coenzyme A	CH_3CO (acetyl)	pantothenate
NADP	nicotinamide adenine dinucleotide phosphate	2H	niacin (a B vitamin)

Though the full names of coenzymes need not be remembered, the initials by which they are conventionally known are important. You will see from Table 4.1 that many of them are derived from *vitamins*, which most animals, including humans, are unable to synthesize for themselves. (Most plants cells, on the other hand, can synthesize all the vitamins they need.)

● What can you conclude from the fact that the vitamin niacin, needed to produce NAD, cannot be made in the human body?

○ Niacin must be obtained from food.

Look at the nutritional components listed on any cereal packet for other examples of vitamins. Given the vital role of coenzymes in metabolism, it is hardly surprising that vitamin deficiency has very serious consequences for health. For example, deficiency of niacin in humans can lead to pellagra (a skin, gut and nerve disorder). As noted above, without this particular vitamin the coenzyme NAD cannot be made.

So far we have considered the role of enzymes and coenzymes in metabolism. We now move on to consider the other important aspect of metabolism introduced in Section 4.2: the way that energy is transferred in cells.

Question 4.2   (a) An enzyme catalyses the dehydrogenation of compound BH_2 to B, a reaction in which the coenzyme NAD also participates. What happens to NAD in this dehydrogenation reaction?

(b) The enzyme also has some effect on the substrate JH_2, but at a rate of only 10% of that with BH_2 as substrate. What is the probable reason for the lower activity of the enzyme with JH_2? ◄

4.5 Energy transfer in living organisms

All the activities characteristic of life need energy. Energy transformation in living organisms does not occur in the same way as, say, in a petrol engine, where the chemical energy of petrol is transformed to the kinetic energy of a speeding car. The high temperatures of burning petrol cannot be tolerated by living organisms. Instead the cell performs highly complex chemical transformations at *moderate* temperatures. Although some heat is generated as a by-product, the transfer of energy from the energy-releasing catabolic activities to the energy-requiring activities takes place by an entirely different mechanism that doesn't involve the flow of heat. In this section, we look at the method of energy transformation in living organisms.

Throughout life, there is a constant *balance* between energy-requiring and energy-releasing activities — between energy *expenditure* and energy *income*. We examine the processes that require energy and the processes that release energy, and then go on to describe the link between them.

4.5.1 Energy-requiring processes

The idea that biosynthesis requires energy was introduced in Section 4.1. Making large molecules, such as proteins, from small molecules needs energy. Clearly, to store energy as chemical energy in a system will require the supply of energy from somewhere else. You have met the idea of energy conservation in Block 5 — energy can be neither created nor destroyed.

However, providing energy for biosynthesis is not the only energy transformation that occurs in living organisms. The idea of a person increasing the gravitational energy or kinetic energy of some object, such as a cricket ball, is a familiar one. Such changes are brought about by muscular work. The activity of nerves also requires energy, as do the processes of cell division, and the transport of ions and molecules into and out of cells by transport proteins embedded in the cell membrane (Section 3.6.3 and Box 4.2).

4.5.2 Energy-releasing processes

We now turn from processes that *require* energy to processes that supply or *release* it. However much energy is required by the various processes discussed above, the same amount must have been supplied originally from some source *outside* the organism (see Section 4.2).

⬤ What is the external source of energy in heterotrophs?

◯ Organic compounds such as sugars, polysaccharides and TAGs taken in as food.

These organic compounds, which store chemical energy, are broken down by various reactions to release energy. Under certain circumstances, proteins can also be used as a further source of energy. Most of these catabolic processes involve oxidizing organic compounds to carbon dioxide and water. This is the process of respiration, which occurs in the vast majority of living organisms.

Question 4.3   Some bacterial cells are suspended in a half-filled, sealed bottle of a solution containing dissolved glucose. Given that these cells obtain energy by glucose respiration, what changes in the composition of the air above the solution would you expect to occur? ◄

Turning to autotrophs, the source of energy for almost all of these — and ultimately for almost all life on Earth — is the Sun. Green plants (and certain prokaryotes) can trap this energy, because they have the necessary metabolic machinery. Chlorophyll is the most abundant light-absorbing pigment, and it allows green plants to use solar energy for the synthesis of sugars from carbon dioxide and water taken in from the environment. As you know, this process is called photosynthesis (discussed in Sections 6 and 7). Once formed inside the autotroph, the fate of the newly-synthesized sugars is almost identical to that of the digested and absorbed molecules in heterotrophs; that is, they are oxidized to release energy or used for energy storage. During the day both photosynthesis and respiration occur in the same plant at the same time. At night when there is no photosynthesis, plants use their energy stores to drive metabolic processes.

● In what form is glucose stored in plants, and in animals?

○ Glucose is converted to starch (mostly amylopectin) in plants and glycogen in animals (Section 3.4).

Storage compounds are very important to living organisms. Animals can get their energy indirectly from either plants or animals by eating and digesting them. Plants can survive considerable periods of darkness by drawing upon their starch reserves, and can load up their offspring (seeds) with sufficient starch or lipid for them to survive and grow until they have developed their own photosynthetic machinery.

Thus in both heterotrophs and autotrophs, energy is made available by means of catabolic processes for a variety of energy-requiring activities, such as biosynthesis. We turn now to the *link* between energy production and energy utilization in cells.

4.5.3 The central role of ATP in energy transfer

We have seen, in Section 4.5.2, that cellular respiration is an energy-releasing process, and that sugars, polysaccharides and TAGs (triacylglycerols) can act as energy-storage compounds. How then is the energy in sugar, for example, actually used to drive energy-requiring activities, such as biosynthesis and movement? The answer lies in the interconversion of two substances, ADP (adenosine diphosphate) and ATP (adenosine triphosphate). We begin by looking at the structure of these molecules.

The simplified structure of **ATP** is shown in Figure 4.8. It consists of an organic part — a 'base' plus sugar combination called adenosine — and a short chain of three phosphate groups; hence the name *tri*phosphate. One of the phosphate groups can be easily removed by hydrolysis to give **ADP** (adenosine *di*phosphate) and an inorganic phosphate ion, which is usually written as P_i.

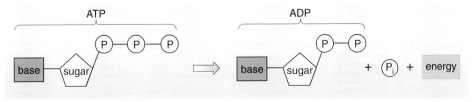

Figure 4.8 The breakdown of ATP (adenosine triphosphate) to ADP (adenosine diphosphate) and P_i (inorganic phosphate). (Note that a 'base' here is not the same as the one you met in Block 6; you will meet these bases again, in a different context, in Section 10.)

In the conversion of ATP to ADP and P_i, a large amount of energy is *released*. Similarly, in the synthesis of ATP from ADP and P_i, the same amount of energy is *absorbed*. During an energy-releasing process, such as the catabolism of sugar, the cell transforms the chemical energy in the sugar molecule into chemical energy stored

Figure 4.9 ATP acts as a molecular link between the various cellular processes that release energy and those that require energy. The energy from energy-releasing processes is coupled to the energy-requiring process of ATP synthesis, as shown on the left.

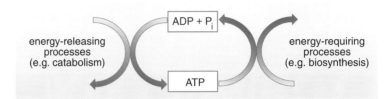

in ATP. These two simultaneous processes — energy release and ATP synthesis — are said to be *coupled*. The left-hand side of Figure 4.9 shows how such coupling may be represented.

What is important to the cell is that the 'reverse' coupling can take place, as shown on the right-hand side of Figure 4.9. Here the conversion of ATP to ADP + P_i releases energy and this reaction is coupled to energy-requiring processes such as biosynthesis. This figure illustrates in diagrammatic form how ATP acts as an *energy transfer molecule* in the cell.

> ATP acts as the molecular link transferring chemical energy between cellular processes that release energy and those that require energy.

ATP is only a *short-lived* energy store, or energy carrier, which is used up much faster than glucose itself, and never allowed to accumulate. It is rapidly recycled. It has been estimated that in the average cell an ATP molecule is converted to ADP + P_i within a minute of its formation. To appreciate how short-lived ATP is, consider the poison cyanide. This exerts its fatal action inside cells by preventing the formation of ATP. A person can survive only as long as their ATP stores last — a matter of minutes after ingesting this poison.

It is through the production of ATP that the energy originally derived from the oxidation of glucose (or TAGs) is released in a conveniently packaged form, for immediate use. This happens in *all* living organisms.

4.5.4 The efficiency of respiration

How efficient is the process of respiration compared with, say, a car fuelled by petrol? This question is best answered by looking at the way that energy is released during respiration, and specifically during the oxidation of glucose.

The complete oxidation of glucose ($C_6H_{12}O_6$) is represented by the equation:

$$C_6H_{12}O_6 + 6O_2 \longrightarrow 6CO_2 + 6H_2O + energy \tag{4.3}$$

When glucose is completely oxidized, to carbon dioxide and water, a very large amount of energy is released — some $2\,900\,kJ\,mol^{-1}$. If this oxidation takes place outside the cell, e.g. by burning glucose on a spoon, all this energy is released in a single step, mostly in the form of heat, as shown in Figure 4.10a. The release of so much energy in one step in a living cell would disrupt the cell's delicate structure. Furthermore, there is no single biochemical process that could make use of so much energy at one go. In living cells, this energy is released piecemeal, by means of a series of small steps, as shown in Figure 4.10b (and introduced in Section 4.2). The energy released comes in small, manageable quantities that can be coupled to the production of ATP from ADP and P_i.

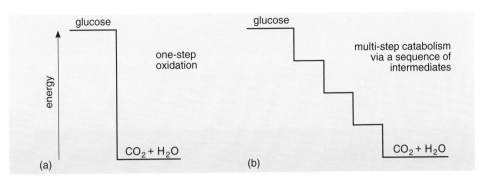

Figure 4.10   Glucose oxidation to carbon dioxide and water. (a) One-step oxidation outside the cell. (b) Multi-step oxidation inside the cell, which occurs via a sequence of intermediates. (The number of intermediates is much greater than shown here.) Notice that the total amount of energy released is the same in (a) and (b).

ATP can be thought of as *energy currency*; converting ADP to ATP is collecting energy *income*, and this energy is then *spent* on the various processes that require energy when ATP is converted back to ADP. So what is the energy-carrying capacity — or energy 'value' — of ATP? The conversion of ADP + P_i to ATP absorbs quite a large amount of energy, around 30.6 kJ mol^{-1}, and conversely, the conversion of ATP to ADP + P_i releases the same amount of energy. The complete oxidation of one mole of glucose to carbon dioxide and water produces a total of 36 moles of ATP.

You may be wondering why chemical interconversions in cells follow such complex pathways. As we saw above, this means that energy is parcelled out, bit by bit, and efficiently transferred to ATP. In fact, cellular respiration is remarkably efficient.

● If 36 moles of ATP are produced for each mole of glucose completely respired (to carbon dioxide and water), and about 30.6 kJ are required to produce each mole of ATP, what percentage of the chemical energy available from glucose oxidation is transferred into the chemical energy of ATP?

○ A total of 36×30.6 kJ = 1 102 kJ of chemical energy are transferred to ATP. Since 2 900 kJ are released in the complete oxidation of one mole of glucose, the percentage of the chemical energy in glucose that is transferred to ATP is

$$\frac{1\,102}{2\,900} \times 100\% = 38\%$$

● What happens to the rest of the energy?

○ It is lost as heat.

So the efficiency with which the energy from sugar is transferred to ATP is about 38%. We can now answer the question that we posed at the beginning of this section: how efficient is the process of respiration compared with a car fuelled by petrol? The answer is that it is considerably more efficient, since a car at best transforms 20% of the chemical energy stored in petrol to mechanical energy. If animals were so inefficient at transferring the energy stored in food into energy stored in ATP they would need to eat voraciously most of the time!

In the next section we will look at the role of enzymes and coenzymes in metabolism, and study the process of ATP production within cells by examining the metabolic pathway of glucose oxidation in more detail.

Question 4.4   When a person runs, what change occurs in the amount of ATP in their muscles? ◄

Question 4.5 Which of the following statements about metabolism are true?

(a) The conversion of ADP + P$_i$ to ATP is coupled to energy-requiring reactions in the cell.

(b) ATP is a carrier of chemical energy.

(c) All the ATP produced in the cell by catabolic pathways is used in biosynthetic pathways.

(d) Energy derived from the oxidation of glucose is packaged as ATP and used within minutes. ◄

4.6 Summary of Section 4

Metabolism is the sum of all chemical reactions in the cell, both biosynthetic and catabolic. A metabolic pathway is a series of biochemical reactions. Catabolism of food molecules, such as glucose, in the cell releases energy; it also provides intermediates for the biosynthesis of other molecules.

Enzymes are biological catalysts which increase the rate of a reaction, but they cannot alter the equilibrium position of a reaction, or initiate reactions that do not already take place. An enzyme binds a specific substrate(s) at the active site to form an enzyme–substrate complex, the reaction occurs and the product(s) are then released.

Coenzymes transfer small groups of atoms (e.g. pairs of H atoms) between different molecules in the cell.

Energy for almost all living organisms is ultimately derived from the Sun by photosynthesis. Respiration (glucose oxidation) occurs in all cells; it proceeds via a large number of small steps, in some of which small quantities of energy are released.

Energy-requiring reactions are coupled to the conversion of ATP to ADP + P$_i$, while the reverse reaction — the conversion ADP + P$_i$ to ATP — is coupled to energy-releasing reactions. ATP thus acts as the link between energy-requiring and energy-releasing processes.

Glucose oxidation

In this section, we look in detail at some of the chemical reactions going on in living organisms, beginning with the cell's main catabolic pathway — glucose oxidation. This is the commonest source of energy in cells, and almost all cells that live in an aerobic (oxygen-containing) environment get substantial amounts of their energy through this process. We saw in Section 4 that energy is required to fuel the huge number of biosynthetic reactions necessary to maintain life and to drive various other activities of life, such as muscular movement. The breakdown of glucose involves a complex series of chemical reactions and we deal only with the main principles here. The CD-ROM activity 'Cells and energy' (Section 7, Activity 7.1) will enable you to consolidate your understanding of the whole process of glucose oxidation. The pathways for the breakdown of fats and proteins channel into the glucose oxidation pathway, hence these compounds are also sources of energy. Later we look at how these various catabolic pathways are linked.

Although the focus of this section is at the molecular level, it will provide the background for understanding the relationship between diet and cell metabolism. The section therefore builds on the information about biopolymers and fats in Section 3 and on the basic principles of metabolism in Section 4 — that is, the role of enzymes, coenzymes and energy transfer in cell chemistry. To check your understanding of these fundamentals, try working through the following questions.

⬤ What is the main difference between the oxidation of glucose in air and its oxidation in the cell?

○ Oxidation in the cell takes place through *many small steps*, each catalysed by an enzyme. The oxidation (burning) of glucose in the air occurs in one large step and does not involve enzymes.

⬤ For the oxidation of glucose to provide energy in a usable form, which substance must be produced?

○ ATP (Section 4.5.3).

⬤ How can the energy in ATP be harnessed to drive an energy-requiring reaction?

○ The breakdown of ATP to ADP and P_i can be *coupled* to the energy-requiring reaction (see Figure 4.9).

ATP can be transported anywhere in the cell and the chemical energy stored in it can be released to drive an energy-requiring process. For each molecule of ATP that is converted to ADP, a definite amount of energy is released.

⬤ If the breakdown of glucose is via *oxidation*, which coenzyme would you expect to feature prominently in this process, and why?

○ NAD. The oxidation of glucose involves the removal of hydrogen atoms; NAD accepts pairs of hydrogen atoms, and the NAD.2H thus formed transfers them to other molecules.

To summarize, the oxidation of glucose involves large numbers of small, enzyme-catalysed steps, resulting in the formation of both ATP and NAD.2H. You will learn more about how these molecules are generated, and about the relevance of NAD.2H formation, as we go on to explore the process of glucose oxidation in some detail.

Question 5.1 Imagine a molecule of glucose, originally produced by photosynthesis, and then used for storage within a plant cell. Outline what must happen to this glucose molecule before it can be broken down inside the cell of an animal that consumes the plant. ◀

5.1 Overview of glucose oxidation

This section gives a brief overview of the complex process of glucose oxidation (respiration) in the cell, which is described in detail in Sections 5.2–5.5. You will find it helpful to bear in mind the basic information given here as you study these later sections. You need to remember the names and key features of the overall process and where the component pathways occur in the cell. Activity 5.1, at the end of this subsection, will help you with this.

There are four distinct stages in the breakdown of glucose to release energy. These stages operate in succession to bring about its complete oxidation to carbon dioxide and water:

$$C_6H_{12}O_6 + 6O_2 + 36ADP + 36P_i \longrightarrow 6CO_2 + 6H_2O + 36ATP \qquad (5.1)$$

(Equation 5.1 is a repeat of Equation 4.3, but with the associated ATP production.)

The information given in Figure 5.1 is important and by the time you have completed your study of glucose oxidation you should be able to reproduce the diagram and explain the information it contains.

The four stages of glucose oxidation are shown in Figure 5.1: *glycolysis*, the *link reaction*, the *tricarboxylic acid cycle* (abbreviated to *TCA cycle*) and *electron transport* coupled to *oxidative phosphorylation*. This figure summarizes the important information on glucose oxidation; the details are explained in later sections, but for now we will consider how the component pathways illustrated relate to the overall equation of glucose oxidation given in Equation 5.1.

Notice from Figure 5.1 that the first three stages sequentially break down the carbon backbone of glucose, a chain of six carbon atoms (6C), and release the carbon as the end-product, carbon dioxide.

- **Glycolysis** (pronounced 'gly-*colli*-sis') brings about the splitting of each 6C glucose to two molecules of a 3C intermediate.

- The **link reaction** converts each molecule of the 3C end-product of glycolysis to a 2C intermediate (with the release of a 1C compound, carbon dioxide).

- The **tricarboxylic acid cycle (TCA cycle)** completes the breakdown of the carbon chain, to 1C, i.e. to carbon dioxide.

In addition to the breakdown of the carbon backbone, the twelve hydrogen atoms of glucose are removed in a stepwise manner. The hydrogen atoms from Stages 1–3 are carried mainly as NAD.2H, the majority of them deriving from the TCA cycle.

The fourth and final stage of glucose oxidation is **electron transport** coupled to **oxidative phosphorylation**. It is during this stage that NAD.2H is oxidized back to NAD and the hydrogen atoms are transferred to molecular oxygen, producing the end-product water.

◯ Look at Equation 5.1 again. Which item have we not yet mentioned?

◯ The ATP produced.

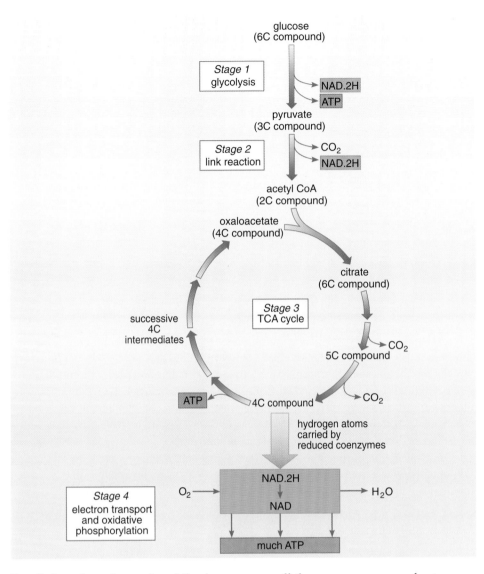

Figure 5.1 The glucose oxidation pathway showing the four distinct stages of the process, the changes that occur in the carbon backbone, and the points at which the end-products carbon dioxide and water are released. (The term 'carbon backbone' refers to those carbon atoms linked together in the glucose molecule.)

Recall that when glucose is oxidized on a spoon, all the energy appears as heat, whereas in the living cell some appears as heat and some as chemical energy in the ATP molecules formed from ADP and P_i. Figure 5.1 shows that most of the ATP is formed during Stage 4, and that this process is intimately linked to the oxidation of NAD.2H back to NAD.

So there are four distinct stages to glucose oxidation, but where in the cell does each of these occur? Figure 5.2 shows a cell with a mitochondrion in the cytosol. This figure also shows that each of the four stages of glucose oxidation occurs in a specific compartment within the cell. Only Stage 1, glycolysis, occurs in the cytosol. The remaining three stages of glucose oxidation take place in the mitochondrion. This organelle has an outer membrane as well as a convoluted inner membrane packed inside it. The inner membrane separates the mitochondrion into an inner fluid-filled centre, called the **matrix,** and a space between the inner and outer membranes, called the **intermembrane space**. Compartmentation is a characteristic feature of cells (introduced in Section 2.1) and is important here for the functioning of the mitochondrion. Both Stages 2 and 3 of glucose oxidation — the link reaction and the TCA cycle — occur in the matrix. Stage 4, the coupled processes of electron

Figure 5.2 The location of each of the four stages of the glucose oxidation pathway in the cell. (The mitochondrion is much enlarged relative to the nucleus in order to show its internal structure.)

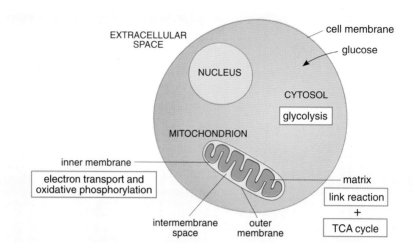

transport and oxidative phosphorylation, takes place at the inner mitochondrial membrane. It is here that most of the ATP is produced in the cell. By the end of the section you should appreciate the role of the mitochondrion in glucose oxidation, and why it is called the 'power-house of the cell'.

Different kinds of cell have different numbers of mitochondria within them, sometimes more than a thousand per cell. Many mitochondria are visible in Figure 2.2, which is an electron micrograph of a single mammalian liver cell. The more work a cell does, of whatever kind (e.g. biosynthesis, movement), the more mitochondria it contains. Thus, for example, a human skin cell contains fewer mitochondria than a human liver or muscle cell. Skin cells are relatively passive metabolically, liver cells are involved in much biosynthesis, and muscles are involved in the transformation of much chemical energy into kinetic energy. Thus the ATP requirements of cells and tissues can vary, and consequently the number of mitochondria they possess also differs.

We will now consider each of the four stages of glucose oxidation (Figure 5.1) in turn, beginning with glycolysis.

Activity 5.1 Producing a summary diagram of glucose oxidation

This activity requires you to add details of the process of glucose oxidation to the pathway given in Figure 5.1, as you study the process in more detail. Such a summary will also be a useful resource when you study the associated CD-ROM activity in Section 7, and for revision purposes. ◀

5.2 Stage 1: glycolysis

We start with a glucose molecule that has just entered the cell. The first stage of glucose breakdown — the process of glycolysis (literally 'sugar splitting') — takes place in the cytosol. Here are found all the necessary enzymes. Glycolysis comprises a number of steps, and these are outlined in Figure 5.3. The pathway begins with the 6C glucose molecule (shown at the top of the figure) and ends with two molecules of a 3C intermediate called **pyruvate** (pronounced 'pie-roo-vate'), shown at the bottom of Figure 5.3. Altogether there are eight intermediates between glucose and pyruvate, each formed from the preceding one by a different, enzyme-catalysed reaction. We will consider only the main reactions, starting with the splitting of the glucose carbon backbone.

Before glucose can be split under the conditions that exist in the cell, it has to be 'activated', so that energetically 'tough' bonds — like the C—C bonds holding the 6C backbone together — are weakened, and hence more readily broken in the enzyme-catalysed reactions that follow. Activation is a complex process, but it can be brought about simply by placing charged groups near the bonds to be broken. Phosphate is one such group because it is negatively charged (Figure 3.16). All the intermediates of glycolysis have at least one phosphate group.

The first step in glycolysis is to phosphorylate ('add a phosphate to') glucose, converting it to *glucose 6-phosphate*. The phosphate group is donated by ATP, and the reaction is catalysed by hexokinase (an enzyme you met in Section 4). There then follows a second phosphorylation step, which produces a doubly activated bisphosphate sugar (6C-bisphosphate in Figure 5.3; 'bis' here means two) This is then split into two 3C sugar phosphate molecules ('3C-phosphate' in the figure).

It may seem odd to *use up* two molecules of ATP right at the beginning of glycolysis, if the whole point of glucose oxidation is to *generate* ATP. But if you look again at Figure 5.3, you can see that this initial investment of ATP is justified by events later in the glycolytic pathway, where two reactions generate ATP, again from ADP. In fact, four ATP molecules are formed because each of the *two* 3C sugar phosphate molecules follows the same route to pyruvate; that is, the second half of the pathway happens twice for each molecule of glucose. In addition, as Figure 5.3 shows, some NAD is reduced to NAD.2H.

The important points to remember about glycolysis are that some of the energy stored in glucose has been tapped off into ATP and the reduced coenzyme NAD.2H. Most of the energy, however, is still stored in the two pyruvate molecules produced at the end of glycolysis.

Activity 5.1 (continued)

Now would be a good time to add the important details of glycolysis to your summary diagram. ◀

5.3   Stage 2: the link reaction

The two pyruvate molecules produced in glycolysis now move from the cytosol to the mitochondrion, passing through both outer and inner membranes and into the matrix (see Figure 5.2). It is here that the link reaction takes place.

In this reaction one carbon atom is lost from the 3C pyruvate molecule as carbon dioxide, leaving a 2C fragment — the very reactive **acetyl** ('asset-ile') group. This is transferred directly from pyruvate to a coenzyme called **coenzyme A** (**CoA** for short) (which was listed in Table 4.1). On combining with an acetyl group, the CoA molecule becomes **acetyl CoA**. At the same time, one molecule of NAD is reduced to NAD.2H. These simultaneous reactions are summarized in Equation 5.2.

$$\text{pyruvate} + \text{CoA} + \text{NAD} \longrightarrow \text{acetyl CoA} + CO_2 + \text{NAD.2H} \qquad (5.2)$$

The important point to remember about the link reaction is that the 2C acetyl group still contains some of the energy originally trapped in the glucose molecule and it is this group that is fed into the TCA cycle. In addition, some NAD.2H has been produced and this is eventually oxidized in the mitochondrion in Stage 4.

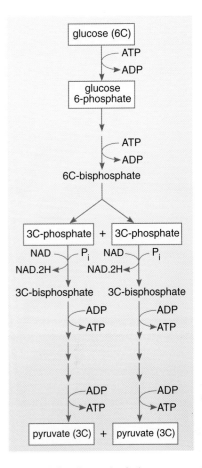

Figure 5.3   Stage 1 of glucose oxidation: glycolysis. Note that the short-hand term '6C-bisphosphate' means a six-carbon compound with two phosphate groups, whereas 'glucose 6-phosphate' is glucose with a phosphate group on its carbon atom 6 (Figure 3.9 shows the carbon atom numbering in glucose).

Question 5.2 Which of the following statements apply to glycolysis, the link reaction, or both?

(a) ATP is produced; (b) a 6C compound is split into two molecules of a 3C compound; (c) it occurs in the cytosol; (d) NAD.2H is produced. ◀

Activity 5.1 (continued)

Now would be a good time to add the important details of the link reaction to your summary diagram. ◀

5.4 Stage 3: the TCA cycle

The 2C acetyl group (carried by CoA) is now dealt with by the TCA cycle (Figure 5.4). Like the link reaction, this circular sequence of enzyme-catalysed reactions occurs in the fluid-filled matrix of the mitochondrion. The overall change brought about by this cycle is the breaking of the C—C bond in the acetyl group, thus producing two molecules of carbon dioxide for each acetyl group entering the cycle.

Figure 5.4 Details of the TCA (tricarboxylic acid) cycle. The numbers 1–8 refer to the reactions that make up the cycle. OAA is the abbreviation for oxaloacetate.

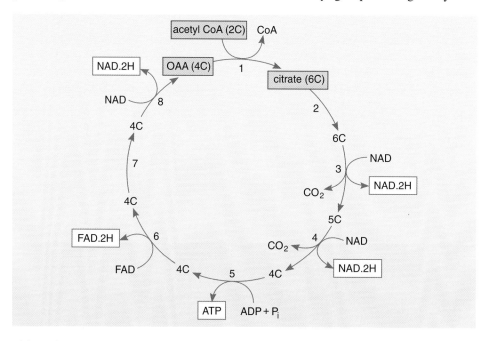

This pathway is a cycle because one of the two compounds that take part in the first reaction (1) is regenerated at the end of the cycle, as shown in Figure 5.4.

⬤ From Figure 5.4, what are the two compounds that react together in reaction 1, and which one of these is regenerated at the end of the cycle?

○ The two compounds that take part in reaction 1 are acetyl CoA (whose acetyl group is removed, releasing CoA again) and the 4C intermediate, oxaloacetate (OAA). Oxaloacetate is regenerated in the last reaction (8) of the cycle.

You can see from Figure 5.4 that the product of reaction 1 of the TCA cycle is *citrate*, a 6C compound — as indeed you would expect from combining 4C oxaloacetate with a 2C acetyl group. The 6C citrate is converted to another 6C intermediate, which is then converted via a 5C intermediate to series of 4C intermediates, the last one of these being *oxaloacetate* (produced in reaction 8).

○ What happens to the two carbon atoms that are lost between 6C and 4C?

○ They are converted to carbon dioxide (in reactions 3 and 4 of Figure 5.4).

During the TCA cycle hydrogen atoms are also 'lost'.

○ Where have these hydrogen atoms gone?

○ They have been picked up by coenzymes, mainly NAD, forming the reduced coenzymes, mainly NAD.2H, that are so important for making ATP in the final stage of glucose oxidation. (Another coenzyme shown in Figure 5.4 (and also listed in Table 4.1) is FAD, which, like NAD, carries pairs of hydrogen atoms.)

You may find it helpful to refer back to your summary diagram or to Figure 5.1, to remind yourself of the whole picture at this point. Some ATP is made directly during each turn of the TCA cycle (reaction 5 in Figure 5.4), like the ATP produced in glycolysis. But as we shall see, most of the cell's ATP is synthesized while dealing with the reduced coenzymes produced in Stages 1–3.

For each turn of the cycle, acetyl CoA has to be fed in from outside, from pyruvate via the link reaction as just described. Because *two* molecules of acetyl CoA are produced from each glucose molecule, the cycle has to turn *twice* to deal with both of them. (Some people remember this by thinking of the TCA cycle as the TCA *bi*cycle!)

The important points to remember about the TCA cycle are listed below.

• The remaining carbon atoms of glucose are released as carbon dioxide.

• A large quantity of reduced coenzyme molecules are formed. (These are oxidized in Stage 4.)

• Some ATP is produced.

• Useful 4C and 5C intermediates are formed. (We shall return to these later.)

Question 5.3   Which of the following statements about glucose oxidation are true and which are false?

(a) Carbon dioxide is produced in glycolysis.

(b) A 4C intermediate of the TCA cycle combines with pyruvate to give a 6C compound.

(c) One turn of the TCA cycle produces one molecule of carbon dioxide.

(d) The carbon dioxide we breathe out is produced in the mitochondria. ◀

Activity 5.1 (continued)

Now would be a good time to add the important details of the TCA cycle to your summary diagram. ◀

5.5   Stage 4: electron transport and oxidative phosphorylation

In the overall equation for glucose oxidation, the one substance that we have not considered so far is oxygen. We spend our lives extracting it from the atmosphere by breathing, and effectively all of it is used in the mitochondria in the last stage of glucose respiration. This stage comprises two processes which are *coupled*: first, *electron transport*, which brings about the oxidation of NAD.2H to NAD by oxygen;

and second, *oxidative phosphorylation*, which is the associated production of ATP from ADP and P_i. The overall reaction of Stage 4 can be summarized as:

$$NAD.2H + \tfrac{1}{2}O_2 + 3ADP + 3P_i \longrightarrow NAD + H_2O + 3ATP \qquad (5.3)$$

(Here we are considering just one molecule of NAD.2H, hence only *half* an oxygen molecule is required to balance the equation.)

Recall that the production of ATP from ADP + P_i is an energy-requiring reaction and is always coupled to an energy-releasing reaction (You met this coupling in Section 4.5.3 and it is illustrated in the left half of Figure 4.9.) We deal first with the oxidation of reduced NAD.2H, and then ask how this reaction releases energy for the phosphorylation of ADP. Although, for convenience, we consider oxidation of NAD.2H and phosphorylation of ADP separately, it is important to realize that the two processes occur simultaneously — they are coupled.

5.5.1 Electron transport

Here we consider the first of the two linked processes, the oxidation of the reduced coenzyme NAD.2H. Looking back at Figure 5.1 will reveal that NAD.2H is produced in all three of the preceding stages of glucose oxidation but that most of it is produced in Stage 3, the TCA cycle. NAD.2H is processed in Stage 4.

The oxidation of reduced coenzymes inside the mitochondrion in Stage 4 does not occur in a single step, but is brought about by a series of steps involving membrane components known as *electron carriers*, which form the **electron transport chain (ETC)**. As Figure 5.5 shows, the ETC is made up of five carriers, numbered 1–5. This figure also shows that at the beginning of the electron transport chain the hydrogen atoms are removed from NAD.2H, and at the end of the chain molecular oxygen comes in to oxidize the hydrogen atoms to water. The overall reaction is summarized in Equation 5.4.

$$NAD.2H + \tfrac{1}{2}O_2 \longrightarrow NAD + H_2O \qquad (5.4)$$

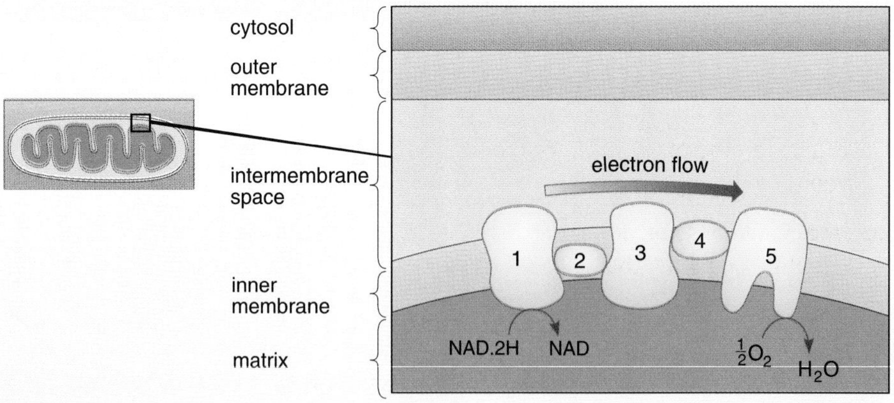

Figure 5.5 The electron transport chain consists of five electron carriers, numbered 1–5 in order of increasing electron affinity. The carriers are alternately reduced and oxidized as electrons are transported down the chain. The relative size and shape of each carrier is shown, as determined by electron microscopy.

However, the situation is more complicated and more intriguing than Equation 5.4 might lead you to believe. As its name implies, the electron transport chain does not transport hydrogen atoms at all; it transports *electrons*. As you know from Blocks 7 and 8, a hydrogen atom is composed of a positively charged proton and a negatively charged electron (e^-), so the H^+ ion that is formed when the electron is removed from the atom is just a single proton. In Stage 4 of glucose oxidation, these two components of the hydrogen atom are processed separately.

The electron carriers can readily accommodate extra electrons. Those carriers that bind electrons more tightly than other carriers are said to have a higher *electron affinity*. Carriers are arranged in the inner mitochondrial membrane in order of increasing electron affinity. In this way they form a chain that can pass electrons from NAD.2H bound to the first carrier, to molecular oxygen bound to the last carrier, as illustrated in Figure 5.5. The electron affinity of the first carrier is high enough to remove a pair of electrons from the hydrogens in NAD.2H, leaving the two protons in the large pool of protons and other ions and molecules in the mitochondrial matrix. Carrier 2 removes the electrons from carrier 1, and so on down the chain. Eventually electrons reach the last carrier, carrier 5, an enzyme known as *cytochrome oxidase*. Cytochrome oxidase releases the electrons to molecular oxygen, which combines with the protons drawn from the surrounding matrix to form water (Figure 5.5).

So even though electrons do not appear in the overall equation for NAD.2H oxidation, their role is vital. We can break down Equation 5.4 into two separate parts that show how the two components of the hydrogen atom are processed separately. At the beginning of the chain NAD.2H loses its 2H as two protons and two electrons:

$$NAD.2H \longrightarrow NAD + 2H^+ + 2e^- \tag{5.5}$$

and at the end molecular oxygen accepts the protons and electrons, so becoming water, as in Equation 5.6.

$$2H^+ + 2e^- + \tfrac{1}{2}O_2 \longrightarrow H_2O \tag{5.6}$$

So the oxidation of glucose is now complete — oxygen has entered the process at last and water has been produced. Look back to Equation 5.1 to remind yourself of the whole reaction. Once relieved of its 2H 'passenger group', the NAD can be recycled to pick up more 2H pairs.

Interestingly, the oxygen-binding site of the last carrier, cytochrome oxidase, can be irreversibly blocked by both cyanide and carbon monoxide, preventing it from binding oxygen. Hence the disastrous effects of these poisons on aerobic organisms (such as ourselves).

● Can you explain what would happen at the biochemical level if potassium cyanide entered the mitochondrion?

○ Electron transport would stop because the final electron carrier would no longer be able to bind oxygen. Consequently, NAD.2H could not be oxidized, so NAD would not be regenerated.

The other vital consequence of the fact that NAD.2H could not be oxidized is that there would be no oxidative phosphorylation, so very little ATP would be produced.

In the next section, we look at the process that links electron transport to oxidative phosphorylation, i.e. the way that the chemical energy made available from the oxidation of reduced coenzymes becomes chemical energy in molecules of ATP.

Question 5.4   Which of the following biological transformations directly involves: (i) the breaking of a C−C bond; (ii) reduction of NAD to NAD.2H; (iii) electron transport within the inner mitochondrial membrane?

(a) $NAD.2H + \tfrac{1}{2}O_2 \longrightarrow NAD + H_2O$

(b) glucose $\longrightarrow$ 2 pyruvate

(c) pyruvate + CoA $\longrightarrow$ acetyl CoA + CO_2

(d) acetyl CoA $\longrightarrow$ CoA + $2CO_2$ ◀

5.5.2 Oxidative phosphorylation

In this section we look at how ATP is produced as electrons are transferred along the electron transport chain. A major outcome of glucose oxidation is the transfer of energy from glucose to ATP, but so far we have mentioned only the few ATP molecules that are produced directly in glycolysis and the TCA cycle. As you have seen, the transfer of hydrogen atoms from NAD.2H to oxygen takes place in several steps. This is not surprising; if the NAD.2H were oxidized directly by oxygen, there would be unacceptably large amounts of energy released (as heat), which might damage the cell, as well as being wasteful. The small oxidation (electron transfer) steps ensure the controlled release of energy, which is tapped off into making ATP. However, the energy released during electron transfer from NAD.2H is not harnessed *directly* into the production of ATP. Rather it is used for 'pumping' protons from the mitochondrial matrix into the intermembrane space, and ATP is generated when protons flow back into the matrix.

The link between the electron transport in Stage 4 and ATP synthesis is described by the **chemiosmotic hypothesis**, which was proposed by the British biochemist, Peter Mitchell (Figure 5.6). For this work he was awarded the Nobel prize for Medicine and Physiology in 1978. An important clue to the nature of this link came from experiments with mitochondria isolated from cells and suspended in a medium supplied with nutrients and oxygen. Such mitochondria can oxidize NAD.2H and simultaneously form ATP, but only if they are not damaged, and in particular, if the inner mitochondrial membrane (see Figure 5.5) is still intact.

The inner membrane is largely made up of electron carriers, as shown in Figure 5.5. However, three of these simultaneously act as **proton pumps**, as shown in Figure 5.7. The discovery of proton pumps in oxidative phosphorylation revolutionized scientists' way of thinking about energy transformations in the cell. Proton pumping provides a way of linking energy from electron transport to ATP synthesis.

Figure 5.6 Peter Mitchell (1920–1992), working in the UK, in 1961 proposed the chemiosmotic hypothesis, according to which electron transport and ATP synthesis are linked by a proton gradient across the inner mitochondrial membrane. He regarded experimental results as of prime importance and made predominant contributions towards establishing the validity of the hypothesis. As with many revolutionary hypotheses, it took a number of years to convince an initially hostile scientific community. In fact, proton gradients have now been found to power a variety of energy-requiring processes in biology, including the synthesis of ATP in chloroplasts.

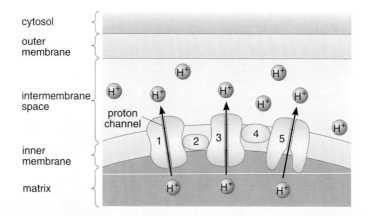

Figure 5.7 Three of the five electron carriers in the electron transport chain are also proton pumps, which transfer protons (H^+) from the matrix across the inner membrane and into the intermembrane space.

Proton pumps are membrane proteins that have a central channel for moving or 'pumping' protons from one side of the membrane to the other. This movement of protons requires energy and the energy used is that made available from electron transport. As electrons are transferred along the ETC, protons are moved out of the mitochondrial matrix, through the proton channels, and into the intermembrane space (Figure 5.7). Thus the concentration of protons in the intermembrane space becomes progressively greater than that in the mitochondrial matrix. Hence a proton *concentration gradient* is formed, with a low concentration in the matrix and a high concentration in the intermembrane space, as shown in Figure 5.7.

The result of proton pumping is that energy from electron transport is now effectively *stored*, because there is a proton concentration gradient between the intermembrane space and the matrix of the mitochondrion. This energy can be released, simply by allowing protons to move in the reverse direction, i.e. *down* their concentration gradient, from high to low concentration. In fact, the protons are allowed to flood back into the matrix through a different channel protein, which is also an enzyme, called **ATP synthase** (Figure 5.8).

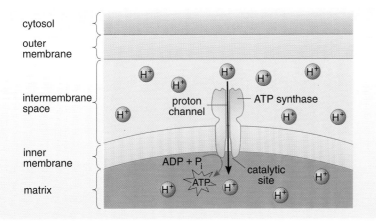

Figure 5.8   ATP synthase, a proton channel protein in the inner mitochondrial membrane, which allows protons to flow down their concentration gradient from the intermembrane space into the matrix and at the same time converts ADP + P_i to ATP. (For clarity, only one ATP synthase molecule is shown here.)

This storage and flow of protons is analogous to a pumped water storage system for producing electricity. In such a system, electricity is used in off-peak periods to pump water from a lower-level reservoir to a higher-level reservoir, where it is stored. This process transforms electrical energy into the gravitational energy of water. During peak hours the water is allowed to flow down from the higher- to the lower-level reservoir through turbines — large water-wheels — coupled to electricity generators. So in this process the stored gravitational energy of the water is converted back to electrical energy. In this analogy, the water is the protons, the pumps are carriers 1, 3 and 5, the higher reservoir is the intermembrane space, the lower reservoir is the mitochondrial matrix, and the turbine is the ATP synthase.

As the name 'ATP synthase' suggests, this enzyme catalyses the formation of ATP from ADP and P_i. Thus the energy released in the transfer of electrons along the ETC to oxygen is first used to pump protons, thereby becoming stored as a proton concentration gradient; as the protons flood back through the ATP synthase channel, this energy is used to convert ADP + P_i to ATP.

● Why must the inner mitochondrial membrane be intact for ATP synthesis to occur?

⬤ To produce the concentration gradient necessary for ATP synthesis, the protons must be pumped across the inner membrane and be stored within the intermembrane space. If the inner membrane is broken, protons will leak back into the matrix.

Thus if the inner mitochondrial membrane is damaged it is impossible to maintain a proton concentration gradient, so the energy from electron transport can no longer be coupled to ATP synthesis. Large amounts of glucose would still be broken down to carbon dioxide and water, because electrons would still flow from NAD.2H to oxygen, but the energy would be lost as heat, and no ATP would be produced. An ideal slimming pill would be a drug that could alter the inner membrane temporarily, and disconnect, or *uncouple*, electron transport from ATP synthesis! Unfortunately no such uncoupler drug has been found to do this safely. A highly unsafe uncoupler was used in World War I, quite by accident. This compound, an explosive called 2,4-dinitrophenol (2,4-DNP) was packed into shells by female munitions workers, many of whom became ill. These women had absorbed 2,4-DNP through the skin, and some of the compound had entered the mitochondria and damaged the inner membrane. If the inner membrane is not intact, no change in proton distribution can build up during electron transport, because protons leak back into the matrix, so no ATP is made. The operation of the electron transport chain without ATP production generates a lot of heat and can lead to severe and sometimes fatal weight loss.

A summary of Stages 2–4 of glucose breakdown (i.e. the stages occurring in the mitochondrion) is shown in Figure 5.9.

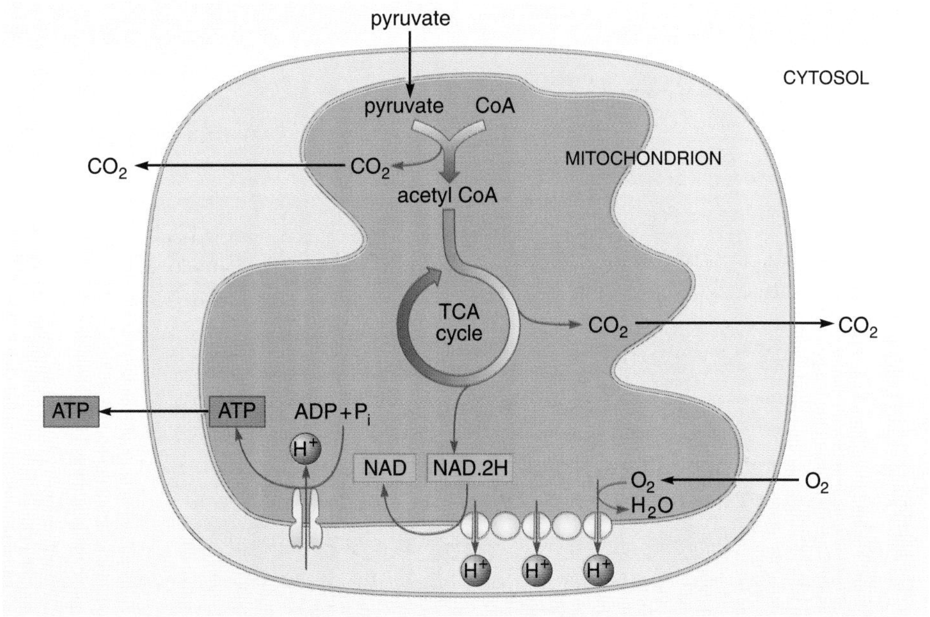

Figure 5.9 A summary of Stages 2–4 of the process of glucose breakdown, all of which take place in the mitochondrion. The starting point is pyruvate, the end-product of glycolysis which occurs in the cytosol. (In reality, the electron carriers and ATP synthase occur along the whole of the inner mitochondrial membrane.)

The vast majority of ATP is made by oxidative phosphorylation in the mitochondria. As we have seen, this process involves an energy-releasing reaction, the oxidation of NAD.2H, coupled to an energy-requiring reaction, the phosphorylation of ADP. This is a different mechanism from the direct production of ATP in glycolysis and the TCA cycle (Figures 5.3 and 5.4), which does not involve electron transport to oxygen. This second type of phosphorylation is called **substrate-level phosphorylation**. Here the intermediates contain phosphate groups that are transferred directly to ADP to produce ATP. In certain conditions, substrate-level phosphorylation can be crucially important to cells, as explained in Box 5.1, *Respiration without oxygen*.

Box 5.1 *Respiration without oxygen*

Cells sometimes temporarily have no, or a much reduced, oxygen supply. One such example is muscle cells in mammals, including humans. Muscles can exhaust their supply of oxygen, for example, in a herbivore escaping from the attack of a carnivore, or a human running for a bus, and under these conditions they resort to **anaerobic respiration** (meaning respiration in the absence of oxygen) instead of the usual aerobic respiration. Thus muscles can continue to contract in the absence of oxygen and ATP is produced entirely by substrate-level phosphorylation.

In anaerobic respiration in muscles, the only energy-producing process in operation is glycolysis. Figure 5.3 showed that during glycolysis some NAD.2H is produced. Because oxygen is not present, this reduced coenzyme cannot be oxidized via the ETC. Under anaerobic conditions, pyruvate — the end-product of glycolysis — serves as the oxidizing agent (hydrogen acceptor). The pyruvate is reduced to lactate by the two hydrogen atoms from NAD.2H. The enzyme involved is one you have met already (Section 4.4.1), lactate dehydrogenase (LDH), which is present in the cytosol.

$$\text{C}_3\text{H}_4\text{O}_3 + \text{NAD.2H} \overset{\text{LDH}}{\rightleftharpoons} \text{C}_3\text{H}_6\text{O}_3 + \text{NAD} \qquad (5.7)$$
$$\text{pyruvate} \qquad\qquad\qquad \text{lactate}$$

Notice that this is the reverse of the reaction in Equation 4.2.

Figure 5.3 also showed that during glycolysis some ATP is produced. In fact, four molecules of ATP are formed but two molecules are used to activate the glucose, making a net gain of only two molecules of ATP per molecule of glucose. This is an extremely small yield compared with the 36 molecules produced by the complete oxidation of glucose (Section 4.5.4). Nevertheless, the production of this relatively small amount of ATP is sufficient for muscle contraction to continue, and since the NAD.2H is converted back to NAD the process of glycolysis can continue — at least for a while.

● Are mitochondria involved in anaerobic respiration?

○ No, because glycolysis occurs in the cytosol.

Anaerobic respiration leads to a build-up of lactate in muscles. You may be aware of this during exercise, because it causes the muscles to feel stiff. When exercise is over, the large amount of lactate that has accumulated is oxidized back to pyruvate, and this reaction is catalysed by lactate dehydrogenase (Equation 4.2). This reaction requires large amounts of oxygen (to oxidize the NAD.2H produced), which is provided by the deep and rapid breathing that continues for some time after physical activity has ceased.

Many organisms can live without any oxygen; for example, the bacterium that causes tetanus is an anaerobic organism. Yeast can live with or without oxygen, depending upon the environment. In aerobic conditions, respiration in yeast is the same as that described earlier. However, under anaerobic conditions, the NAD required for the continuation of glycolysis is regenerated, not via lactate formation, but by the process of *fermentation*. Here, the pyruvate is converted, via two steps, to alcohol and carbon dioxide — hence the use of yeast in the brewing and bread-making industries.

Question 5.5   Stage 4 of glucose oxidation includes oxidative phosphorylation. (a) What is oxidized and (b) what is phosphorylated in this process? ◄

Question 5.6   What changes, if any, take place in the distribution of protons on either side of the inner mitochondrial membrane during electron transport:

(a) when the membrane is intact?

(b) when 2,4-dinitrophenol (2,4-DNP) is present?

(c) when the oxygen-binding site of cytochrome oxidase is blocked by carbon monoxide? ◄

Activity 5.1 (continued)

Now would be a good time to add the important details of both Stage 4 of glucose oxidation and anaerobic respiration to your summary diagram and then to review your completed diagram. ◄

Activity 5.2 The 'power-house of the cell'

This activity will help you to review your understanding of the series of reactions involved in the transfer of energy stored in pyruvate to ATP production in the mitochondrion, by drawing a flow diagram. ◄

5.6   Integration of metabolism

Besides carbohydrates, most heterotrophs also consume substantial quantities of triacylglycerols (TAGs) and proteins. And in both animals and plants there is continuous synthesis and breakdown of TAGs and proteins as part of cellular turnover. Therefore, we would expect there to be effective biochemical systems for catabolizing these substances — and indeed there are. In this section, we examine these systems, focusing mainly on animals, particularly mammals.

Since this section will involve a discussion of TAGs and proteins, introduced in Section 3, it will help you first to revise the structures of these molecules. We begin, however, by looking at glycogen, because this is the energy source that animals use first.

● Describe the structure of glycogen.

○ It is composed of branched chains of glucose monomers (Section 3.4).

● What are the breakdown products of TAGs?

○ Fatty acids and glycerol (Section 3.6.1).

● What are the monomer units of proteins and what is the name of the type of bond that links these monomers together in a polypeptide chain?

○ Amino acids are linked by peptide bonds in a polypeptide chain (Section 3.3.2).

Fatty acids, glycerol and amino acids, produced by the hydrolysis of TAGs and proteins, are used by cells for both biosynthetic and catabolic processes. The points at which they feed into the glucose oxidation pathway are shown in Figure 5.10. This *central pathway* is shown by the thicker arrows in the figure. The other arrows indicate pathways that are linked to the central pathway. Thus the pathway of glucose breakdown is central to metabolism, and the information summarized in Figure 5.10 is the focus of Sections 5.6.1–5.6.3.

5.6.1   Blood sugar levels and glycogen

The control mechanisms that coordinate the breakdown of different energy sources in cells are complex. But in addition to these control mechanisms within individual cells, of crucial importance is regulation at the level of the whole organism. In mammals, including humans, one such vitally important mechanism keeps blood glucose level constant. This is particularly important for the brain, which has no energy reserves of its own and relies on glucose from the blood.

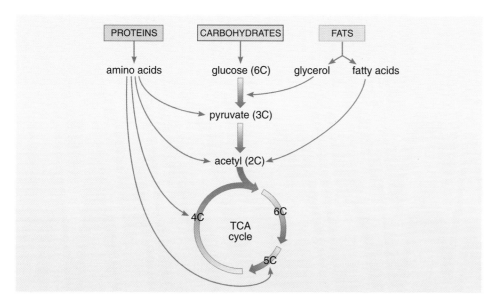

Figure 5.10 Links between the glucose oxidation pathway and the oxidation of other nutrients, which feed into this central pathway. For example, there are amino acids that join the central pathway at various points.

Immediately after a meal, glucose floods into the bloodstream, and most of it is converted into glycogen in the liver and muscles, where it is stored. As blood glucose level falls between meals, glycogen is hydrolysed to glucose. In the muscles, this glucose is used directly by the tissue, whereas in the liver it is released slowly back into the bloodstream. In this way, an adequate blood glucose concentration is maintained. Between meals, glucose is taken up from the bloodstream continuously by the cells of the body, so the blood glucose pool has to be continuously replenished by mobilization of the glycogen stores. This is summarized in Figure 5.11.

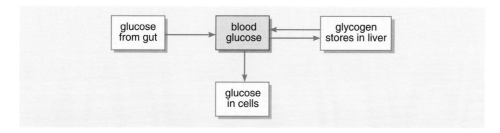

Figure 5.11 The balance between glycogen stores and blood glucose. The two full arrows between blood glucose and liver glycogen stores indicate that the glycogen synthesis pathway is not simply the reverse of the pathway that releases glucose from glycogen. Each pathway comprises a different set of reactions.

In order to appreciate the regulation of blood glucose level, consider the following data. The normal level of blood glucose in humans before breakfast is 4.5–5.5 millimoles per litre ($mmol\,l^{-1}$). After a meal containing carbohydrates (for example, a breakfast of cornflakes with milk and sugar) the level will rise temporarily to around $7\,mmol\,l^{-1}$. Going without food for 24 hours will cause the level of blood glucose to fall to around $3.5\,mmol\,l^{-1}$, but the level will not normally fall further even if fasting is prolonged. This minimum level is maintained by the release of glucose from glycogen stores. So constant topping up from glycogen stores ensures that the blood glucose level is kept within narrow limits. How is this level maintained? The answer to this question is given in Box 5.2, *Hormones and the regulation of blood glucose level*.

Box 5.2 Hormones and the regulation of blood glucose level

The balance between blood glucose level and glycogen stores is regulated by hormones which are secreted into the bloodstream. A hormone is a 'chemical messenger', which is produced in very small quantities in one part of an organism and transported, via the bloodstream, to a *target tissue*, where it exerts an effect. (You met the hormone adrenalin in Block 8.) One of the hormones that regulates blood sugar level is a protein called *insulin*. Food intake triggers the release of insulin from an abdominal organ called the pancreas. The main effects of insulin are to promote the transfer of glucose from the bloodstream into cells, particularly liver and muscle cells, and to promote its conversion into glycogen. Hence the rise in blood glucose level after a carbohydrate-containing meal is only temporary.

Individuals who produce only a low level of insulin in their blood have one form of *diabetes*, and can be treated by injecting insulin. A constant supply is essential, since insulin is rapidly broken down in the body.

○ Why do you think insulin has to be given by injection, rather than by mouth?

○ Since insulin is a protein, if taken by mouth, it would be broken down by digestive enzymes in the gut before it could reach the bloodstream (see Box 4.2).

{Another form of diabetes is common in older people whose bodies no longer respond to the insulin they secrete. Injecting insulin clearly will not help these diabetic individuals, and the treatment here is by diet and/or drugs.}

As blood glucose level falls between meals, or during bouts of exercise, when the muscles use large quantities of glucose, insulin secretion is greatly reduced and another hormone, *glucagon* ('glue-ka-gon'), is released into the blood. Glucagon stimulates the breakdown of glycogen stores in the liver and muscles and the release of glucose from the liver into the bloodstream. Thus the effects of glucagon on liver and muscle cells are opposite to those of insulin.

So stored glycogen can be used to provide glucose to fuel the metabolism of body cells. However, glycogen stores are limited, even in a well-fed animal. During prolonged exercise, or if there is a long period without food intake, the body must turn to its alternative energy stores — TAGs (fats).

5.6.2 Energy from triacylglycerols

As well as sugars, both fatty acids and glycerol (released by the hydrolysis of TAGs) can be used by cells to provide energy. The hormone glucagon not only stimulates the release of glucose from the liver but also promotes the mobilization of fat reserves from adipose tissue. (We use the terms 'TAGs' and 'fat' interchangeably here.) Quantitatively, fat is usually more important as an energy store than glycogen. On average, an adult human stores enough glycogen to last for only about a day of typical activities, but enough fat to last at least a month. This is partly because the body stores a much greater quantity of fat than glycogen and partly because the oxidation of fatty acids generates about six times as much energy as the oxidation of the same mass of glycogen.

When TAGs are broken down to generate energy, they are first hydrolysed to fatty acids and glycerol. The glycerol is eventually converted to a 3C intermediate of glycolysis, as shown in Figure 5.10. The fatty acids are converted via another catabolic pathway into acetyl groups, which are carried by CoA (Figure 5.10). This acetyl CoA then feeds into the TCA cycle.

CoA can accept acetyl groups from either fatty acids or pyruvate (in the link reaction). However, whether the acetyl groups come from fatty acids or from glucose depends on the availability of these fuels. As long as there is sufficient glucose, the oxidation of fats is suppressed. A high-energy diet, rich in both carbohydrates and fats (as is common in the Western world) may eventually lead to obesity, because the carbohydrates meet most of the energy needs of the body and so the excess fat consumed get stored in adipose tissue. (Carbohydrate consumed in excess of requirements can also be converted into fat and stored.)

● Imagine a person on a low-energy diet. What will be happening to their TAG stores?

○ They will be slowly broken down, via fatty acids to acetyl CoA, which will be catabolized in the TCA cycle, thereby making up the shortfall in energy provision from the diet.

Such a diet would lead to weight loss over time as more and more of the stored TAGs would be mobilized to provide energy for the rest of the body.

5.6.3 Catabolism of proteins

Protein breakdown happens all the time as part of body maintenance, as discussed in Section 4.1. But proteins can also serve as an energy source. When amino acids from protein digestion in the gut (Box 4.2) are in excess of the body's requirements for growth and maintenance, they are broken down to provide energy, and in periods of extreme starvation body proteins, particularly muscle proteins, can be catabolized to provide energy.

When proteins are broken down, they are first split into the individual amino acid monomers. Since there are 20 of these (Section 3.3.2), there are 20 different starting points to their catabolic routes. However, we will concentrate only on the general principles of amino acid catabolism. In all cases the amino group (NH_2) is first removed, and the remaining non-nitrogenous acids, either directly or after further catabolism, feed into the central pathway at one of a number of points: to pyruvate (at the end of glycolysis), to acetyl CoA (after the link reaction) or to one of several TCA cycle intermediates (see Figure 5.10). A proportion of the amino groups are recycled in the process of amino acid biosynthesis and the rest are ultimately excreted; for example, as urea, in the urine of humans.

In conclusion, we emphasize that the catabolism of all energy stores proceeds ultimately via the central pathway of glucose catabolism.

5.7 Biosynthetic pathways

Growth and survival depend on a well ordered system of cell biochemistry, involving an adjustable balance of interrelated catabolism and biosynthesis — the point in Section 4 where we began. The main focus of Section 5 is catabolic pathways, but here is a good point to introduce biosynthetic pathways and look at the relationship between the two types of pathway. As well as providing energy for biosynthesis, catabolic processes also provide a whole range of *precursors*, the small organic molecules or groups from which other molecules are made (Figure 4.1). For example, the acetyl group is a precursor of cholesterol (a type of lipid) in mammals and vitamin A in plants.

Oxidation and reduction reactions are central to energy metabolism. We have seen that the chemical energy in food molecules is *released* in catabolic oxidative reactions. However, the synthesis of biological molecules involves reduction reactions and *requires* energy. Because of the energy requirements, biosynthetic pathways, (e.g. glycogen synthesis, fatty acid synthesis) are not simply the reverse of the corresponding catabolic routes, although there may be some reactions that are common to both (such as the interconversion of pyruvate and lactate; Section 4.4.1 and Box 5.1).

In this block we consider two biosynthetic processes. One is protein synthesis, which in most cells requires more energy than any other biosynthetic activity. The production of proteins must be highly regulated within the cell, because each cell type has its own characteristic set of proteins (as described in Section 3.3) and each protein has a specific sequence of amino acids (Section 3.2.2). The synthesis of proteins in the cell is achieved by a complex sequence of steps. Recall from Section 2 that ribosomes, studded in the endoplasmic reticulum which pervades the cytosol (Figure 2.2), are the sites of protein synthesis. How the cell synthesizes proteins, each with its own specific sequence of amino acids, is the subject of Sections 10 and 11.

The other biosynthetic process that we look at in this block is one that stands apart from all others. This is photosynthesis, and is the focus of the next section.

Question 5.7   Which of the following statements about metabolism in mammals are true?

(a) Biosynthetic pathways involve the conversion of ATP to ADP + P_i.

(b) The breakdown of amino acids involves first removing the carboxylic acid (COOH) group.

(c) Insulin helps to control the blood glucose level by stimulating the uptake of glucose by cells that can synthesize and store glycogen.

(d) The pathways of fat and protein catabolism both merge with the glucose oxidation pathway. ◄

5.8   Summary of Section 5

Glucose is oxidized in the cell in four consecutive stages: glycolysis, which takes place in the cytosol; the link reaction and the tricarboxylic acid (TCA) cycle, both of which take place in the mitochondrial matrix; and electron transport coupled to oxidative phosphorylation, which occur in the inner mitochondrial membrane.

In glycolysis, each molecule of glucose is broken down to two molecules of pyruvate, a 3C compound. Only two molecules of ATP are gained per molecule of glucose broken down.

In the link reaction, each pyruvate molecule is further broken down to carbon dioxide and an acetyl group, which is transferred to coenzyme A. Thus for each glucose molecule broken down, two acetyl groups are formed.

Each acetyl group is transferred, at the beginning of the TCA cycle, to a 4C molecule, oxaloacetate (OAA), forming a 6C compound, citrate. The latter is converted, via a series of 6C, 5C and 4C intermediates, to OAA again, thus completing one turn of the cycle. Two molecules of carbon dioxide, one ATP molecule and several molecules of reduced coenzymes — mainly NAD.2H — are formed with each turn of the cycle. For each glucose molecule broken down the cycle turns twice.

The ATP formation that occurs in glycolysis and the TCA cycle is called substrate-level phosphorylation.

The reduced coenzymes are reoxidized as electrons from the hydrogen atoms they carry are passed along the electron transport chain (ETC). The ETC is a series of electron carriers arranged in the inner mitochondrial membrane in order of increasing electron affinity. The last electron carrier, cytochrome oxidase, passes the electrons to oxygen.

Three of the carriers in the ETC are also proton pumps. Using the energy of electron transport they pump protons against their concentration gradient (from low concentration to high), out of the mitochondrial matrix and into the intermembrane space. The protons flood back across the inner mitochondrial membrane through the proton channel of ATP synthase, and the energy released is used to synthesize ATP from $ADP + P_i$. This is oxidative phosphorylation. Most of the ATP obtained by the oxidation of glucose is produced in this way.

Anaerobic respiration occurs in mammals in the absence of oxygen. Glycolysis continues one step beyond pyruvate with the reduction of pyruvate to lactate by NAD.2H (produced earlier in glycolysis). This regenerates NAD and so allows glycolysis to continue.

In mammals, glucose is stored as glycogen in muscle and liver. Between meals, glycogen is hydrolysed to release glucose. Blood glucose level is regulated by hormones, including insulin and glucagon.

Glycerol from hydrolysis of fat (TAG) stores enters the central pathway at a point within glycolysis. Fatty acids are converted to acetyl groups and feed into the TCA cycle, as acetyl CoA.

The catabolism of amino acids links to the central pathway at a number of points: to pyruvate (at the end of glycolysis), to acetyl CoA (after the link reaction) and to several TCA cycle intermediates.

Oxidation and reduction reactions are central to the production and utilization of energy in cells.

6 Photosynthesis

Nearly all life depends on the energy of sunlight (solar energy). All green plants and some bacteria need light in order to survive (Blocks 2 and 4). They convert solar energy into chemical energy by the process of photosynthesis, and store this chemical energy as sugars and polysaccharides. These organisms are autotrophs, since carbon dioxide is their source of carbon (Block 4, Section 2.3).

Photosynthesis is one of the most important chemical processes in nature because it is the process on which most of metabolism depends. We begin by revising the overall process of photosynthesis by comparing it with the complementary process of respiration, and then examine it in some detail. The CD-ROM activity 'Cells and energy' (Section 7, Activity 7.1) will enable you to consolidate your understanding of the main principles of photosynthesis.

6.1 Overview

The essential feature of photosynthesis is that solar energy is converted by means of the pigment chlorophyll in the chloroplasts into chemical energy in sugar. (You met chloroplasts in Section 2.1.) The overall reaction for photosynthesis is:

$$6CO_2 + 6H_2O + \text{solar energy} \longrightarrow C_6H_{12}O_6 + 6O_2 \qquad (6.1)$$

Look back at Equation 5.1, which is the equation for glucose oxidation (respiration). What is the relationship between the substrate for respiration and the main product of photosynthesis?

They have the same molecular formula — that of a 6C sugar, $C_6H_{12}O_6$.

We shall look at the sugars produced in photosynthesis in more detail later, but for now we will assume that all the sugar produced is glucose. Photosynthesis produces sugar, which has two main fates:

(a) It can be oxidized by respiration to liberate energy for the numerous energy-requiring activities of the plant.

(b) It can be used for the biosynthesis of all the other organic molecules that make up the plant. (Of course (a) is also required to provide the energy for these biosynthetic activities.)

Comparing Equations 5.1 and 6.1 again, what is the relationship between the raw materials of photosynthesis and the final products of respiration?

They are the same. The carbon dioxide and water that are combined into sugar by photosynthesis are released when sugar is broken down by respiration.

In chemical terms, photosynthesis is the exact reverse of respiration. Whereas in respiration *sugar is oxidized* and *energy is released*, in photosynthesis *carbon dioxide is reduced*, and *energy* (solar energy) is *required*. Look back at Figure 3.9, which shows the structural formula of glucose. For each of the six carbon atoms of glucose there is just one oxygen atom and two hydrogen atoms, whereas the starting compound, carbon dioxide, CO_2, has two oxygen atoms (and no hydrogen atoms) per carbon atom. In photosynthesis, it can be shown that the hydrogen atoms in glucose come from water, H_2O — just the reverse of respiration, in which hydrogen atoms are added to oxygen to *produce* water.

○ What is the general mechanism for transferring hydrogen atoms from one compound to another in a metabolic reaction?

○ Hydrogen atoms are attached to a coenzyme (such as NAD) in one reaction and transferred from the reduced coenzyme (e.g. NAD.2H) to the other compound in a second reaction. (See Section 4.4.)

In photosynthesis, the hydrogen-carrying coenzyme is *not* NAD but a phosphorylated form of this molecule, i.e. **NADP** (nicotinamide adenine dinucleotide phosphate, listed in Table 4.1). NADP behaves very much like NAD, but is generally the hydrogen carrier in biosynthetic reactions (whereas NAD is mostly involved in catabolic reactions).

6.2   Light and dark reactions

There are two distinct stages to the process of photosynthesis: the *light reactions* and the *dark reactions*. Before examining each of these stages, we will consider where they occur in the cell. In plants, both the light and the dark reactions take place in specialized organelles, the chloroplasts, which you saw in Figure 2.3. Like mitochondria, chloroplasts lie in the cytosol, are bounded by an outer membrane and also have internal membranes. In chloroplasts, the internal membranes are folded back on themselves many times to form stacks called **grana**, as can be seen in Figure 6.1. This figure shows a chloroplast at a much greater magnification than those shown in Figure 2.3.

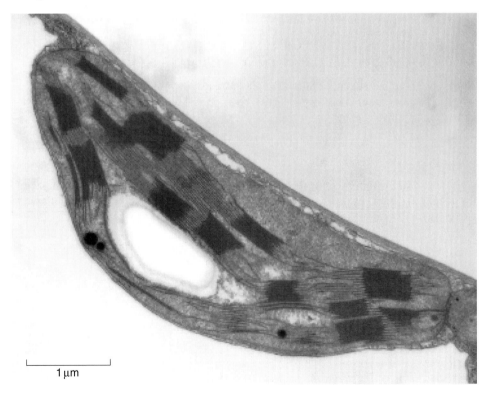

1 µm

Figure 6.1   Electron micrograph of a chloroplast from a cell of a leaf of Busy Lizzy (*Impatiens* sp.). The stacks of internal membranes, or grana, are where the light reactions occur. The stroma between the grana is where the dark reactions take place. The pale, oval structure is a starch grain.

The light and dark reactions take place in different parts of the chloroplast: the light reactions occur in the grana, since this is where the chlorophyll molecules are located; the dark reactions take place in the fluid **stroma** (equivalent to the matrix of the mitochondrion) between the grana. So the chemical division of labour is matched by the physical separation of the two reactions within the chloroplast.

In the **light reactions**, a unique photochemical reaction takes place, in which the green pigment chlorophyll traps the energy of sunlight. This energy is used to synthesize ATP from ADP and P_i and to reduce NADP to NADP.2H. Thus the light reactions can be summarized as Equation 6.2.

$$ADP + P_i + NADP + H_2O + \text{solar energy} \longrightarrow ATP + NADP.2H + \tfrac{1}{2}O_2 \qquad (6.2)$$

How is solar energy used to produce ATP and reduced coenzyme? ATP production in the chloroplast is a process similar to mitochondrial ATP synthesis, in that electrons are transferred along a chain of electron carriers that differ in electron affinity. The photosynthetic electron transport chain is very much like the one used in Stage 4 of glucose oxidation. In the chloroplast, the energy derived from sunlight is used to remove electrons from water and oxygen is produced (see Equation 6.2), whereas in the mitochondrion oxygen is used and water is produced (Equation 5.4). At the end of the photosynthetic electron transport chain, the electrons are transferred to NADP, which combines with protons present in the stroma to form NADP.2H. Thus photosynthetic electron transport uses (solar) energy to produce reduced coenzyme, while in respiration reduced coenzyme is oxidized and energy is released.

As in the inner mitochondrial membrane, the energy released during electron transport is used to pump protons to one side of the inner chloroplast membrane, thereby creating a proton concentration gradient. As the protons flow back down their concentration gradient through a membrane channel protein — which is also an ATP synthase, as in the inner mitochondrial membrane — ATP is synthesized from ADP and P_i. The formation of ATP in this way is called **photophosphorylation** (meaning *light*-driven *phosphorylation*).

Neither ATP nor NADP.2H appears in the overall Equation 6.1, because they are only intermediates and are used up in the second stage of photosynthesis, collectively termed the **dark reactions**. In fact, it can be said that the products of the light reactions *drive* the dark reactions, for the dark reactions would not occur in the absence of these light-reaction products. The relationship between the light and dark reactions is shown in Figure 6.2. Note that the dark reactions are not directly dependent on light, nor do they occur only in the dark! They use the ATP and NADP.2H from the light reactions, in a cyclic sequence of reactions, to reduce carbon dioxide, so converting it to sugars. This process is often referred to as 'carbon fixation' and the cycle of reactions is called the **Calvin cycle** (after its principal discoverer, Melvin Calvin, in 1945). Equation 6.3 summarizes the dark reactions of photosynthesis. Notice the large amounts of ATP and NADP.2H that are required to produce each molecule of 3C sugar phosphate from carbon dioxide. (You do *not* need to recall this equation.)

$$3CO_2 + 9ATP + 6NADP.2H \longrightarrow 3C \text{ sugar phosphate} + 9ADP + 8P_i + 6NADP \quad (6.3)$$

As shown in Equation 6.3 and Figure 6.2, the first carbon compound to be produced in the chloroplast is a 3C sugar phosphate — in fact, an intermediate in glycolysis. This 3C sugar phosphate is transported to the cytosol; here, some is used directly as an energy source, but much of it is converted into glucose phosphate and fructose phosphate, both 6C molecules.

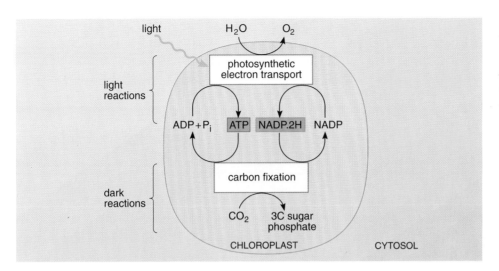

○ How does this synthesis of 6C sugars from 3C molecules in the cytosol compare with events in respiration?

○ It is the opposite of the first stage of respiration, i.e. glycolysis, where a 6C compound is split into two 3C compounds (Figure 5.3).

Glucose and fructose phosphates in the cytosol then combine to produce the disaccharide sucrose, with the loss of their phosphate groups. Sucrose is the major form in which sugar is transported between plant cells; just as glucose is transported in the blood of animals, sucrose is transported from the leaves (where most of it is made) to the rest of the plant. As well as sugars, both fatty acids and amino acids are synthesized in the plant cells from the 3C sugar phosphate product of the dark reactions. Most of the 3C sugar phosphate molecules that remain in the chloroplast are converted to glucose molecules which are then polymerized into starch. A starch grain is visible in the chloroplast in Figure 6.1. As you learnt in Section 3.4, starch, like glycogen, is a large biopolymer that serves as a sugar reserve. The production of starch occurs in daylight. At night the starch can be broken down to meet the metabolic needs of the plant.

○ What is the other product of photosynthesis, besides sugar?

○ Oxygen (see Equation 6.1).

In fact almost all the Earth's supply of atmospheric oxygen comes from photosynthesis. Without the evolution of photosynthetic autotrophs, the Earth's atmosphere would have remained anaerobic. (This will be discussed in more detail in Blocks 10 and 12.)

As you learnt in Section 2.2, most of a plant's chloroplasts are located in the inner layers of cells of the leaves. How can the carbon dioxide needed for photosynthesis get to the chloroplasts in these cells? Carbon dioxide enters the leaf through small pores in its surface. These pores, called *stomata* (singular stoma), were introduced in Block 1, Section 6.4.1, and are shown in Figure 6.3. Stomata can open to allow the exchange of gases (oxygen and carbon dioxide), and close to reduce water loss from the plant. This opening and closing of stomata is controlled by pairs of guard cells which surround them (Figure 6.3).

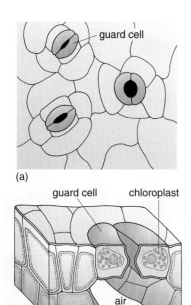

(a)

guard cell

guard cell   chloroplast

(b)

air space

Figure 6.3 (a) View of leaf surface showing three stomata, each of which is surrounded by two guard cells. (b) One of these stomata has been cut and is viewed from the side. Guard cells can change in size and so alter the size of the stoma.

Not surprisingly, photosynthesis is subject to stringent controls by the cell, ensuring that light and dark reactions keep in step and that the plant makes maximum use of the available light and carbon dioxide. An understanding of the mechanisms of control of photosynthesis is very important for maximizing plant growth and crop production, particularly in countries where many people go hungry. Currently, there is a great deal of interest in the mechanism of the light reactions, since this is the stage which uses a truly renewable energy source — solar energy. In the long term, its key components may perhaps be assembled artificially into light-driven fuel cells.

Question 6.1 State two reasons why photosynthesis is a vital process for life on Earth.◀

Question 6.2 In what way are the dark reactions dependent on the light reactions of photosynthesis? ◀

Question 6.3 Chloroplasts isolated from spinach can be broken open and then separated into membranous material and soluble components, which we will call M and S, respectively. Both M and S are biochemically active. Which of the following features apply to each of these two chloroplast components?

(a) Contains chlorophyll; (b) converts carbon dioxide to sugar; (c) produces oxygen from water.◀

Question 6.4 List the similarities and the differences between the processes of oxidative phosphorylation and photophosphorylation.◀

6.3 Summary of Section 6

The essential feature of photosythesis is that solar energy is converted by means of the pigment chlorophyll into chemical energy in sugar. In overall terms, photosynthesis is the reverse of respiration.

Photosynthesis consists of two sets of reactions. In the light reactions, light energy is absorbed by chlorophyll present in the internal chloroplast membranes (the grana), and this energizes electrons removed from water, which are then transferred along an electron transport chain. The energy released during electron transfer is used to pump protons across the inner chloroplast membrane, and the return flow of these through ATP synthase drives the synthesis of ATP, a process called photophosphorylation. At the end of the photosynthetic electron transport chain, electrons are transferred to NADP, which combines with protons to form NADP.2H.

In the dark reactions (or Calvin cycle) the products of the light reactions — ATP and NADP.2H — are used to reduce carbon dioxide, converting it to a 3C sugar phosphate. The dark reactions occur in the stroma between the internal membranes of the chloroplast (the grana).

Much of the 3C sugar phosphate is transported out of the chloroplast into the cytosol where it is converted into glucose and fructose phosphates, which are then combined to form sucrose. The 3C sugar phosphate is also the precursor of amino acids and fatty acids. However, the majority of the 3C sugar phosphate that remains in the chloroplast is converted, via glucose, into starch for storage.

The carbon dioxide needed for photosynthesis enters the leaves through the stomata.

Energy in cells: a review

The two processes of respiration and photosythesis are biologically very important. We have seen that in overall chemical terms, respiration is the exact reverse of photosynthesis (Sections 5 and 6), and that they both involve a sequence of chemical reactions that occur in a number of cellular compartments.

The main purpose of this section is to review these two processes, and to consolidate your understanding of them. Activity 7.1 will help you to do this, but before carrying out this activity we will review briefly both the striking similarities and the differences in structure and function between the two organelles that are involved in these two processes: mitochondria and chloroplasts.

Mitochondria, which are present in all eukaryote cells, and chloroplasts, which occur only in plants, are membrane-bound organelles with a large amount of internal membranes. The internal membranes of these organelles carry key components, for example the electron transport chain (Sections 5.5.1 and 6.2) and ATP synthase (Sections 5.5.2 and 6.2). Functionally, both organelles convert energy to forms that can be used to drive chemical reactions; large amounts of ATP are produced by the same fundamental mechanism: the energy derived from sugar and fats (in mitochondria) or from light (in chloroplasts) is used to drive proton pumps. The proton pumps in both organelles provide a way of linking energy released from electron transport to ATP synthesis (Sections 5.5.2 and 6.2).

Although the similarities between the two organelles are striking, there are significant differences between them. Mitochondria are involved in the oxidation of sugars and fats to carbon dioxide and water, and enable much of the energy stored in these metabolic fuels to be temporarily stored in ATP before it is used to drive a variety of energy-requiring reactions in the cell. In contrast, chloroplasts convert carbon dioxide and water to sugars and oxygen, and in the process they store some of the energy trapped from sunlight. The differences between the two organelles are thought to be a consequence of their different origins from different bacterial ancestors, as described in Section 2.3.

Activity 7.1   Cells and energy

This CD-ROM activity will give you an opportunity to consolidate your understanding of the processes of respiration and photosynthesis, which were discussed in Sections 5 and 6. The visualization of these processes will help to bring them alive. ◀

8 Meiosis and the genetic lottery

This block has demonstrated the degree of uniformity of organisms in their cell structure, chemical components and metabolism. Living organisms use the components of the world around themselves and convert these into their own living material. An acorn grows into an oak tree using only water, oxygen, carbon dioxide, some inorganic materials from the soil, and light energy. Similarly a human baby grows into an adult by digesting and metabolizing food and drink. The parents in each case pass to their progeny, or offspring, the information and specification for building cells from materials around them. This information lies in the genetic material, or DNA, which is found in the chromosomes within the nucleus (Block 4), and which is transmitted from generation to generation. Chromosomes can be regarded as strings of genes, the units of inheritance. It is to the study of chromosomes and genes that we now turn.

The idea of passing on information from parents to offspring raises an important question: *how* are the units of inheritance transmitted from one generation to the next? This section takes two approaches to answering this question. First, we look at what happens to the chromosomes of animals and plants during the process of sexual reproduction. Second, we examine how genes are transmitted in particular patterns from generation to generation. Then these two approaches are combined to show how the patterns of inheritance can be explained by the behaviour of chromosomes during sexual reproduction. Since genes are an integral part of chromosomes, following the behaviour of chromosomes allows us to trace the movement of genes. Thus the focus of this section will be at both the gene and chromosomal levels of explanation.

The majority of the study time will be dedicated to learning about genes and chromosomes and their patterns of inheritance. Your study of inheritance will involve the CD-ROM activity 'Mitosis, meiosis and recombination', which explores the relationship between division of the nucleus and the inheritance of genes. You will practise some basic maths skills, particularly the use of ratios (introduced in Block 1) and you will revisit the mathematical idea of probability (which you met in Block 7).

8.1 Meiosis and the life cycle

The type of nuclear division called meiosis is intimately linked to the life cycle of organisms that reproduce sexually. You were introduced to the essential features of life cycles in Block 4 and you should check your understanding of these now by doing Activity 8.1.

Activity 8.1 Revision: chromosomes and the life cycle

This activity will help you to recall the main features of, and the interrelationship between, chromosomes and life cycles of organisms that reproduce sexually, as well as the biological terms used to describe them. ◀

Chromosomes are present in the cells of all eukaryotes. Their number varies enormously and is characteristic for each species. The parasitic worm *Ascaris lumbricoides* has only four chromosomes whereas some ferns, such as the adder's tongue fern (*Ophioglossum vulgatum*), have more than 1 000 chromosomes. Most eukaryotes have between 10 and 50 chromosomes; for example, as you learnt in Block 4, humans have 46. However, there is no obvious relationship between chromosome number and an organism's complexity of organization.

When the chromosomes are aligned along the centre of the cell during metaphase of mitosis (Figure 3.8b in Block 4), they are in their most condensed state so their number, size and shape can be most easily studied. Figure 8.1 shows the metaphase chromosomes of a human female. These have been stained and spread out so that they are readily distinguishable. The array of chromosomes that a particular species possesses is called the **karyotype**. For any one species, the male and female karyotypes may differ slightly because of the sex chromosomes (Block 4, Section 3.2). By cutting out the chromosomes from photographs taken down the microscope and lining them up according to their size and shape, the distinctive features of the karyotype can be revealed (Figure 8.2).

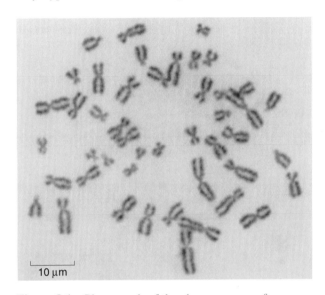

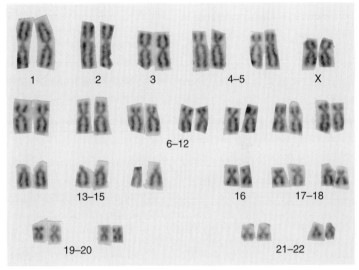

Figure 8.1 Photograph of the chromosomes of a human female. These chromosomes were prepared from a cell in the blood. Each chromosome is made up of a pair of identical chromatids, joined at the centromere.

Figure 8.2 Photograph of chromosomes of a human female arranged as a karyotype. The pairs of autosomes (chromosomes that are not sex chromosomes) are numbered 1–22, and the pair of sex chromosomes is labelled X. Pairs of chromosomes that are difficult to separate from each other are grouped together, e.g. pairs 6–12.

◯ What is the most striking feature of the karyotype shown in Figure 8.2?

◯ All the chromosomes are present in pairs; each member of a pair has the same structure and appearance.

Each member of a pair of chromosomes is said to be **homologous** to its partner, that is, to have the same size, shape and function. Another feature of the karyotype in Figure 8.2 is the different appearances of the chromosomes; non-homologous chromosomes can be distinguished from each other by their length and the position of the centromere, and although many look very similar, to the trained eye and using more sophisticated staining techniques, each pair is different.

◯ How can you tell that the karyotype in Figure 8.2 is of a diploid cell?

◯ The chromosomes are present in pairs — homologous pairs — hence they must be from a diploid cell.

Sexual reproduction includes two distinctive processes:

1   The production of haploid gametes, such as sperm and ova, which involves the specialized nuclear division called **meiosis**. (Later, in the CD-ROM activity 'Mitosis, meiosis and recombination', you will learn how this is brought about.)

2   The fusion of gametes at *fertilization*, which results in the restoration of the diploid number of chromosomes.

The relationship between these two processes, and the changes in chromosome number that each process brings about, is shown in outline in Figure 8.3. This figure represents a hypothetical organism with only four chromosomes, that is, two pairs of homologous chromosomes — one long pair and one short pair — as shown for each of the parents in the first row in the figure. The chromosomes of the female parent (*maternal* chromosomes) are shown in red and those of the male parent (*paternal* chromosomes) are shown in blue. As a result of meiosis, the chromosome number is halved in the gametes, each of which contains two chromosomes, as shown in the second row in Figure 8.3. Notice that the set of chromosomes in the gametes is not a random collection; it is made up of one member of each homologous pair — one long chromosome and one short. The bottom part of the figure shows that fertilization restores the original number of four chromosomes in the zygote, which contains a pair of the long homologous chromosomes and a pair of the short homologous chromosomes. Note that in the zygote, half the chromosomes are shown in red and half in blue, since one member of each homologous pair comes from the female parent and its partner comes from the male parent.

Figure 8.3   How the number of chromosomes changes at gamete production (meiosis) and at fertilization in a hypothetical organism with only two pairs of homologous chromosomes. For simplicity, each chromosome is shown as a single strand, rather than as a pair of chromatids (Figures 8.1 and 8.2).

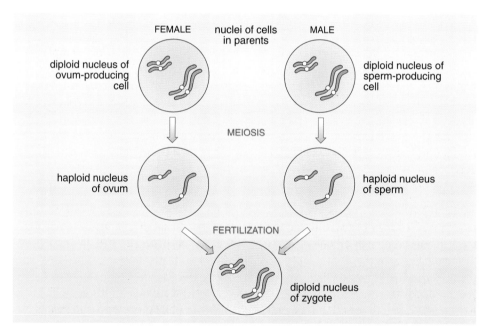

What would happen to the chromosome number in future generations if gamete production did not involve the halving of the diploid chromosome number?

If the chromosome number were not reduced by half during gamete formation, to produce the gametes containing the haploid number, a zygote would have twice the diploid number; the chromosome number would double in each subsequent generation.

The distribution of one member of each homologous pair of chromosomes to each gamete is a consequence of the precision of the process of meiosis. An understanding of the distribution of chromosomes, both during the production of gametes and at fertilization, is important for exploring the inheritance of genes.

Question 8.1   Insert the missing term in each of the following sentences.

(a) ————— chromosomes are pairs of chromosomes which are present in diploid cells and have the same appearance and function.

(b) The number, size and shape of all the chromosomes in a cell is called the ————— and is characteristic for a species.

(c) The process of ————— is involved in the production of gametes, which have the haploid number of chromosomes.

(d) The process of combining two gametes to produce a zygote is called —————. ◄

8.2   Like begets like

It is possible to follow a character, such as eye colour or hair colour in humans, that is handed down from generation to generation. Such characters are said to be **inherited characters** (or heritable characters) and are determined by genes. A **gene** can be considered as a unit of inheritance, which determines a particular character and which is passed on from parent to offspring.

Genes maintain the differences between species, such as oak and human, but they also contribute to differences between individuals within a species. For example, consider hair colour or eye colour within a family. Brothers and sisters may share features such as brown hair, that they also share with their biological parents, but in addition they have their own particular combination of characters that make them recognizable as individuals. For example, one sister may have blue eyes whilst her siblings have brown eyes; a brother may have curly hair whilst his siblings have straight hair, and so on. To understand the differences and similarities in characters between individuals, we need to look at how copies of genes are transmitted from parent to offspring. In so doing, we shall discover the rules that govern inheritance.

While at one level there is continuity from one generation to the next, at another level a degree of variation occurs. In fact there is so much variation that every human alive today is different from all others — we are all genetically unique (with the exception of identical twins, who have identical genes). Some of this variation can be seen with the unaided eye, whereas other variation, such as blood groups or the activity of a particular enzyme, is revealed only by more sophisticated molecular biological techniques. The sum of all the characters that an individual organism possesses, not only structural features but also biochemical, behavioural and physiological features, is described as the **phenotype**. All aspects of an organism's phenotype depend ultimately on that organism's chemical composition and on the biochemical reactions that go on inside it.

The full complement of an individual's genes is called the **genotype**. The phenotype of each individual is the result of the combined action of their genes (their genotype) and their environment, some characters being influenced more by the environment than are others.

⬤ From your own experience, can you suggest a human character that might be influenced by environmental factors?

◯ One example is body mass, which is greatly influenced by the amount and type of food that people eat and the amount of exercise they take.

Phenotype, as well as meaning the sum total of *all* an individual's characters, also has a more restricted meaning; it is used as a shorthand way of referring to the expression of just *one* character, for example, 'blue-eyed phenotype'. Similarly, genotype is also used to refer to the specific genes associated with a particular character, for example, 'blue-eyed genotype'.

Question 8.2   Which of the following is the same for every individual of a species: (a) karyotype; (b) genotype; (c) phenotype? Explain your answer. ◀

8.3 Patterns of inheritance

We can trace the inheritance of characters in animals and plants by following the phenotype from generation to generation, in breeding experiments. We will describe work with maize (*Zea mays*), alternatively called corn (sweetcorn, or corn on the cob), which occurs throughout the world as an extremely important commercial crop plant, and which is used extensively in genetic research. We can also study the inheritance of characters at the level of the genotype. In this section we will jump between these two levels, and in so doing we shall be jumping from the fundamental work of 19th century biologists, who could only trace phenotypes, to that of present-day geneticists, who work at the level of the gene.

We begin with one of the simplest known examples of inheritance, that of grain colour in maize. We will consider two of the possible colours: purple and white. A cob in which all the grains are purple has the 'purple phenotype'; a cob with white grains has the 'white phenotype'. The two cobs are said to have **contrasting characters**.

Maize cobs consist of hundreds of grains (seeds) arranged in columns. Each of the grains on the cob is the result of a separate fertilization of a female gamete inside each ovule (Figure 8.4). Before fertilization, each maize plant carries hundreds of flowers in the flower heads, but the male flowers are separated from the female ones, as shown in Figure 8.4. The male flowers produce pollen grains (each containing a male gamete) which, in maize, do not normally fertilize female gametes from the same plant. (Male and female gametes on the same plant mature at different times.) This ensures that the pollen from one plant fertilizes the female gametes of another plant, a process called *cross-fertilization*. We use the terms 'ovule' and 'pollen grain' as shorthand for the female and the male gametes, respectively (Book 4, Section 6.2), although these structures are not actually the gametes of plants but *contain* the gametes.

Thus a maize cob is the result of several hundred cross-fertilizations, and each grain has the potential to develop into a new, individual plant. Each single cob therefore provides a wealth of information about inheritance in the maize plant.

A variety is said to be **pure-breeding** for a character if all its members have the same character, such as purple grains, and all breeding within that variety leads to offspring that have the same character. For example, purple-grained maize and white-grained maize are both pure-breeding varieties. But why should grain colour be different in

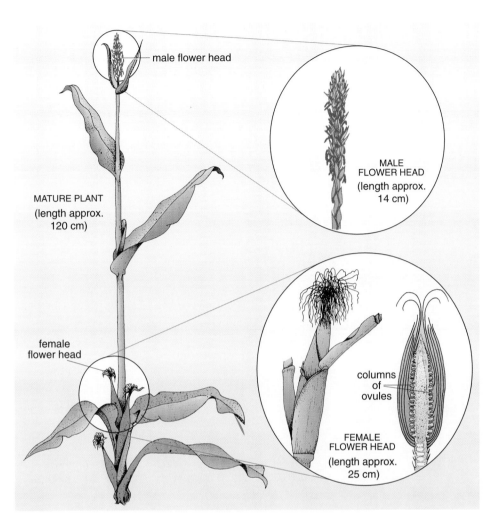

Figure 8.4 The arrangement and structure of male and female flowers on a maize plant.

male flower head

MATURE PLANT
(length approx.
120 cm)

MALE
FLOWER HEAD
(length approx.
14 cm)

female
flower head

columns
of
ovules

FEMALE
FLOWER HEAD
(length approx.
25 cm)

the two varieties of maize? And if plants of these two varieties were cross-fertilized, what would be the grain colour of the offspring? In order to answer these questions we will describe a breeding experiment, carried out in two stages, using these two maize varieties.

8.3.1 A breeding experiment: stage one

In the first stage of the breeding experiment, shown in Figure 8.5, plants from the pure-breeding purple-grained variety are crossed with (fertilized by) plants from the pure-breeding white-grained variety. This can be done by artificially dabbing pollen grains from one plant onto the female flowers of another plant. These plants are the **parental generation** (abbreviated to **P**), and the cobs resulting from the cross are the first offspring generation or **first filial** (pronounced 'phil-ee-al') **generation**, (abbreviated to F_1). The subsequent generations in such an experiment are called F_2, F_3, and so on. Incidentally, if you read information on seed packets, you may well be familiar with F_1 hybrid seeds, which are the product of crossing two pure-breeding parental varieties.

Returning to our maize cross (Figure 8.5), the most striking observation is that these cross-fertilizations result in F_1 cobs all of which have purple grains. On average, each cob contains 500 grains, so examining the grains on only one cob means that we are examining a large number of offspring (or fertilizations).

Two important features of the results of this cross should be noted:

1 No F_1 cobs have any white grains. This is true even if we examine large numbers of F_1 cobs. Hence, one of the two characters present in the parental generation, white grain colour, has vanished in the F_1 offspring generation.

2 It doesn't matter which way round the cross is carried out; that is, the result is the same whether the pollen comes from the purple-grained variety and the ovules from the white-grained variety, or vice versa. This rules out the possibility that grain colour is determined by the plant on which the cob has grown.

Figure 8.5 The result of crossing maize plants of a pure-breeding purple-grained variety with those of a pure-breeding white-grained variety. (The F_1 offspring are still on the parent plant — the one that contributed the female gametes.)

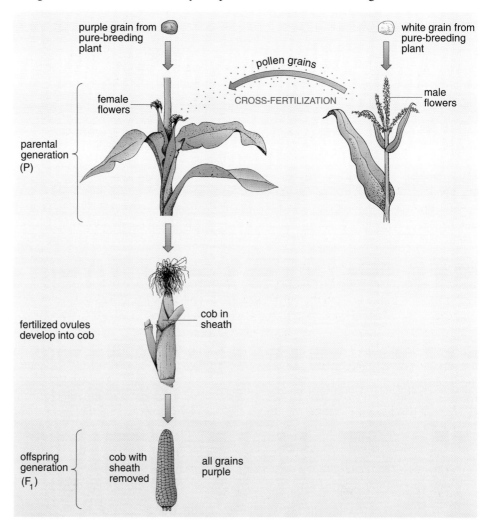

Now that we have examined the phenotype of the grains in the breeding experiment, we will explore what is happening at the level of the gene. We can consider a gene as a small section of the DNA in a chromosome, which issues instructions for a specific phenotypic character such that a maize grain is either purple (presence of purple pigment) or white (absence of purple pigment); for brevity it can be called the gene for grain colour. Most importantly for understanding the patterns of inheritance of genes, it is known that a gene has a particular location on a chromosome, such as band A in Figure 8.6. As this figure shows, a diploid cell contains two copies of a gene for a particular character situated at corresponding locations on the two homologous chromosomes. The technical term for the location of a gene on a chromosome is **locus** (plural loci).

● Where do each of these two copies of a gene in a diploid cell come from?

○ One comes from the female gamete and the other from the male gamete. (Fertilization restores the chromosomes as homologous pairs, as shown in Figure 8.3.)

● Why is the outcome of the breeding experiment described above the same regardless of which of the parental phenotypes provides the ovules and which provides the pollen?

○ The simplest explanation is that the instructions that a gene issues are the same, irrespective of whether the gene is from the male or female parent.

Each gene can exist in one or more forms; each form is a different **allele** (pronounced 'a', as in apple, 'leel'). The existence of alleles of a gene is a powerful source of variation. It is conventional in genetics to represent each allele by a letter (either upper or lower case), printed in italics; alleles are given the same letter symbol to show that they are forms of the same gene. In the case of grain colour we will use the letter *G* (for grain) for the allele that is associated with purple grains and *g* for the different allele that is associated with white grains.

The terms 'allele' and 'gene' can be confusing because the terms are used interchangeably in some situations. For example, the 'allele for purple grain' and the 'gene for purple grain' both refer to the same thing in an interchangeable way. This stems from the fact that the forms (alleles) of any gene are of course genes themselves.

Now consider what happens at the gene level when we cross the pure-breeding purple-grained plant with the pure-breeding white-grained plant. We will designate the two copies of the gene in the purple-grained parent as *G G* and the two copies of the gene in the white-grained parent as *g g*, as shown in Figure 8.7. (The reason for this designation will become clear later in the section.) Note the convention of the multiplication sign to represent a breeding cross. Of course, the gametes contain a copy of each of the other maize genes too, but here we are considering only the gene for grain colour.

● Looking at Figure 8.7, what are the genotypes of the gametes produced by each parent?

○ *G* and *g*. Gametes from the purple-grained parent all contain the *G* allele and those from the white-grained parent all contain the *g* allele.

Recall from Figure 8.3 that meiosis ensures that each gamete contains one member of each homologous pair of chromosomes and hence only one copy of each gene.

● What would be the possible genotypes of the offspring of such a cross?

○ They would all be *G g* or *g G*, and these are the *same* genotype.

The convention is to write the allele with the capital letter first, so the genotype of all the F₁ offspring would be written as *G g*. Notice that not only do all the F₁ offspring have the same genotype, *G g*, but that this genotype is different from that of either parent. Where the two copies of a gene are different, as in the offspring of this cross, they are said to be **heterozygous** (pronounced 'het-er-oh-zye-guss') and the individual is referred to as a **heterozygote** (pronounced 'het-er-oh-zye-goat') for that particular gene. When the two copies of the gene are the same (as in the case of each parent), they are said to be **homozygous** and the individual is a **homozygote** for the gene for grain colour.

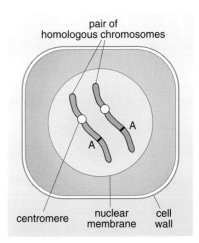

Figure 8.6 A gene, labelled A, is a small section of a chromosome at a particular locus. For simplicity, only one pair of homologous chromosomes is shown in this hypothetical plant cell. The length of the gene relative to length of the chromosome is very much smaller than shown here.

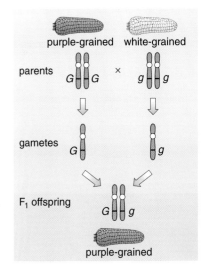

Figure 8.7 The cross between pure-breeding purple-grained maize (genotype *G G*) and pure-breeding white-grained maize (genotype *g g*). The diagram shows the fate of the grain colour genes and of the chromosomes on which they are carried, during gamete production and fertilization.

But what is the phenotype of the F_1 offspring with the heterozygous genotype $G\,g$? You may recall (Figure 8.5) that the phenotype of all the F_1 offspring of this cross was purple. The character that is expressed, or manifest, in the heterozygote, purple grain in this case, is said to be the **dominant** character because it masks the presence of the alternative character, white grain. The character that is not expressed in the heterozygote is said to be **recessive**. In this case, white grain is recessive to, or masked by, the dominant character, purple grain. Strictly speaking, it is the phenotype — rather than the allele — that is dominant or recessive; however, alleles are usually referred to as being dominant or recessive on the basis of the associated phenotype.

Question 8.3   Match each of the terms (a)–(g) with one of the descriptions (i)–(vii).

(a) F_1; (b) alleles; (c) locus; (d) heterozygous; (e) homozygote; (f) dominant; (g) recessive.

(i) An individual in which both copies of the gene are the same.

(ii) The alternative forms of a gene.

(iii) The generation derived from a mating between two pure-breeding varieties.

(iv) The location of a gene on a chromosome.

(v) A phenotype that masks the presence of the allele for a contrasting character.

(vi) A genotype with two different alleles of a gene.

(vii) A phenotype not expressed in the heterozygote. ◀

8.3.2   A breeding experiment: stage two

We now turn to the second stage of the breeding experiment, but this time we will follow the phenotypes and genotypes simultaneously. The purple ($G\,g$) grains of the F_1 generation are planted and when these have developed into mature F_1 plants they produce male and female flowers. These F_1 plants are crossed with each other, as shown in Figure 8.8. The fertilized ovules develop into grains borne on cobs, and these grains are the beginning of the **second filial generation (F_2)**.

The mating diagram and the outcome of the fertilizations of this cross are given in Figure 8.8. First consider the gametes produced by the F_1 generation.

⬤   What are the genotypes of the gametes produced by the F_1 purple-grained plants?

◯   The gametes are either G or g, since all F_1 plants are $G\,g$.

⬤   In what ratio would these two genotypes be produced, and why?

◯   The ratio would be $1\,G : 1\,g$ because the pair of homologous chromosomes on which they are located separate into different gametes in equal proportions.

Now consider the possible fertilizations between the gametes produced by the F_1 generation, as shown in Figure 8.8, and the genotypes and phenotypes of the F_2 generation that arises from these fertilizations.

Looking at Figure 8.8, you can see that the allele G of plant 1 might combine with either the G or the g allele of plant 2 at fertilization. Over a large number of fertilizations a G-bearing ovule of plant 1 would combine with a G-bearing pollen grain of plant 2 in half of the fertilizations and combine with a g-bearing pollen grain of plant 2 in the other half. Similarly, the allele g of plant 1 might combine with either the G or g allele of plant 2. Hence, in the F_2 generation three different genotypes are produced: $G\,G$, $G\,g$ and $g\,g$.

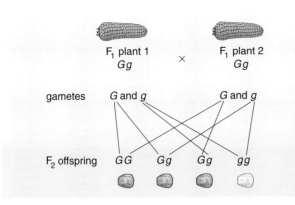

Figure 8.8 Crossing F$_1$ plants with F$_1$ plants gives F$_2$ cobs, bearing F$_2$ grains. Drawings of the F$_2$ offspring grains are included, to show the phenotypes. The recessive phenotype reappears in the F$_2$ generation. Unlike Figure 8.7, the chromosomes bearing the grain-colour alleles are not shown; it is conventional to simplify mating diagrams in this way.

⬤ What is the expected ratio of the three genotypes in the F$_2$ generation?

◯ The expected ratio is 1 *G G* : 2 *G g* : 1 *g g* (see Figure 8.8).

This ratio follows for two reasons. First, the two different gametes, *G* and *g*, are produced in equal numbers. Second, which ovule is fertilized by which pollen grain occurs at random; that is, a *G* ovule is equally likely to be fertilized by either a *G* pollen grain or *g* pollen grain.

The phenotype of each of these genotypes in the F$_2$ generation can be determined since we know that the allele *G* (purple grain) is dominant to *g*.

⬤ What are the phenotypes corresponding to each of the genotypes, *G G*, *G g* and *g g* of the F$_2$ generation?

◯ *G G* and *G g* plants are purple-grained and *g g* plants are white-grained.

⬤ In what ratio would grains with the purple phenotype and grains with the white phenotype be expected to occur in the F$_2$ generation?

◯ The expected ratio is three purple (the dominant phenotype) : one white (the recessive phenotype), since three of the four possible fertilizations have at least one dominant *G* allele (see Figure 8.8).

The phenotypic ratio of 3 : 1 (three of the dominant phenotype : one of the recessive phenotype) and the genotypic ratio of 1 : 2 : 1 (one homozygous dominant : two heterozygous : one homozygous recessive) are of fundamental importance in genetics.

Figure 8.9 presents the same information about the breeding experiment as shown in Figure 8.8, but the information is laid out in a different way. Either way of presenting the details of a cross can be used, and when producing your own diagrams you can use whichever is easier for you (although you are not expected to draw the phenotypes).

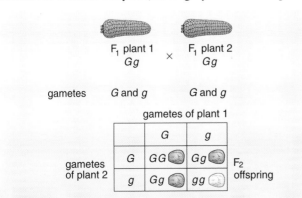

Figure 8.9 An alternative way of laying out the cross shown in Figure 8.8.

Figure 8.10 A monk, Gregor Mendel, laid the foundation of the modern science of genetics. The results of his experiments, carried out in the monastery gardens in Brunn, Moravia (subsequently incorporated in Czechoslovakia), were published in 1865. His work was largely ignored or unnoticed until 1900 when it was 'rediscovered' by other workers after they had come to similar conclusions from their own work. Mendel had died 16 years before his work was recognized.

In Figure 8.9 the fertilizations between the various combinations of gametes from the F_1 generation are shown in boxes at the bottom. Along the top you can see the two types of gamete produced by plant 1 of the F_1 generation; down the left-hand side you can see the two types of gamete produced by plant 2 of the F_1 generation. Inside the other boxes are the genotypes of the products of fertilization between the various kinds of gamete, that is, the F_2 generation. Thus, for example, the top left-hand box records the outcome of fertilization between a G ovule and a G pollen grain. An examination of the contents of the four boxes should convince you that the expected ratio of genotypes of the F_2 generation is $1\,GG : 2\,Gg : 1\,gg$ (one homozygous dominant : two heterozygous : one homozygous recessive) and that the expected phenotypic ratio is therefore three purple : one white (three of the dominant phenotype : one of the recessive phenotype).

This breeding experiment in maize, which we just have described, is similar in essence to a famous series of experiments carried out by Gregor Mendel (Figure 8.10) on the garden pea, *Pisum sativum*. Mendel introduced the scientific approach to breeding experiments by:

- following a *single* pair of contrasting characters in each investigation;
- breeding beyond one generation;
- counting the individuals showing each of the phenotypes;
- working with large numbers of offspring.

Although the existence of genes and chromosomes was not known in Mendel's time, he predicted the separation or **segregation** of units (now called genes and alleles) during gamete formation. We now know that meiosis ensures that each gamete contains only one copy of a gene, because the pairs of chromosomes on which the genes are located separate into different gametes (Figure 8.7). This segregation of genes (units) has been given formal recognition as Mendel's **law of segregation**.

The breeding experiment in maize shows that characters due to dominant or recessive alleles, such as grain colour, show a particular pattern of inheritance from generation to generation: the F_1 offspring all resemble one of the parents (Figure 8.7), and the F_2 offspring have the phenotypic ratio of $3 : 1$ and the genotypic ratio of $1 : 2 : 1$ (Figures 8.8 and 8.9). The action of dominant alleles explains why the recessive character 'disappears' in the F_1 generation and why this character reappears in the F_2 generation. Most importantly, this pattern of inheritance is a consequence of two events.

1 The two copies of a gene separate into different gametes in equal numbers.

2 The combining of a female gamete and a male gamete at fertilization occurs at random.

The conclusions we have drawn from the breeding experiment in maize are the same as those drawn by Mendel and apply to all sexually reproducing eukaryotes, including humans. The main features of the experiment that we have described so far, and that can be explained by the theory of inheritance, are summarized in Table 8.1.

Table 8.1   A summary of features of the maize breeding experiment.

1   The phenotype of pure-breeding varieties for a particular character is constant when crossed with members of the same variety.

2   One parental character disappears in the F_1 generation when parents differ in the character for which each is pure-breeding (the recessive character is masked by the dominant character).

3   The outcome of a cross is independent of which parent provides the ovules and which the pollen.

4   The vanished (recessive) character reappears in about one-quarter of the F_2 generation.

5   The two copies of a gene segregate to different gametes at meiosis and in equal numbers.

6   Gametes combine at random at fertilization.

Question 8.4   In what respect does each of the following *hypothetical* breeding experiments produce results that differ in an important way from the results described in the breeding experiment in maize? Note down in each case how the results differ.

Experiment 1   100 pure-breeding red-flowered plants are crossed with 100 pure-breeding white-flowered plants. All of the offspring have red flowers. These offspring are then crossed with each other. About three-quarters of their offspring have white flowers, and about one-quarter have red flowers.

Experiment 2   100 pure-breeding red-flowered plants are crossed with 100 pure-breeding white-flowered plants. All of the offspring have pink flowers.

Experiment 3   When the pollen from 100 pure-breeding red-flowered plants fertilizes the ovules of 100 pure-breeding white-flowered plants, all of the offspring have white flowers. When the pollen from 100 pure-breeding white-flowered plants fertilizes the ovules of 100 pure-breeding red-flowered plants, all of the offspring have red flowers. ◀

8.3.3 Predicting the outcome of crosses

By knowing the pattern of inheritance of genes as described above, it is possible to make some predictions about the phenotypes and genotypes of each generation in breeding experiments. This section considers some examples of such predictions.

First consider whether it is possible to determine the genotype for certain characters, such as grain colour, from observing an organism's phenotype.

- Is it possible to determine the genotype of all white-grained cobs just by observing their phenotype?

- Yes, it is possible; since white grain colour is recessive, white-grained cobs must be $g\,g$.

- Is it possible to determine the genotype of all purple-grained cobs just by observing their colour?

- No, it is not possible, because purple-grained cobs may be either $G\,G$ or $G\,g$. It is possible to say that one copy of the gene must be G but it is not possible to predict the identity of the second copy without further information.

Think back to our original pure-breeding parents (Figure 8.7). The white-grained parent was $g\,g$ and any crosses between individuals of that variety would involve only g gametes. All offspring, therefore, must also be $g\,g$. Hence this is a pure-breeding variety because all breeding within the variety would lead to offspring that have the same character. Similarly, all the white-grained plants in the F_2 generation (Figures 8.8 and 8.9) would also be pure-breeding for grain colour when crossed with each other.

Now consider the parental pure-breeding purple-grained variety (Figure 8.7).

○ Why must this variety be $G\,G$ and not $G\,g$?

○ To be pure-breeding all the offspring must have the same phenotype as the parents — this is the definition of pure-breeding. If the parent variety had the genotype $G\,g$, then a cross between individuals of this variety would produce offspring some of which would be purple-grained and some of which would be white-grained (similar to the cross shown in Figures 8.8 and 8.9). Hence it would not be pure-breeding.

Therefore, all members of a pure-breeding variety not only have the same phenotype, but they also have the same genotype.

One of the important things that can be learned from the study of genetics, particularly in the case of humans and agricultural breeding, is that many of the outcomes of inheritance are statistical ones; that is, they are to do with probability, as explained in Box 8.1, *Chance and probability in genetics*. (Probability was introduced in Box 3.1 in Block 7.)

Box 8.1   Chance and probability in genetics

When tossing a coin there is an even chance that heads or tails will turn up, i.e. each is equally likely. The probability of throwing heads is described mathematically as 1 out of 2, or $\frac{1}{2}$. In general, the probability of a particular outcome, such as heads, is defined mathematically as:

$$\text{probability of outcome} = \frac{\text{number of ways to get that particular outcome}}{\text{total number of possible outcomes}}$$

In the case of throwing a six-sided die and getting a 4, there is only one way of getting that outcome, but there are six possible outcomes, so the probability is $\frac{1}{6}$.

● What would be the probability of throwing an even number with the die?

○ $\frac{3}{6}$ or $\frac{1}{2}$, since three of the six possible different outcomes are even numbers.

● What is the probability that a gamete produced by a $G\,g$ plant will have the white-grained allele?

○ The probability is $\frac{1}{2}$, since there are two possible outcomes and each one is equally likely. Only one of these corresponds to the white-grained allele.

● Recall the reason why each of these two possibilities is equally likely.

○ It is because the two copies of a chromosome separate from each other into different gametes at meiosis, and in equal numbers.

● What is the probability that an offspring of a cross between two maize plants that are heterozygous for grain colour ($G\,g$) will have the white-grained genotype? (Hint: You might find it helpful to draw out such a cross, or to look at the one drawn in Figures 8.8 and 8.9.)

○ The probability is $\frac{1}{4}$, since there are four possible outcomes ($G\,G$, two $G\,g$, and $g\,g$), and only one of these corresponds to the white-grained genotype.

Again, recall that this probability is based on two events: first on an equal number of G and g gametes being produced by each $G\,g$ plant; and second, on male and female gametes combining at random at fertilization.

Question 8.5   What is the probability that an F_2 maize grain, shown in Figures 8.8 and 8.9, will contain at least one g allele? ◄

So far in Section 8.3 we have considered only two types of cross, one between two pure-breeding varieties which gives rise to the F_1 generation, and one between F_1 individuals which gives rise to the F_2 generation. However, other crosses can be carried out and they show that inheritance of the copies of a gene follows the same basic rules. An understanding of probability, the relationship between dominant and recessive alleles, and the way that the two copies of a gene segregate at meiosis, enables us to predict the outcome of many breeding experiments.

Let's consider an example. Suppose a breeding experiment was carried out in which plants from a pure-breeding white-grained variety of maize ($g\,g$) were crossed with heterozygous maize plants of genotype $G\,g$. What are the expected genotypes and phenotypes in the offspring arising from this cross, and in what ratio would they occur? We can begin to answer this question by first determining the genotypes of the gametes produced by each of the parents. The pure-breeding white-grained plants ($g\,g$) will produce gametes that all carry the g allele, as shown in Figure 8.11. The heterozygous $G\,g$ plants will produce gametes, half of which carry the G allele and half the g allele (Figure 8.11).

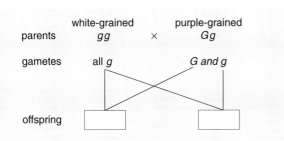

Figure 8.11   A cross between a pure-breeding white-grained variety of maize and a heterozygous purple-grained variety. Unlike Figures 8.8 and 8.9, drawings to show the phenotypes are not included; it is conventional to simplify mating diagrams in this way.

Question 8.6   Complete Figure 8.11 and hence determine the ratios of the genotypes and phenotypes of the offspring. ◄

The expected outcome of the cross reveals a further important genetic ratio of $1:1$. This ratio confirms that during meiosis alleles G and g in a $G\,g$ plant segregate from each other into *equal* numbers of gametes containing G and g alleles, and that

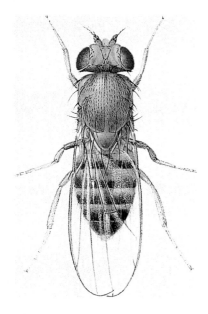

Figure 8.12 The common fruit-fly, *Drosophila melanogaster* (about 10 times actual size).

(From *Flies and Disease*, Vol. 1, 1971, by Bernard Greenberg, published by Princeton University Press, 1971. F. Gregor, artist.)

fertilizations between these gametes and those of the other parent occurs at random and therefore both possible combinations are equally likely.

We have seen that the phenotypes of members of each generation in a breeding experiment can be understood by using a model of inheritance. This model involves representing alleles by letters. The relative proportions of the possible combinations of letters then account for the ratio of the phenotypes. In fact this is an example of *mathematical modelling*; the mechanism of inheritance is regarded as equivalent to a mathematical process whose consequence can be calculated by the well-established laws of chance and probability.

In the next two questions you are asked to predict the results of some different sorts of crosses using the same rules of dominant/recessive alleles, the segregation of the two copies of a gene and the combining of gametes at random.

Question 8.7 A breeding experiment was carried out in which plants from a pure-breeding purple-grained variety of maize were crossed with plants that were heterozygous for grain colour. Draw the mating diagram for this cross and then predict the genotypic and phenotypic ratios of the offspring. ◀

Question 8.8 Which, if any, of the following breeding experiments in the common fruit-fly (*Drosophila melanogaster*), shown in Figure 8.12, could have involved parents that were pure-breeding for eye colour? Assume that red eye colour is dominant to brown eye colour. Give reasons for your choice, and reasons for rejecting any options you do not choose.

(a) 300 brown-eyed flies are crossed with 300 red-eyed flies. All the offspring are red-eyed.

(b) 300 brown-eyed flies are crossed with 300 red-eyed flies. Half of the offspring are brown-eyed and half are red-eyed.

(c) 300 brown-eyed flies are crossed with 300 brown-eyed flies. All of the offspring are brown-eyed. ◀

Activity 8.2 Tackling problems in genetics

This activity provides hints on how to tackle problems in genetics that you will be expected to solve. ◀

8.4 Why not an exact 3 : 1 ratio?

Before we leave the maize breeding experiments we will look more closely at some actual values obtained for the F_2 generation and how closely they fit the expected phenotypic ratio of 3 : 1. Table 8.2 gives the ratios of purple to white grains for eight cobs of the F_2 generation, counted by members of the S103 Course Team.

Notice the variability of the results between cobs in Table 8.2. One of the most striking features of biological results is their variability. First, consider the total number of grains in each cob. None of the figures in the table is the 'right' answer; each set reflects the particular feature of the individual cob from which they were taken. Some of the cobs may have more grains than others because there were more female flowers and hence more ovules, or because a larger proportion of the ovules were fertilized.

Table 8.2 Numbers of purple and white grains in eight maize cobs of the F_2 generation.

Total no. of grains	No. of purple grains	No. of white grains	Ratio of purple to white grains
565	434	131	3.31:1
487	364	123	2.96:1
554	436	118	3.69:1
521	398	123	3.24:1
760	562	198	2.84:1
426	316	110	2.87:1
544	398	146	2.73:1
676	501	175	2.86:1

Now consider the variation around the 3 : 1 ratio. Why is there a variation in the ratio of purple to white grains, i.e. why is this ratio not exactly the expected ratio of 3 : 1? The short answer is 'chance'. The *predicted* or *expected* ratio does not tell us the *actual* ratio of purple to white grains in a particular cob, but rather the most probable ratio, as explained in Box 8.2, *More about chance and probability in genetics*.

Box 8.2 *More about chance and probability in genetics*

The observed deviations in genetics experiments from predicted ratios like 3 : 1 are similar, in principle, to what you observe when you toss a coin. The *expected* ratio of heads to tails is 1 : 1 because each is equally likely. If you were to toss a coin a million times, the result would be a ratio very close to 1 : 1. If you tossed it only ten times, however, the result *might* be quite a marked deviation from a 1 : 1 ratio (e.g. six heads and four tails — a ratio of 3 : 2, or 1.5 : 1 — instead of five heads and five tails).

In an experiment with maize, suppose that exactly half of the ovules on a female flower head contained the allele G and the other half contained g. Imagine also that of the millions of pollen grains that are artificially dabbed onto the female flowers in a breeding experiment, exactly half contain G and the other half contain g. Which of the millions of pollen grains produces the few hundred gametes that win the race to fertilize the ovules is totally independent of whether the gametes contain G or g. Purely by chance, the proportion of G-bearing gametes that succeed in this way may be rather higher than one-half for one flower head. The cob would then develop rather more than the 3 : 1 ratio of purple to white grains. On another flower head the opposite might occur, with a disproportionately higher number of g-bearing pollen grains fertilizing the ovules. Similarly, the proportion of g-bearing ovules fertilized may be more (or less) than one-half. If a sufficiently large number of flower heads are investigated, giving a very large total of the number of grains counted, then the ratio will be very close to 3 : 1, but for any one flower head it may deviate quite markedly from 3 : 1.

Adding all the purple grains and all the white grains of the cobs given in Table 8.2, gives an overall ratio close to the expected ratio of 3 : 1, in fact a ratio of 3.03 : 1.

Returning to our examination of the expected phenotypic ratio of 3 : 1, a cob of the F_2 generation is shown in Figure 8.13. You can see how the purple and yellow grains (the latter are white when fresh) are distributed at random throughout the cob. This distribution reflects the chance events of which allele, G or g, each ovule bears and whether it was fertilized by a G-bearing or a g-bearing pollen grain.

Figure 8.13 Photo of an F₂ maize cob.

Activity 8.3   The 3:1 phenotypic ratio

This activity involves you in calculating the ratio of the two phenotypes in the cob in Figure 8.13, and thinking about what this tells you. ◄

Question 8.9   Table 8.3 gives the numbers of the two contrasting phenotypes in the F₂ generation for two of Mendel's pea-breeding experiments. In the seed colour experiment he counted the largest number of F₂ progeny and in the pod colour experiment he counted the smallest number of F₂ progeny. In both cases, the phenotype printed in italics is the dominant one.

(a) Calculate the actual F₂ phenotypic ratios in these two experiments.

(b) Comment on the ratios that you have calculated. ◄

Table 8.3   Results of the F₂ generation of two of Mendel's experiments.

Character	Numbers of each phenotype		Ratio of phenotypes
seed colour (*yellow* or green)	6 022 *yellow*	2 001 green	
pod colour (*green* or yellow)	428 *green*	152 yellow	

8.5   Inheritance of more than one pair of contrasting characters

We have considered the inheritance of one pair of contrasting characters that involves the segregation of the two copies of one gene in maize. A single chromosome carries many genes, of the order of 2 000 to 4 000 in each human chromosome, each carrying its own information, and each with its specific location, its own locus, on the chromosome. In a pair of homologous chromosomes, there will be many pairs of genes strung along their length.

These observations raise some intriguing questions. What happens when a cross is made that involves two pairs of genes affecting two different characters? Are genes that are present on the same chromosome inherited together? These are some of the questions that are considered in Activity 8.4.

Activity 8.4   *Mitosis, meiosis and recombination*

This CD-ROM activity reviews the nuclear division of mitosis and considers the nuclear division of meiosis. It demonstrates the segregation of the two copies of a gene, and then explores the patterns of inheritance of two pairs of genes affecting two different characters. ◄

Question 8.10   A heterozygous plant with the genotype $E e\, T t$ produces four kinds of gametes, $E\,T$, $e\,t$, $E\,t$ and $e\,T$ in the ratio $1:1:1:1$. Another heterozygous plant, with the genotype $E e\, Q q$, produces four kinds of gametes, $E\,Q$, $e\,q$, $E\,q$ and $e\,Q$ in the ratio $8:8:1:1$. How can these differences between the two ratios be explained? ◄

Question 8.11   If the genes making up the genotype of an animal were shown to be organized into five groups of linked genes, how many chromosomes would you expect to find: (a) in each gamete; (b) in each fertilized ovum? ◄

8.6   Summary of Section 8

The number of chromosomes is characteristic of each species and can vary enormously between species.

Sexual reproduction always includes two distinctive processes: the production of gametes, which involves meiosis, and fertilization. The two processes are accompanied by changes in the chromosome number, from diploid to haploid and from haploid to diploid, respectively.

Genetics is based on the concept of the gene as the unit of inheritance. A particular phenotypic character is determined by the two copies of a gene that an organism possesses and these two copies are identical in a pure-breeding variety.

When organisms with contrasting characters for which they are pure-breeding are crossed, the dominant character appears in the F_1 generation and the recessive character is masked. Crossing the F_1 offspring gives rise to the F_2 offspring with a phenotypic ratio of $3:1$ (three with the dominant phenotype : one with the recessive phenotype) and a corresponding genotypic ratio of $1:2:1$ (one homozygous dominant : two heterozygous : one homozygous recessive). A cross of a heterozygote with a homozygous recessive individual produces offspring with a $1:1$ phenotypic and genotypic ratio (one heterozygous : one homozygous recessive).

The genotypic ratios of a cross result from the separation of the two copies of a gene to different gametes in equal numbers, and because gametes combine at random at fertilization. The expected ratios in genetics do not tell us the actual ratios observed, but rather the most probable ratios.

The behaviour of chromosomes at meiosis explains the segregation of the two copies of a gene and the independent assortment of genes. The linkage of genes on a chromosome can be broken by means of crossing over.

Recombination — the production of new combinations of alleles — arises during meiosis from independent assortment of chromosomes and crossing over between homologous chromosomes.

The amount of crossing over between linked genes differs according to their distance apart. This observation is the basis for mapping the order of genes along a chromosome, and hence drawing up genetic (or linkage) maps.

9 Variations on a gene

The range of phenotypes and patterns of inheritance associated with some genes is more complex than for the examples considered so far. We have looked at examples of the inheritance of one or two pairs of contrasting characters where one allele of each gene is dominant to the other allele of the gene, and we have seen how the segregation and recombination of genes and alleles can be correlated with the behaviour of chromosomes at meiosis. These are the basic principles of genetics. However, these are only a base for understanding inheritance and in this section we will consider a number of extensions to these basic rules. However, rather than creating a bewildering situation, these examples reveal a unifying set of principles. The examples include widely different situations, from sex-linkage to the inheritance of characters that show continuous variation, such as height in humans. In addition, we will consider the process of *mutation* — the ultimate source of new variation.

Activity 9.1   Sources of phenotypic variation

In this activity you are asked to compile a list of the sources of phenotypic variation as you study this section. Your list will be useful for revision purposes. ◀

9.1   Sex and sex-linked inheritance

All the genes that we have considered so far have been on autosomes. This section looks at the patterns of inheritance of genes on the sex chromosomes. Since the same rule of segregation applies to the sex chromosomes and the copies of genes present on them, this section will help you review your understanding of the behaviour of chromosomes at meiosis and the segregation of the two copies of a gene.

In humans, males and females can be distinguished by a particular pair of chromosomes, the sex chromosomes, which direct the development of the sex of the individual. The sex chromosomes (introduced in Block 4) are of two types, called X and Y, the Y chromosome being much smaller than the X. Females have two X chromosomes; these are clearly visible in the human female karyotype shown in Figure 8.2. Males have one X chromosome and one Y chromosome, as shown in Figure 9.1. Hence, females are said to be XX and males are said to be XY.

Figure 9.1   Electron micrograph of a pair of human male sex chromosomes: the X chromosome (on the left) and the Y chromosomes (on the right). (Parts of other chromosomes are also visible.)

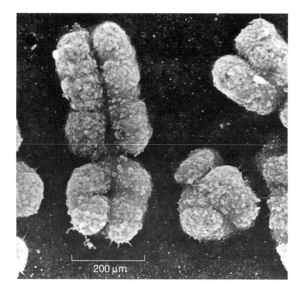

200 µm

The sex chromosomes segregate from each other at meiosis in the same way as the pairs of autosomes, with the consequence that in females all the ova contain 22 autosomes and an X chromosome.

● With respect to the sex chromosomes of a human male, what do the gametes (i.e. the sperm) contain?

○ Half the sperm contain an X chromosome and the other half contain a Y chromosome.

Question 9.1 To determine the distribution of sex chromosomes during gamete formation, and the expected ratio of male to female offspring, complete the mating diagram in Figure 9.2. ◀

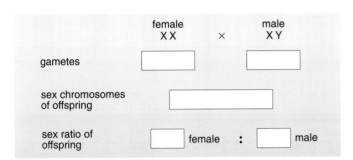

Figure 9.2 Mating diagram for use with Question 9.1.

The completed Figure 9.2 shows that it is the presence of the Y chromosome that determines maleness in humans.

● From your completed figure, what is the notable feature of the expected progeny?

○ Equal numbers of males and females are expected.

Hence, the segregation of sex chromosomes to gametes results in the maintenance of approximately equal numbers of male and female individuals.

The small Y chromosome carries very few genes, all of which are involved in directing the embryo to develop male characters. However, the larger X chromosome carries a number of other genes not involved in sex determination, called **sex-linked genes**. Consequently females carry two copies of each sex-linked gene, one on each X chromosome, but males carry only one copy of each sex-linked gene on the single X chromosome, there being no counterpart on the Y chromosome. This difference between the sex chromosomes results in genes on the X chromosome having a pattern of inheritance that is different from genes on the autosomes, a pattern that is described as **sex-linked inheritance**.

The XX/XY system of sex determination is not universal but is found in all mammals and also in some insects, including the common fruit-fly (*D. melanogaster*).

Activity 9.2 Applying genetic principles to sex-linked genes

In this activity you will look at the pattern of inheritance in *D. melanogaster* of contrasting characters that are determined by alleles of a sex-linked gene. ◀

The answer to Activity 9.2 shows that the genetic results are consistent with the segregation of the X and Y chromosomes at meiosis and with the absence of sex-linked genes on the Y chromosome. It also shows why males are more likely to manifest a recessive sex-linked character than are females.

Note how the inheritance of sex-linked genes follows the same basic principles of Mendel's law of segregation. The modification of the pattern of inheritance is a consequence of the absence of sex-linked genes on the Y chromosome.

Question 9.2   With respect to humans, why does a son not inherit a sex-linked character from his father? ◀

9.2   Multiple alleles

When considering alleles of a gene, all the examples discussed so far have involved two different alleles, one of which is dominant to the other, such as purple and white grain colour in maize. However, early in the history of genetics, it became clear that many genes have more than two alleles; these are called **multiple alleles**.

One such example is the ABO blood group system in humans, of which there are four different phenotypes, A, B, AB and O. If you have to be given a blood transfusion, first a sample of your blood has to be taken to match your blood to that of potential donors. If this is not done, the results can be disastrous because some of the blood groups are incompatible with each other, resulting in the clumping together of red blood cells.

The genetic basis of the ABO system is well-known and is based on three alleles at a single locus, denoted by the symbols A, B and O. Note that, for historical reasons, the nomenclature of these alleles is different from the standard convention. Any individual carries only two copies of the gene, which might be the same or different alleles.

 Why can an individual not carry all three alleles of the gene?

Each gene has a fixed locus, one on each member of an homologous *pair* of chromosomes. For three alleles to be carried by one individual, three homologous chromosomes, instead of two, would have to be present in each cell.

 Activity 9.3   Applying existing knowledge of genetic principles to multiple alleles

In this activity you will explore the relationship between different combinations of pairs of the A, B and O alleles and their associated phenotypes. ◀

The comments on Activity 9.3 reveal that the genotype AB manifests the phenotype of both the A and the B alleles, i.e. the corresponding phenotype is AB. This phenomenon is called **codominance**. In a sense, codominance is no dominance at all, since the presence of one allele does not mask the presence of the other allele but rather the effects of both alleles are manifested! The ABO system also shows that alleles of a gene can show different dominance relationships with one another, for the A and B phenotypes are both dominant to the O phenotype but not to each other.

This example reveals an important feature of inheritance: the phenotype of a particular character is a result of the relationship between the two alleles of a gene and this relationship varies between different combinations of alleles. Recall that, although we talk of 'dominant alleles' (see Section 8.3.1), it is the phenotype that is dominant, not the alleles.

9.3   Many genes — one character; one gene — multiple effects

An organism is a highly complex 'machine' in which all functions interact to a greater or lesser extent. Similarly a single gene does not act in isolation; its effects depend not only on its own activity but also on the activities of other genes (and on the environment). The most noticeable examples of gene interaction can be observed where a number of genes affect the same character.

One such character that has been studied extensively is coat colour in mammals. Although the details of these studies need not concern us here, they have revealed a striking interplay between different genes affecting a particular character. Take the domestic cat, for example, where genes at more than four different loci affect coat colour; two of these genes are known to have multiple alleles. The allele for one sex-linked gene, when homozygous, gives a yellow (ginger) coat colour, whereas the other allele for this gene, when homozygous, gives a black colour. The dominant allele at a second locus, gives the 'tabby' coat colour, consisting of alternating darker and lighter stripes. This is the colour pattern characteristic of the remote wild ancestors of the domestic cat. The recessive allele of a third gene, when homozygous, gives the 'Maltese dilution', which transforms black into smoky grey, tabby into grey with traces of tabby pattern, and yellow into a pale sandy coat. The large irregular white spots, of varying sizes, are due to various multiple alleles of yet another gene. All these genes interact during development to produce the coat colour phenotype, although the fundamental laws of the transmission of each of the genes are the same.

All aspects of phenotype depend on the organism's chemical composition and the kind of biochemical reactions that take place inside it. The different coloration of the forms of the domestic cat is ultimately dependent on chemical processes that determine the overall coat colour phenotype. Cats with different coat colours will have slightly different biochemical processes, causing different coloration.

In addition to many genes affecting one character, the opposite may also apply: one gene may affect two or more different characters. For example, a recessive allele in fruit-flies when homozygous gives rise to flies with very small, or *vestigial*, wings, as shown in Figure 9.3. Yet when flies with normal wings are carefully compared with those that have vestigial wings, many differences come to light. Apart from short wings, vestigial-winged flies have bristles of an unusual shape, the shape of the spermatheca (a sac in the female for storing sperm) is changed, the number of ova is decreased and lifespan is reduced. All these phenotypic changes are a consequence of the 'vestigial wing' allele when homozygous.

Notice that the extensions of genetic analysis discussed in Sections 9.1 to 9.3 do not involve new laws of inheritance; the basic rules of inheritance described in Section 8 still apply.

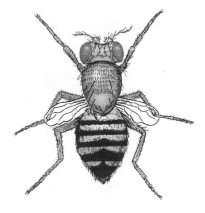

Figure 9.3   The common fruit-fly (*D. melanogaster*) with vestigial wings. (About 10 times actual size)

Activity 9.1   Phenotypic variation (continued)

Now would be a good time to update your summary of the sources of phenotypic variation, if you have not already been doing so. ◄

9.4   Effect of environment on phenotype

We have seen that an organism's genotype contributes to the development of its phenotype. However, the environment also plays a crucial role in the development of the phenotype and is another source of variation between individuals. The environment is never the same for any two individuals. Even two plants growing side by side in a field do not receive precisely the same amount of light, water and minerals; no two animals receive exactly the same type and/or amount of food at the same stage of growth.

Breeders of agricultural plants and animals are always on the look-out for genotypic variants that, when raised under farm conditions, give greater yields of grain, milk, meat, or wool, for example. However, yields are influenced also by environmental factors, such as the quality of the soil, the amount of moisture, heat and light.

One striking example of the effect of the environment on the phenotype is seen in the coat colour of Siamese cats. In these cats (Figure 9.4), the pattern of brown extremities — feet, face, ears and tail — and cream-coloured body are transmitted to their descendants. (Note that the gene involved is a different one from the coat colour genes mentioned in Section 9.3.) The kittens are all cream-coloured at birth and some days later, pigment appears in their new fur, first along the margins of their ears and gradually over their extremities. If the kittens grow and develop in a warm environment, the amount of brown fur is smaller than if they develop at cold temperatures. Although it appears that the brown and cream pattern is itself inherited, in fact what is really inherited is the capacity of the fur to form brown pigment or not to form it, depending on the particular temperature at the time of growth. So a single genotype may produce different phenotypes, depending on the environment in which the organism develops.

Figure 9.4   Siamese cats showing the variation in the distribution of brown colour on the body. The cat in (a) grew and developed in a colder environment than the cat in (b) and hence has more brown fur.

(a)

(b)

This example illustrates that no character is inherited ready-made; the phenotype arises during the growth and development of the individual in a particular environment. This takes us to the important point that what is biologically inherited is not a character in itself (you do not actually inherit your father's nose) but the *information* to produce that character.

9.5 Characters that show continuous variation

All the characters that we have considered so far have one of a number of contrasting phenotypes which can be classified into discrete classes. Such *qualitative* characters that vary in this way show **discontinuous variation**. However, not all differences between individuals are of this kind. Characters such as weight in humans and economically important traits in domestic animals and cultivated plants, such as amount of milk produced and yield of fruit, do not fall into distinct classes. Such characters that can be measured in some way to give a number with a unit attached to it, are described as *quantitative* characters. They show **continuous variation** in the population. This section examines the differences in inheritance between characters showing discontinuous variation and those showing continuous variation.

A good example of a character that shows continuous variation is height in humans, as shown in Figure 9.5. This figure shows data on height for 1 164 adult British men in 1946. The symmetrical distribution with the appearance of a bell-shaped curve shows that the majority of individuals have a height that is close to the mean value for the population, with numbers decreasing on either side of this mean value. Very few individuals — very tall and very short — are found at the two extremes. Such a pattern is described as a **normal distribution**.

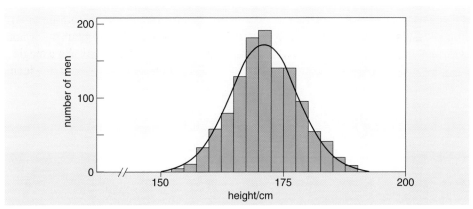

Figure 9.5 A normal distribution curve for a quantitative character: height for 1 164 adult British men in 1946. The original measurements are presented as a histogram with 2.5 cm height intervals and interpreted as a smooth curve. (The mean height of adult British men nowadays is considerably greater than it was in the 1940s.)

The fact that the phenotype varies continuously does not mean that the variation is the result of some genetic mechanism different from that of the genes we have been dealing with. The development of the phenotype of continuously varying characters is due to the joint action of several genes, each of which has, individually, a very small effect on the phenotype. So height, for example, is the cumulative effect of a number of genes located at different loci. However, genes are not the only determinants of continuously varying characters; as with those that vary discontinuously, a major role is also played by environmental factors.

🔵 Can you suggest environmental factors that might affect a person's height?

⚪ Diet, and bouts of infections and disease during childhood. (The latter is particularly important in developing countries.)

The critical difference between characters that vary continuously and those that vary discontinuously is not the number of segregating genes but the range of the phenotypic differences between genotypes. In the case of characters that show discontinuous variation there is a small number of clearly defined phenotypes, as in the case of grain colour in maize. In contrast, for characters that show continuous variation (such as height) there is a potentially infinite number of slightly different phenotypes.

9.6 Mutation

Genetic analysis, as we have seen, must start with parental differences, such as purple versus white grains. Without variation, no genetic analysis is possible. Where do these variants come from? The answer is that the genetic material has an inherent tendency to undergo change in a spontaneous process called *mutation*. Geneticists recognize two different levels at which mutation takes place. In **gene mutation** an allele of a gene changes and gives rise to a different allele. A different kind of mutation involves parts of or whole chromosomes and is called **chromosome mutation**.

9.6.1 Gene mutation

Gene mutations may bring about a change of one allele to another, such as a change in an allele for white grain in maize to an allele for purple grain, or vice versa. All present variation in organisms that we consider to be 'normal' variation, such as blue and brown eyes or blood groups in humans, must have arisen some time ago by mutation. Some mutations may have no effect on the phenotype, some are useful and some, such as haemophilia — a recessive sex-linked disease in humans in which blood clotting is impaired — can have harmful consequences, whilst others are lethal.

Most importantly, only mutations in the cells that give rise to the gametes can be perpetuated from one generation to the next. Some gene changes transmitted in gametes are new, and arose very recently as new gametes were formed. In fact, it is highly probable that each of us has received at least one new mutation from one of our parents. Other gene changes transmitted in gametes, however, are descended from mutations that happened many generations ago, and these mutations have been copied and passed on from parent to offspring. One famous example is a mutation for haemophilia in the generations of interrelated royal families in Europe. The original haemophilia allele arose as a mutation in the reproductive cells of either Queen Victoria or one of her parents. One of Queen Victoria's sons, Leopold, Duke of Albany, suffered from the disease, as did many of her grandsons and great grandsons. For example, the son of the last czar of Russia, Alexis, inherited the allele from his mother, Alexandra, granddaughter of Queen Victoria.

9.6.2 Chromosome mutations

Meiosis is a well-ordered sequence of events that involves a large number of interdependent processes, including the separation of homologous chromosomes and the separation of chromatids into different gametes. However, occasionally things go wrong.

Sometimes errors occur during the separation and distribution of chromosomes during nuclear division. The commonest example of such an error in humans leads to Down's syndrome (Figure 9.6). A typical karyotype of a person with Down's syndrome is shown in Figure 9.6b.

 Compare the karyotype of a person with Down's syndrome (Figure 9.6b) with a typical human karyotype (Figure 8.2). How do these karyotypes differ?

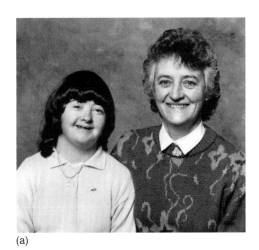

(a)

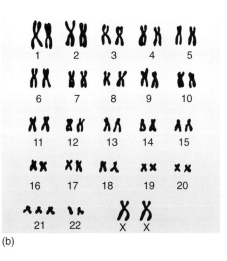

(b)

Figure 9.6   Down's syndrome. (a) A photograph of Cathy who has Down's syndrome, with her mother Chris. (b) The karyotype of a female with Down's syndrome.

The Down's syndrome karyotype has 47 chromosomes instead of 46; there are three copies of chromosome 21, instead of the usual two copies.

The presence of an extra chromosome has a profound effect on the phenotype; Down's syndrome children usually have a particularly loving nature, short stature, poor muscle tone, a small round head, as well as showing varying degrees of learning disability. Why the presence of an extra chromosome 21 has these effects on the phenotype is an area of current intensive research.

The presence of an additional chromosome in an individual's cells is an example of a chromosome mutation. The reason for its occurrence is that occasionally a pair of chromosomes fails to separate during meiosis (in the first division). Instead, both chromosomes move to the same end of the cell and this results in a gamete with *two* copies of the same chromosome. When this gamete combines with a normal gamete at fertilization, the result is a zygote with *three* copies of this chromosome.

Intriguingly, the presence of an extra chromosome in a gamete is more frequent in women than in men and occurs more frequently in older than in younger women. Why should this be so? The main clue comes from the difference in the duration of meiosis in men and women. In men, meiosis begins at puberty and is maintained throughout life. The process takes about three hours, and the production of fully motile mature sperm is complete within three weeks. In contrast, meiosis begins in a developing female embryo whilst still inside her mother's womb, but the process is arrested at an early stage (prophase I) before the baby is born and is completed at some time between puberty and the menopause. During a woman's reproductive life, one cell completes the meiotic division and gives rise to one ovum during each menstrual cycle. A cell that completes meiosis shortly after puberty has thus been arrested at prophase I for about 10–15 years. By contrast, a cell that completes meiosis late in a woman's reproductive life will have been arrested at prophase I for up to 50 years. As the duration of meiosis increases, the risk of chromosome mutations, such as the failure of homologous chromosomes to separate, also increases.

Hence, the longer meiosis is arrested, the greater the chance that chromosomal abnormalities will occur. Thus the older a woman is, the greater the likelihood that she will produce an ovum with a chromosome mutation such as an extra chromosome 21. This is clearly demonstrated by comparing the proportion of Down's syndrome babies born to mothers of different ages, as shown in Figure 9.7.

Looking at the graph in Figure 9.7, what is the frequency (as number per 100 births) of individuals born with Down's syndrome for mothers aged 20 years and those aged 45 years?

The frequency of individuals born with Down's syndrome is very low (less than 0.1 per 100 births) in mothers aged 20 years but rises steeply to about three per 100 births in those aged 45 years.

Figure 9.7 A graph showing the increase in frequency of Down's syndrome with maternal age.

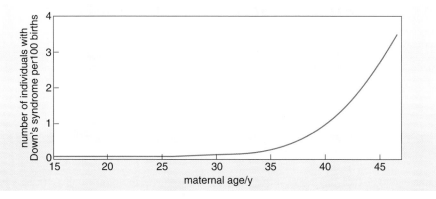

Chromosome mutations in general play a prominent role in determining disability in humans. However, the number of individuals with chromosome mutations that we know about is a small fraction of the total number of zygotes produced that carry a chromosome mutation. The vast majority of human embryos with a major chromosome abnormality spontaneously abort. In fact, chromosome mutations account for about half of spontaneous abortions.

In conclusion, all the sources of variation considered in Sections 8 and 9 contribute to the overall range of phenotypes in individuals of a species and help to explain why each individual is phenotypically unique.

In Sections 8 and 9 we have considered the gene as a unit of inheritance with a specific location on a specific chromosome. Through genetic analysis we have studied the inheritance of particular genes and chromosomes. But we have not yet considered the physical nature of genes and chromosomes, and it is to the structure of genes and chromosomes that we turn in Section 10.

Question 9.3 Match each of the situations found in maize and described in (a)–(d) with one of the explanations (i)–(v) in the list below.

Situation

(a) When two maize plants, each with round-shaped grains, were crossed, most of the progeny had round-shaped grains but about one-quarter of the progeny were found to have wrinkled grains.

(b) Cob size in maize is very variable between varieties. Crosses between varieties revealed no predictable ratio of long to short cobs although there were relatively few of the extremely long and extremely short cobs in the F_2 offspring and a relatively large number of intermediate cob length.

(c) Two maize plants, when crossed, produce white-grained cobs. However, one of the cobs produced by crossing these two plants had one grain that was purple in colour — the phenotype that is dominant to white.

(d) In maize, if a mutated recessive allele of any one of 15 particular genes is present, the leaves of the seedlings are virtually white instead of the normal green colour, are unable to photosynthesize and so die.

Explanations

(i) A new mutation occurred during gamete formation in the parents.

(ii) The affected offspring are homozygous for the recessive allele of the gene.

(iii) This character is a quantitative one, determined by the combined action of a number of genes.

(iv) This character is not genetically determined.

(v) This character shows discontinuous variation and is affected by the combined action of a number of genes. ◀

Activity 9.1   Phenotypic variation (continued)

You should now complete your summary of the sources of phenotypic variation and then compare your list with ours. ◀

9.7   Summary of Section 9

The absence of genes on the Y chromosome, other than those involved in sex determination, results in sex-linked genes (those on the X chromosome) having a pattern of inheritance that is different from that of the genes on the autosomes.

The phenotype of a particular character is a result of the relationship between the two copies of a gene that are present in an individual, and this relationship varies between different alleles (e.g. dominance, codominance). A gene can have more than two alleles but there are only two in any individual.

Some characters are affected by more than one gene, and one gene may affect more than one character.

The phenotype is determined by the interaction of the genotype and the environment.

Characters that show continuous variation are influenced by several genes as well as by environmental factors.

Mutation is a source of heritable variation. Gene mutation involves the change of one allele of a gene to a different allele. Errors sometimes occur in the separation of homologous chromosomes at meiosis and this can result in chromosome mutations.

10 What are genes made of?

So far, we have considered genes as units of inheritance and this section goes on to explore the chemical nature of genes. Genes are composed of DNA, and a knowledge of the structure of DNA is essential to understand how it can function as hereditary material. This biopolymer illustrates beautifully the precise relationship between chemical structure and biological function discussed in Section 3. DNA has three key properties: it is relatively stable and hence an appropriate store for vital information; its structure suggests an obvious way in which the molecule can be duplicated, or replicated; and it can convey information which is used continuously within a cell. In this section, we will examine the chemical nature of DNA, which accounts for both its stability and the way it can be replicated — the first two of these three key properties. The third property, how DNA functions as the genetic material, is the subject of Section 11.

10.1 The chemical structure of DNA

It was in 1953 that James Watson and Francis Crick deduced the three-dimensional structure of DNA. It was the year that might be described as the dawn of molecular biology, for their publication was to have far-reaching consequences in terms of our understanding of how cells function at the molecular level. So monumental was this work that they were awarded, together with Maurice Wilkins, the Nobel Prize for Medicine and Physiology in 1962. In this section we shall examine in some detail the structure of this biopolymer. You were introduced to the essential features of the three classes of biopolymer — proteins, polysaccharides and nucleic acids — in Section 3 and you should review your understanding of these before you continue.

Activity 10.1   Revision: structure of biopolymers

This activity will help you to review the main features that proteins, polysaccharides and nucleic acids have in common. ◀

Watson and Crick showed that DNA has a *double helix* structure; it is this that accounts for the stability of DNA, one of the key features of the hereditary material. Its simplest representation is shown in Figure 10.1a and in this context 'double' means the *two* intertwined strands of this simplified sketch. We will first consider the composition of each separate strand by taking it apart to reveal the monomers of this biopolymer. Then we will show how the two strands interact to form the characteristic double-helical molecule of DNA.

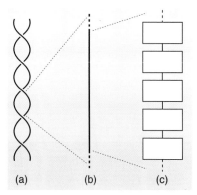

Figure 10.1   A simplified sketch showing the structure of DNA. (a) The double helix — two intertwined strands. (b) A small section of one of the strands, straightened out and greatly magnified. (c) This same section, magnified further, showing how a strand is made up of monomers, each of which is represented as a rectangular box.

Figure 10.1b shows a small straightened-out section from one of the strands of the DNA molecule. Each strand is a polymer comprising a string of monomers, shown diagrammatically as rectangles in Figure 10.1c. Each monomer is a **nucleotide** and is more complicated in structure than the monomers of proteins and polysaccharides. Each nucleotide consists of three component parts: a phosphate group, a sugar molecule and a nitrogen-containing organic molecule called a *base*. (You were introduced to an organic base in the structure of ATP shown in Figure 4.8; as mentioned there, in this block the term 'base' has a different meaning from the one you met in Block 6.) Figure 10.2a shows these separate parts and the relationship between them in a simplified structure of a nucleotide. The sugar is a 5-carbon molecule called *deoxyribose* (Figure 10.2b), and so these nucleotides are known as *deoxyribonucleotides*. From here on we will simplify this cumbersome term to merely nucleotide. Note though, that because of the presence of deoxyribose, the polymer of nucleotides that we are describing is known as **deoxyribonucleic acid**, usually abbreviated to **DNA**.

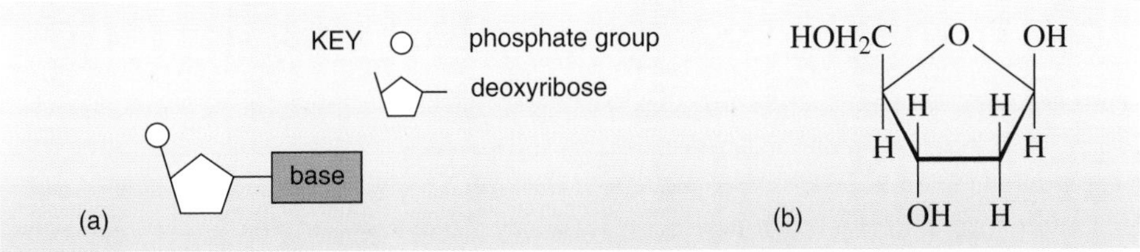

Figure 10.2 (a) Simplified structure of a generalized nucleotide of DNA. (b) The full structure of the sugar deoxyribose. (As with the sugar structures given in Section 3, ring carbon atoms are not shown.)

In the nucleotide shown in Figure 10.2a, the base is undefined. However, there are four different **bases** in DNA: adenine, guanine, cytosine and thymine. Their structures are shown in Figure 10.3. (You are not expected to memorize these structures, although you should remember the names of the bases.)

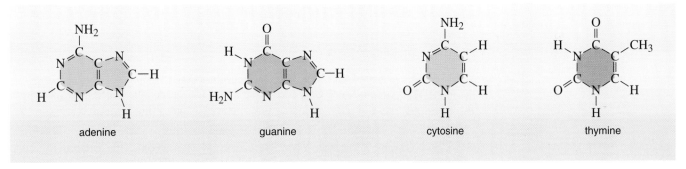

adenine   guanine   cytosine   thymine

● Look at the structure of each of the four bases shown in Figure 10.3. How might you distinguish, in simple terms, the structures of adenine and guanine from those of cytosine and thymine?

Figure 10.3 The structures of the four DNA bases.

○ Both adenine and guanine have *two* nitrogen-containing rings, whereas cytosine and thymine each have only *one* such ring. Consequently adenine and guanine are larger than cytosine and thymine.

The single strand of DNA separated from its pair (a portion of which is shown in Figures 10.1b and c) is a polymer of the nucleotides shown in Figure 10.2a. In each strand, the phosphate of one nucleotide forms a bond with the sugar of another nucleotide, and so on down the strand, as shown on the left (in white) in Figure 10.4. As with other biopolymers, the bonds joining the chain of monomers — in this case

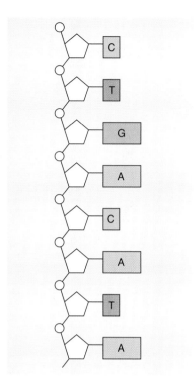

Figure 10.4 A short segment of a polynucleotide, in which the bases, adenine, guanine, cytosine thymine, are denoted simply as A, G, C, and T, respectively. The sugar–phosphate backbone is shown in white. (This figure represents one strand of the DNA double helix.)

nucleotides — are covalent bonds. The strand of alternating phosphate groups and sugars is known as the *sugar–phosphate backbone*, and the bases protrude out from this towards the other strand of the helix. A length of such a polymer with a number of nucleotides joined together, as shown in Figure 10.4, is described as a *polynucleotide*. The size differences between the bases is illustrated diagrammatically in this figure by the different-sized rectangles that denote the bases; the larger rectangles represent either an adenine or a guanine base and the smaller rectangles represent either a cytosine or a thymine base. When illustrating a polynucleotide we can simplify the name of each base to a single capital letter, so that A = adenine, G = guanine, C = cytosine and T = thymine, as shown in Figure 10.4.

⬤ How many nucleotides are shown in the polynucleotide segment in Figure 10.4?

○ The simplest way of answering this question is to count the number of rectangles that represent the bases; there are eight.

There is a simplified way of describing the structure of DNA in text, and that is to write out the sequence of bases in a single polynucleotide strand, representing each base by its initial letter A, G, C or T. We will use this chemical shorthand extensively from now on.

⬤ What is the base sequence in the portion of a DNA molecule shown in Figure 10.4, starting from the top?

○ CTGACATA.

These sequences are usually written or printed in lines like the letters or characters on this page. This is a convention, like reading left to right and top to bottom of this page. There may be many hundreds of thousands of bases within a single DNA molecule, in a long linear sequence. Such a sequence might appear as follows (reading from left to right in successive lines):

…AACGCGCGTATATAAATCGCTAGCTTCAACGACTGCTGACGTAGTTCCCT GCAAACACAAGTCACGAAGCAGTTTGCAGCAGCTGCAACATCTAGCAGCT…

DNA molecules are by far the largest known molecules in living organisms; some have relative molecular masses of many billions! If you consider the comparatively short sequence of 100 bases shown above, and think about how a simple coding language of just four letters could be rearranged in such a sequence, you will gain some appreciation of the huge variety of sequences that are possible. Take, for example, a short chain (i.e. a polynucleotide) of just eight nucleotides. Since there are four *different* bases, there are four options for each position, and therefore $4 \times 4 \times 4 \times 4 \times 4 \times 4 \times 4 \times 4 = 4^8 = 65\,536$ possible different sequences for a polynucleotide of this length! The much longer sequence shown above has 100 bases in it, so the number of different possibilities here is 4^{100} or 1.6×10^{60}. A DNA molecule consisting of thousands of bases therefore represents a vast store of potential information, the full consequences of which should become more apparent as you study subsequent sections.

So far we have considered a single strand of DNA, but Figure 10.1a showed that DNA has a *double*-helical structure. The DNA double helix in fact consists of two polynucleotide chains spiralled around each other, as shown in Figure 10.5, which is an enlarged and more detailed version of Figure 10.1a. Here each of the two ribbons represents the sugar–phosphate backbone of Figure 10.4, whilst the horizontal bars represent the bases of the two strands and the bonds between them.

The key to understanding the structure of DNA and how it functions in the cell lies in the interaction between the bases at the core of the molecule. Along the length of a polynucleotide chain within the double helix, each base makes specific pairing and bonding with a corresponding base in the other polynucleotide chain. These interactions are known as **base-pairing**, for which there are very precise rules, as illustrated in Figure 10.6.

> The base-pairing rules in DNA are as follows: T (thymine) pairs only with A (adenine), whilst C (cytosine) pairs only with G (guanine). Thus there are two pairs of **complementary bases**: T and A; C and G.

These pairs of complementary bases sit flat within the spiral of the DNA double helix, rather like the steps of a spiral staircase. The other important point to note about base-pairing is that T is bonded to A, and C to G via weak bonds, shown as the orange dashed lines in Figure 10.6. These weak bonds are hydrogen bonds, and you saw examples of situations where they are important for the higher-order structure of biopolymers in Section 3. Figure 10.6 clearly illustrates the difference between the A–T base pair and the C–G pair in terms of the number of hydrogen bonds: the A–T pair has only two hydrogen bonds, whereas the C–G pair has three.

The base composition of DNA is related to the base-pairing rules just outlined.

- If you were to extract some DNA from cells, isolate and purify the four bases, how much adenine would you expect to find relative to thymine? Similarly, how much cytosine would you find relative to guanine?

- A consequence of the base-pairing rules is that the amount of adenine in a DNA molecule is always equal to the amount of thymine; the same applies to the amount of cytosine relative to that of guanine.

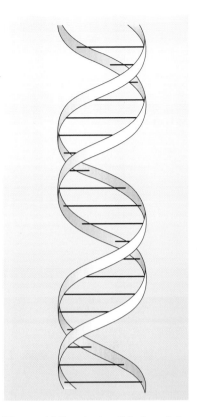

Figure 10.5 A simplified model showing the double-helical structure of DNA. The bars represent base pairs, and the ribbons represent the sugar–phosphate backbones of the two polynucleotide chains which make up the DNA molecule.

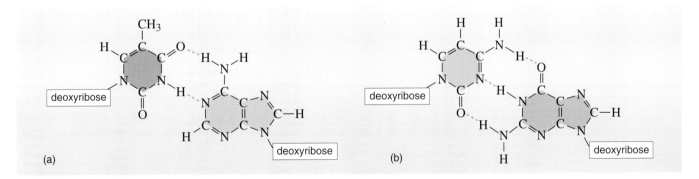

(a)　　　　　　　(b)

Figure 10.6 Base-pairing between DNA bases. (a) Thymine (T) pairs with adenine (A), and (b) cytosine (C) pairs with guanine (G). The orange dashed lines represent the hydrogen bonds between these two pairs of bases. The covalent linkage of each of the bases to deoxyribose in the sugar–phosphate backbone is also shown.

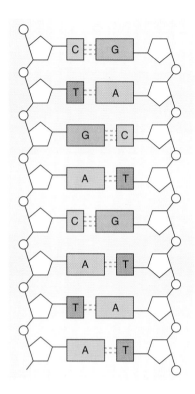

Figure 10.7   A portion of a DNA molecule with the helix unwound, showing the complementary base pairs held together by hydrogen bonds (orange dashed lines) between the two polynucleotide chains.

The alignment of base pairs within a DNA molecule is shown in Figure 10.7. Here the helix is shown unwound, with the two sugar–phosphate backbones now parallel but still on the outside; the complementary base pairs with their hydrogen bonds form the core of the molecule. Notice here the significance in the different sizes of the bases, even though Figure 10.7 shows them only in a diagrammatic form: a complementary A–T pair is a similar size to a complementary C–G pair, whereas in contrast a G–A pair would be too large to fit into the available space, and a C–T pair would be too small. Since the sequence of bases on one strand is complementary to the sequence of bases on the other strand, the two strands of the double helix are described as *complementary*.

The structure of DNA can be summarized as follows. The hydrogen-bonded complementary base pairs sit at the core of the molecule, and are arranged flat like the steps of a spiral staircase. The two sugar–phosphate backbones lie to the outside of the helix, each spiralled around the other.

Watson and Crick, in their famous 1953 paper published in the journal *Nature*, wrote:

> We wish to suggest a structure for … deoxyribose nucleic acid (DNA). This structure has novel features which are of considerable biological interest … It has not escaped our notice that the specific pairing we have postulated immediately suggests a possible copying mechanism for the genetic material.

In the following section we consider how new DNA molecules are synthesized, and show how true Watson and Crick's prediction was.

Question 10.1   In a fragment of double-stranded DNA, there is a total of 100 bases, of which 30 are cytosine (C). Calculate the total number of each of the following items in the DNA fragment: (a) complementary base pairs; (b) nucleotides; (c) deoxyribose groups; (d) guanine (G) bases; (e) thymine (T) bases; (f) adenine (A) bases; (g) hydrogen bonds. ◀

10.2 DNA replication

You know from Block 4 that eukaryote cells divide by means of mitosis to produce two progeny cells which contain identical genetic material, which is also identical to that of the original parent cell. This is how unicellular organisms form large populations of individual cells, and how a zygote grows into an adult multicellular organism. Prokaryote cells also undergo cell division, whereby one cell divides completely to become two. Recall from Section 2 that these cells do not contain nuclei, so the process of cell division is somewhat simpler. Whatever the cell type, for one cell to become two new ones, the DNA within it must undergo a process in which an identical copy is made, otherwise the two new cells would not be genetically identical to the original parent cell.

We begin at the molecular level by examining how DNA is replicated and then turn to the level of the chromosome to explore the relationship between DNA molecules and chromosome structure.

10.2.1 How DNA is replicated

As noted above, Watson and Crick postulated that DNA base-pairing provides a mechanism by which the DNA might be copied. This DNA copying mechanism, usually referred to as **DNA replication**, is the process we consider here.

○ Recall the significant feature of the bonding between the two bases of a base pair, and compare this with the bonding in the sugar–phosphate backbone.

○ The hydrogen bonds between a C–G pair and between an A–T pair are *weak* bonds, implying that these could be readily broken. The stronger covalent bonds of the sugar–phosphate backbone are very much more difficult to break.

Indeed, the breaking of the hydrogen bonds between base pairs and the separation of the two polynucleotide strands of DNA is an early event in the process of DNA replication. Once the strands have been separated, new DNA strands are synthesized; the enzyme that catalyses this process is called *DNA polymerase*.

Figure 10.8 shows the principal stages of DNA replication. The two strands of the double helix shown in Figure 10.8a unwind, starting at one end, to expose the bases on each strand. The two complementary single strands are shown separated in Figure 10.8b. Each of these strands now acts as a *template*, a mould, for DNA replication. The base-pairing rules are the basis of this process; that is, the nucleotides are added in a complementary manner — C always opposite G and A always opposite T, with the hydrogen bonds being formed in the process. At the same time, the two new sugar–phosphate backbones are synthesized by the formation of covalent bonds between alternating phosphate and deoxyribose molecules. The result is the production of two identical double-stranded DNA molecules (Figure 10.8c). Initially the DNA is unwound, as shown in Figure 10.8c; later the paired strands wind around each other to form the characteristic double-helical structure.

This process has been termed **semi-conservative replication**, meaning 'half-conserved' replication. This is because in each new daughter DNA molecule, *one* of the two original polynucleotide strands is unchanged from the original parent molecule; these are labelled as the parental strands in Figure 10.8b. The second polynucleotide strand has been newly synthesized in its entirety; these are labelled as the new strands in Figure 10.8c. Or, to put it crudely, each daughter double helix is only 'half new'; each has one parental strand and one new strand.

Figure 10.8 The process of DNA replication. (a) A portion of a DNA double helix showing 10 labelled complementary base pairs. (b) Part of the double helix has unwound and come apart at one end, revealing two single-stranded polynucleotide chains. (c) Part of each polynucleotide chain has been replicated, but the two paired chains have not yet wound into double helices. The new DNA strands are shown in green and the hydrogen bonds are shown as orange dashed lines. The process continues until all of the parent DNA molecule has been replicated.

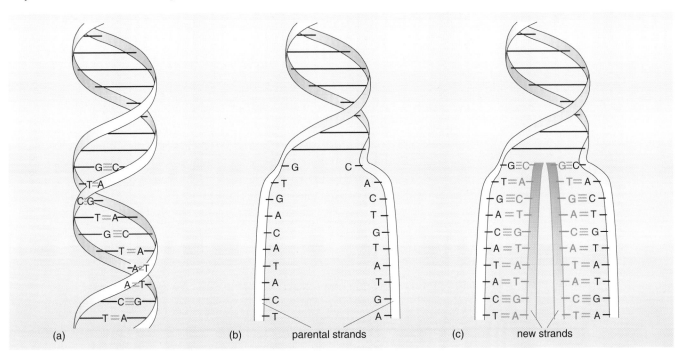

(a) (b) parental strands (c) new strands

Figure 10.8 shows just a small portion of DNA being replicated. The process continues until the whole of the DNA molecule has been replicated, and the two daughter DNA molecules form the characteristic double-helical structures, as opposed to the unwound products of replication shown in Figure 10.8c. Before the cell can divide to produce identical progeny cells, *all* the DNA molecules in the cell have to replicate to produce two identical copies.

This, in outline, is how DNA is copied during most cycles of cell division. If you compare Figures 10.8a and 10.8c you will see that both DNA molecules in (c) are a faithful copy of the sequences of bases of the parent molecule in (a), although in (c) they have not yet formed helices.

An important feature of DNA structure is that the genetic information it contains is copied into more DNA with the same genetic information.

Activity 10.2 Understanding DNA replication

This activity will help you to consolidate your understanding of DNA replication. ◀

10.2.2 Chromosome structure and DNA replication

DNA replication is closely linked to chromosome replication, which in turn is linked to mitosis (see Activity 8.4). This raises an intriguing question: What is the structural relationship between chromosomes and DNA molecules? In other words, how many DNA molecules are present in a chromosome?

Chromosomes are composed of DNA intimately associated with protein. The DNA of the chromosomes is replicated during interphase of mitosis, and when the chromosomes first become visible at prophase they are double structures; that is, they are each composed of two chromatids. (The chromosomes in Figures 8.1 and 8.2 are clearly visible as paired chromatids.) During mitosis, the two chromatids of each pair separate to opposite poles (ends) of the cell so that at the end of mitosis each chromosome is a single unit. Evidence suggests that such a single (unreplicated) chromosome contains one continuous double-stranded DNA molecule running along its length, as shown in Figure 10.9a. That makes a very long molecule! This shows that since genes are linked together along the length of a chromosome (Activity 8.4), each gene is a short section of a double-stranded DNA molecule. Each DNA double helix is associated with protein, and the DNA–protein complex coils, loops, and supercoils to form a chromosome.

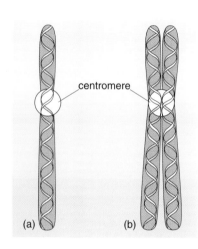

centromere

(a)   (b)

Figure 10.9 The number of DNA molecules in a chromosome. (a) A chromosome prior to replication contains a single DNA molecule. (b) A chromosome that has replicated and consists of two chromatids, each comprising a single DNA molecule. In reality, each DNA double helix would be associated with protein, forming a DNA–protein complex.

Before the next round of cell division begins, each chromosome duplicates longitudinally to form two paired chromatids, as shown in Figure 10.9b. At the molecular level, the original DNA double helix has formed two identical daughter DNA double helices and the total mass of DNA in the cell has doubled. Each chromatid contains one DNA double helix along its length (Figure 10.9b). Since the double helix in each chromatid has a base sequence identical to that in its partner chromatid (Figure 10.8c), the gene copies carried by pairs of chromatids are also identical.

The faithful replication of DNA is remarkable, considering that the copying of millions of bases is involved. However, as you will see in the following section, such accurate replication does not always occur.

Question 10.2   Figure 10.10 shows part of a double-stranded DNA molecule during the process of replication. Each square represents a base. (a) Identify the missing bases and write the correct letter (A, G, C or T) in each of the blank squares. (b) At what stage of the cell cycle would DNA be undergoing replication? ◄

10.3 Errors in replication, and damage to DNA

The structure of DNA accounts for its stability. Nevertheless, errors can arise during the process of DNA replication, leading to mutations. Gene mutation as a fundamental source of heritable variation was considered in Section 9.6. This section examines these mutations at the level of DNA and shows that a gene mutation is an error in DNA sequence.

The machinery of DNA replication is generally remarkably efficient and accurate, so that a parent DNA molecule is faithfully reproduced as two new, identical helices. However, this process is not always perfect and mistakes sometimes occur, with the result that 'wrong' bases are inserted into the growing polynucleotide chain. For example, the replication machinery may add a T into the growing polynucleotide chain where a C should have been, or it may add a G instead of an A. Alternatively, slightly larger errors might be made, such as when a short sequence of the parental template strand is skipped over, or a few extra bases are inserted. Such errors in replication bring about changes in the DNA sequence. The 'wrong' sequence would be copied as faithfully in future cell divisions as would the 'correct' sequence, so the mutation would be perpetuated.

Not all these mistakes go undetected by the cell, however. There are 'surveillance' processes in cells which detect most of these replication errors. For example, there are DNA repair pathways containing enzymes that can identify a wrongly placed base in the growing polynucleotide chain, remove it, and replace it with the 'correct' base. These DNA repair mechanisms can be viewed as being analogous to quality control systems in an industrial production line, such that 'faulty' products are removed before they leave the 'factory'. Hence the mutation is usually short-lived, since the incorrect base(s) are removed and replaced by the correct one(s).

In addition to errors brought about by mistakes made by the DNA replication machinery, environmental agents can produce mutations. Many of these environmental agents are chemicals, some of which are used experimentally in the laboratory to produce mutants which are useful in gene identification and mapping. Others are physical agents, such as various forms of radiation, including UV radiation from the Sun.

As with mistakes made by the replication machinery, many mutations brought about by chemical or physical means can be detected by DNA repair mechanisms. For example, in the much studied bacterium *Escherichia coli*, one such repair mechanism has been termed the SOS system. As its name implies, it responds to a 'distress signal', produced as a result of damage to DNA caused by UV radiation.

However, if errors pass undetected by the repair mechanisms — an event which must happen relatively rarely, considering the total number of DNA bases replicated — they result in mutations. We shall return to a consideration of mutation after we have considered how DNA functions as the genetic material, which is the major topic of the following section.

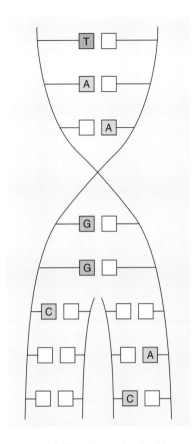

Figure 10.10   Part of a double-stranded DNA molecule during replication.

10.4 Summary of Section 10

DNA (deoxyribonucleic acid) is composed of two polynucleotide chains linked together by hydrogen bonds and wound around each other to form a double helix.

Four bases, A (adenine), G (guanine), C (cytosine) and T (thymine), make up the core of the DNA double helix. These form complementary base pairs, so that an A of one polynucleotide chain always pairs with a T of the other chain, whilst C and G always pair with each other. The outer part of the double helix consists of the two sugar–phosphate backbones.

The information carried by DNA is in a simple coding language of just the four bases, A, G, C and T. Using just these four letters, a DNA molecule represents a vast store of information.

The process of DNA replication is semi-conservative. During replication, the DNA double helix unwinds, and each of the two parental polynucleotide strands forms a template on which a new strand is synthesized. DNA polymerase adds DNA nucleotides according to the base-pairing rules. Two identical double helices are thereby produced, each consisting of a parental strand and a newly synthesized strand.

An unduplicated chromosome consists of a long double-helical DNA molecule and proteins. The two chromatids of a duplicated chromosome each have a DNA double helix, in which the base sequences and hence the gene copies are identical.

Although the structure of DNA is relatively stable, errors sometimes occur in DNA replication and, if they are not identified and rectified by the cell, are perpetuated as mutations. Changes to DNA sequence are also brought about by environmental factors, such as certain chemicals and radiation.

Using genetic information

One important property of DNA is that it carries genetic information. The simple coding language of just four letters (bases), which can be arranged in a huge variety of sequences, represents a vast potential store of information. This section examines how this information is accessed and used by the cell. We have seen in Section 10 that DNA's double-helical structure both gives rise to its stability, and permits its faithful replication to produce two identical daughter double helices. The key structural features of complementary base pairs joined by hydrogen bonds which play an important role both in stability and replication are also the basis for how DNA functions as genetic material.

How does the simple coding language of DNA relate to the nature of the gene; that is, how do genes function and how do they control phenotype? For example, how can one allele of a gene result in white grain colour in maize and another allele lead to purple grain colour, as we saw in Section 8? The focus of this section, therefore, is on the gene as a unit of function.

The phenotype of an organism largely depends on its chemical composition and on the biochemical reactions that go on inside it. So, for example, the different colour forms of maize grains will have slightly different biochemical processes, causing different colours to be produced. All the biochemical reactions of a cell are catalysed by enzymes, which are proteins (Section 4.3). The enzymes present in a cell, and structural proteins too, are determined by that cell's genotype. Genes specify polypeptides. *How* genes do this is the topic of this section and the essence is that the structure of the DNA can be related to the structure of proteins. As you saw in Section 3, proteins come in a huge range of sizes and shapes, and this diversity arises from different combinations of just 20 amino acids. We will examine how the simple coding language of DNA of just four letters contains information for thousands of different proteins, each with its own unique sequence of amino acids.

The production of proteins is a far more complex process than the more straightforward process of DNA replication, partly because many other molecules are involved. We begin by viewing the overall scheme in barest outline and then go on to examine each step in turn. The video sequence in Activity 11.4 provides an animation of the flow of information from DNA to polypeptide. This will enable you to consolidate your understanding of the processes involved and help to bring them 'alive'. Finally, we revisit the process of mutation and examine how a small change in the DNA can affect the activity of a protein for which it codes, and hence the phenotype of the individual, such as the cystic fibrosis phenotype in humans.

11.1 One gene — one polypeptide

The concept that genes contain hereditary information leads inevitably to the question: 'information for what?'. Most genes contain the information for the production of a specific polypeptide or protein. Recall that these terms are used interchangeably. However, in the context of protein synthesis, it is actually the polypeptide chain that is being made; it becomes a fully functional protein molecule later.

You have seen that a gene is part of a long DNA molecule, which comprises a linear sequence of base pairs (Section 10.2.2). So, a gene is divisible into a specific sequence of DNA base pairs.

What can you recall about the monomers in a polypeptide?

A polypeptide has a linear sequence of amino acids. (Recall that by convention this is written with the N-terminal amino acid on the left and the C-terminal one on the right (Section 3.3.2 and Figure 3.19).)

There is a direct and specific relationship between the linear sequence of base pairs in a DNA molecule which goes to make up a gene, and the linear sequence of amino acids in a polypeptide molecule. This relationship is presented in a very simplistic manner in Figure 11.1, which shows (in particular in Figure 11.1b) that the *base sequence* of the DNA in a gene can be related precisely to the *amino acid sequence* of the polypeptide. This colinearity of sequence between a gene and a polypeptide is known as the **one gene — one polypeptide hypothesis**.

The one gene — one polypeptide hypothesis states that a given gene has a very precise linear sequence which codes for the linear sequence of amino acids in one polypeptide molecule.

Figure 11.1 (a) The linear relationship between a gene and the polypeptide for which it codes. (b) More detail of this relationship: the linear sequence of base pairs corresponds directly to the linear sequence of amino acids in the polypeptide. (Leu, Thr, Val and Ser are the abbreviations for four consecutive amino acids in this polypeptide: leucine, threonine, valine and serine.)

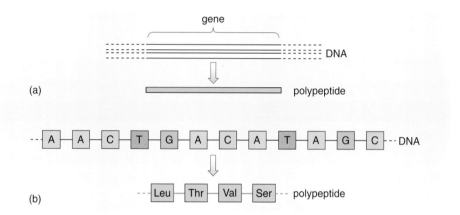

This linear relationship has been a remarkably useful working hypothesis which holds true for many polypeptides in many organisms, but with some modification in the case of others, as you will see in Section 12. However, for the moment it is convenient to view the base sequence of a DNA molecule as having a direct relationship to the amino acid sequence, or primary structure, of a polypeptide. How the DNA base sequence gives rise to the polypeptide molecule is the subject of the rest of Section 11.

11.2 The flow of information from DNA to RNA to polypeptide

The genetic information encoded within a gene is carried via an intermediary class of molecules, **RNA (ribonucleic acid)**. Information within a cell can therefore be seen as passing from DNA, via RNA, to a polypeptide. This flow of information is often called the *central dogma* (a dogma is a widely-held belief) of molecular biology and can be expressed in another way:

DNA makes RNA makes polypeptide.

The central dogma implies that there are two separate steps in this information flow: from DNA to RNA and from RNA to polypeptide; these are called, respectively, *transcription* and *translation*. **Transcription** of DNA produces RNA (Section 11.3) and the subsequent **translation** of this RNA produces polypeptides (Section 11.4). These steps are summarized in Figure 11.2.

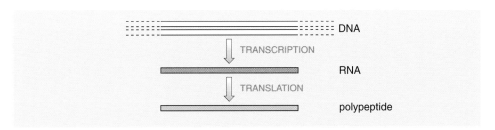

Figure 11.2 Information flow from DNA to RNA to polypeptide.

11.3 From DNA to RNA: transcription

In the process of transcription, the information in a gene, i.e. the DNA base sequence, is transcribed, or copied, to form an RNA molecule. RNA is therefore an intermediate in the flow of information from DNA to polypeptide. Before we consider the details of transcription, we will first look at the structure of RNA.

11.3.1 The structure of RNA

The name ribonucleic acid, for which RNA is an abbreviation, suggests that chemically it is related to DNA, deoxyribonucleic acid. Like DNA, RNA is a polymer of nucleotides, a polynucleotide, and each nucleotide consists of three parts, covalently joined together: a sugar, a phosphate group and a base (Figure 11.3a). However, there are some important differences between DNA and RNA.

One way in which RNA and DNA differ is in the sugar component; RNA has ribose, not deoxyribose as in DNA (compare Figures 11.3b and 10.2b). A second difference is in the constituent nucleotide bases. RNA has four bases: adenine (A), guanine (G), cytosine (C) and uracil (U), whereas the DNA bases are adenine, guanine, cytosine, and thymine (T). Figure 11.4 compares the structures of thymine and uracil. Why one of the four bases in RNA is different from the equivalent base in DNA is not understood.

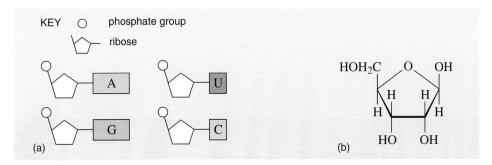

Figure 11.3 (a) The simplified structures of the four nucleotides of RNA. (b) The structure of the sugar ribose. (As for sugar structures given earlier, ring carbon atoms are not shown.)

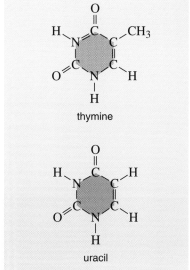

Figure 11.4 The structures of the bases thymine (T) and uracil (U). Note that T occurs only in DNA, whereas U occurs only in RNA. You do not need to memorize these structures.

There is another important structural difference between DNA and RNA. Recall that DNA is a double helix of two spiralled polynucleotide chains, i.e. it is double-stranded. In contrast, RNA is usually a single-stranded polynucleotide chain.

11.3.2 DNA makes RNA

Having considered the structure of RNA and contrasted it with DNA, we now move on to examine how RNA molecules are synthesized — the process of transcription.

○ Before we describe transcription, you might like to speculate in outline how it occurs, bearing in mind what you now know of DNA replication and of the similarities in structure between DNA and RNA.

○ You might have come to the conclusion that RNA is synthesized in a manner similar to DNA replication, i.e. using the DNA as a template.

This is indeed what happens. The process of transcription is illustrated diagrammatically in Figure 11.5. As in DNA replication, the starting point is a double-helical molecule of DNA (Figure 11.5a). The hydrogen bonds between the complementary base pairs are broken, the DNA unwinds and the two polynucleotide strands separate (Figure 11.5b). Here the process of transcription diverges from the familiar one of DNA replication, because synthesis of RNA molecules occurs on only *one* of the two strands: only one DNA strand is the template for RNA synthesis, and this is termed the **template strand**. The other DNA strand, which is not used as a template in RNA synthesis, is termed the **non-template strand** (Figure 11.5b). Apart from this important difference, the basic mechanism of RNA synthesis is the same as that for DNA, in that pairing of complementary bases is the key to the process.

Figure 11.5 The synthesis of RNA on a DNA template. (a) The DNA double helix with 10 labelled base pairs. (b) The hydrogen bonds between the base pairs have been broken and the two strands have separated; note that only one of the strands is used as the template for RNA synthesis. (c) A short length of RNA (shown in red) has been synthesized. In reality the RNA molecule would be much longer than the chain of 10 nucleotides shown here.

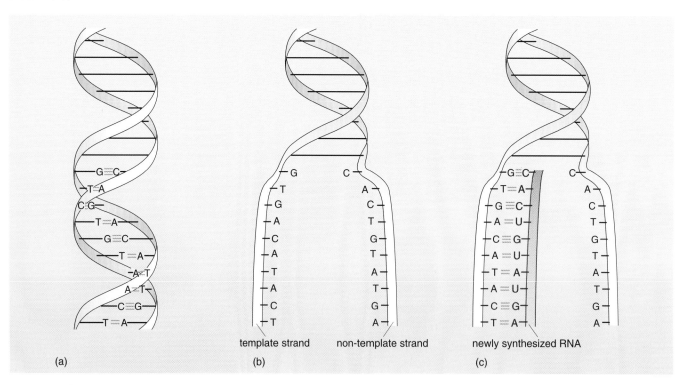

template strand   non-template strand   newly synthesized RNA

(a)   (b)   (c)

○ Which bases are paired together in DNA?

○ C pairs with G, and A pairs with T.

○ Considering these base-pairing rules in DNA, together with the information in Figures 11.3–11.5, what base-pairing rules would you expect to apply to transcription?

○ The T of DNA is replaced with U in RNA, so A–U is a 'new' base pair. The C–G base pair remains the same. T–A is still a possible base pair, but clearly the T has to be in the DNA template and not in the newly-synthesized RNA.

The base-pairing rules in transcription are summarized in Table 11.1.

Thus, the template strand of DNA forms the template on which an RNA molecule is synthesized, according to the base-pairing rules shown in Table 11.1. The enzyme *RNA polymerase* binds to the DNA template strand and moves along it, extending the growing RNA chain by the successive addition of nucleotides containing bases complementary to those in the template strand. The formation of the covalent links between phosphate groups and the ribose sugar molecules produces the sugar–phosphate backbone of the RNA, as shown in Figure 11.5c.

Table 11.1 Base-pairing rules in transcription.

DNA base	RNA base
A	U
G	C
C	G
T	A

Another important difference between DNA replication and transcription is that, in transcription, only relatively short regions of the DNA molecule, corresponding to genes, are transcribed into RNA molecules. This raises the intriguing questions of where on the DNA molecule does RNA synthesis begin, and where does it end? RNA polymerase binds to the template strand of DNA at a particular sequence of bases at one end of the gene, called a transcriptional start site. Transcription comes to an end at a termination sequence, a specific sequence of bases in the DNA at the other end of the gene. At this point the RNA polymerase leaves the DNA, as does the newly synthesized RNA molecule. The DNA double helix reforms and transcription has been completed.

Question 11.1 In what ways do the structures of DNA and RNA differ? ◄

Question 11.2 Which of the descriptions (i)–(x) apply to: (a) both DNA and RNA; (b) DNA but not RNA; (c) RNA but not DNA; (d) neither DNA nor RNA?

(i) Polynucleotide chain(s) of covalently linked nucleotides; (ii) contains the sugar ribose; (iii) contains the sugar deoxyribose; (iv) typically found as a single strand; (v) typically found as double helix; (vi) contains as many T bases as A bases; (vii) contains both T and U; (viii) contains U but not T; (ix) contains T but not U; (x) synthesized on a DNA template. ◄

11.4 From RNA to polypeptide: translation

The second process in the production of polypeptides is translation. Here the base sequence of an RNA molecule is converted into the amino acid sequence of a polypeptide chain. This is a more complex process than transcription. As you have seen, the base sequence of a gene is transcribed into an RNA base sequence, the language of which consists of a mere four characters. Translation is the conversion from the four-character language of RNA into the corresponding 20-character language of a polypeptide. In any language, not all characters are used in every word, and in the same way not all 20 amino acids are used in every polypeptide.

11.4.1 Different forms of RNA

The term RNA covers a collection of somewhat different molecules, which can be classed together under three main headings: *messenger RNA (mRNA)*, *transfer RNA (tRNA)* and *ribosomal RNA (rRNA)*. All three types of RNA are produced on a DNA template, and in a similar way. We outline their respective roles here, but details will follow in Sections 11.4.2–11.4.4.

Messenger RNA (mRNA) has preserved within it the sequence of DNA bases, although now in an RNA code, which determines the precise amino acid sequence of a particular polypeptide. The code in mRNA consists of consecutive three-base sequences, or triplets (e.g. AUG, CCU). Each triplet is termed a **codon**, and there are many different ones. Each codon contains the information for a particular amino acid, and this relationship between codon and amino acid forms the basis of the *genetic code*. For example, the mRNA codon AUG codes for the amino acid methionine (abbreviated to Met), and CCU codes for the amino acid proline (Pro). Examination of the sequence of codons within a molecule of mRNA enables the sequence of amino acids in the polypeptide for which it codes to be determined, since there is a colinear relationship between the two sequences. The details of the genetic code will be examined in detail in Section 11.5. In the context of translation, all you need to appreciate for now is that an mRNA molecule consists of a very specific sequence of consecutive codons.

The other significant feature of the genetic code is that, because the sequence of bases in an mRNA molecule is determined by the base sequence of the DNA, the genetic code in the RNA is a copy of the code present in the DNA on which the mRNA was synthesized during transcription.

The consequence of the genetic code being carried in an mRNA molecule is that a given polypeptide has a particular mRNA molecule coding for it. Since there are thousands of different proteins, there are thousands of different mRNA molecules, each transcribed from a different section of DNA, that is, from a different gene.

There are two other types of RNA, neither of which code for polypeptides, but which have important roles to play in the process of polypeptide synthesis.

Transfer RNA (tRNA) molecules carry individual amino acids, which join together to form polypeptides.

Ribosomal RNA (rRNA) molecules, together with proteins, make up the ribosomes (Section 2.1). These large macromolecular aggregates are the sites of polypeptide synthesis.

Ribosomes, mRNA, tRNAs with their associated amino acids, and several different enzymes, together form the protein-synthesizing machinery, the functioning of which will now be described.

11.4.2 Recognition of the codon by tRNA

Transfer RNA (tRNA) is the molecule that brings an individual amino acid to the mRNA where it will be incorporated into a growing polypeptide molecule. The generalized structure of a tRNA molecule is shown in Figure 11.6a, and a stylized version is shown in Figure 11.6b.

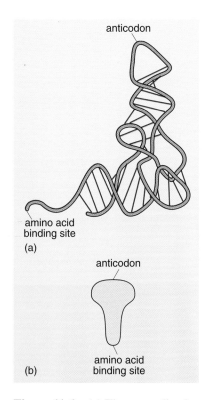

anticodon

amino acid binding site
(a)

anticodon

amino acid binding site
(b)

Figure 11.6 (a) The generalized structure of a tRNA molecule showing its three-dimensional shape, and functional regions. The straight lines represent the paired bases. (b) A stylized version of (a), which is used in subsequent figures.

Look at Figure 11.6a. Follow the ribbon, which represents the sugar–phosphate backbone. Is tRNA a single-stranded or a double-stranded molecule?

There is just one ribbon of a sugar–phosphate backbone, so tRNA is single-stranded.

Note, however, that parts of the molecule are folded up around itself, allowing some base-pairing. Figure 11.6a shows more than 20 such base pairs.

Figure 11.6a shows two other significant features of tRNA, which demonstrate the relationship between the structure and function of the molecule. First, there is a 'loose' arm, which is available to bind an amino acid. Second, there is a region at the other end of the molecule where there are *three* free, or unpaired, RNA bases; these constitute the **anticodon**.

Assuming that each tRNA can bind specifically to only one kind of amino acid, what can you predict about the number of different tRNA molecules present in a cell?

There must be at least 20 different tRNA molecules, one for each amino acid.

This is indeed what is found; for each amino acid there is a different tRNA molecule. Enzymes are involved in joining each amino acid to its specific tRNA to produce a specific tRNA–amino acid complex (i.e. a tRNA and an amino acid covalently linked together).

11.4.3 mRNA and its codons

A crucially important molecule involved in translation is mRNA. This has a linear sequence of RNA bases which is translated into the amino acid sequence of a polypeptide, a process which depends on the interaction between mRNA and tRNA, as shown in Figure 11.7.

The three bases that make up the tRNA anticodon pair with the three bases of the corresponding mRNA codon. The amino acids are inserted at the correct position because the tRNA molecule recognizes the mRNA codon; the tRNA molecules are the link between mRNA codon and amino acid recognition. Thus tRNA allows the mRNA code to be interpreted as (i.e. translated into) a sequence of amino acids.

What base-pairing rules must apply to the interaction between the codon and the anticodon?

Here RNA is base-pairing with another RNA molecule, so the base-pairing rules would be C–G (and vice versa) and A–U (and vice versa).

Some RNA base pairs are shown in Figure 11.7. What is the nature of the interactions within these base pairs?

The base pairs are held together by hydrogen bonds (shown in the figure as orange dashed lines).

What is the significance of the interaction between the mRNA codon and tRNA anticodon being via weak bonds?

These bonds can be readily formed and are easily broken.

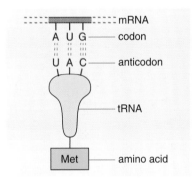

Figure 11.7 The interaction between one tRNA molecule attached to the amino acid methionine (Met) and a short mRNA sequence.

There is another important feature to be emphasized about the relationship between the binding of tRNA to mRNA, as illustrated in Figure 11.7. The relationship between the mRNA codon and the amino acid that is bound to the specific tRNA is *precise* because complementary base-pairing occurs between the codon of the mRNA and the anticodon of the tRNA.

Thus, the interaction between mRNA and tRNA forms the basis of translation, as shown in Figure 11.8. The first tRNA to bind at the mRNA does so at a very particular **start codon** (labelled codon 1 in this figure), which always has the base sequence AUG and codes for methionine. Once this first tRNA has bound, a second follows suit (Figure 11.8a).

● To synthesize a polypeptide chain from individual amino acids, what type of bonds must be formed? (If you're not sure, look back at Section 3.3.2.)

○ Peptide bonds link the constituent amino acid units together in a polypeptide chain.

In Figure 11.8b a peptide bond is formed between the first two amino acids that have arrived at the mRNA. Protein synthesis is a very energy-demanding process, and in most cells consumes more energy than any other biosynthetic process.

Once a peptide bond has been formed, the first tRNA molecule is released from the mRNA (Figure 11.8c). The binding and subsequent release of tRNA molecules is repeated along the length of the mRNA chain, with amino acids being added sequentially, one at a time, to the growing polypeptide chain. After the binding of the sixth tRNA, the polypeptide chain consists of six amino acids covalently linked together by five peptide bonds (Figure 11.8d). Note that throughout this series of events there are never more than two tRNA molecules bound to the mRNA at any one time.

The final event in polypeptide synthesis is termination of translation. This is brought about by a specific **stop codon** in the mRNA, which 'tells' the translation machinery that its job is complete. Each polypeptide has a precise number and particular sequence of amino acids in its primary structure. When the stop codon is reached, synthesis stops and the completed polypeptide dissociates from the mRNA.

The final point to notice from Figure 11.8 is the direction in which the polypeptide chain is synthesized. Recall from Section 3.3.2 that each polypeptide chain has an N-terminal amino acid and a C-terminal amino acid. You can now see from Figure 11.8 that the first amino acid added is the N-terminal one, and the last amino acid added to the growing polypeptide chain will be the C-terminal one. Polypeptides are therefore synthesized from their N-terminus to their C-terminus.

11.4.4 The role of ribosomes in translation

The ribosomes are the sites at which the process of translation, outlined in Figure 11.8, actually takes place. Ribosomes are very similar in structure and function in all organisms. They are large aggregates of several different protein and rRNA molecules that fit together to form a complex with a relative molecular mass of many millions. The ribosome has three binding sites; it binds mRNA and up to two tRNA molecules. The stage of translation shown in Figure 11.9 is the same as that shown in Figure 11.8b. Here two tRNA molecules plus their attached amino acids have bound to the mRNA at a ribosome, and a peptide bond has formed between the two amino acids (methionine (Met) and proline (Pro)). The two tRNA molecules remain at the

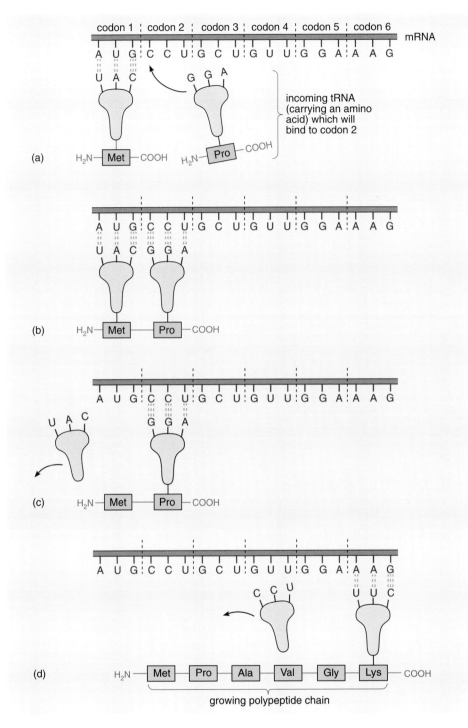

Figure 11.8 Simplified scheme for translation. (a) One tRNA molecule is already bound to mRNA and a second is about to bind. (b) Two tRNA molecules are now bound to mRNA, and a peptide bond has formed between the first two amino acids of the polypeptide chain. (c) The first tRNA molecule is released. (d) A few steps further on in the process — the growing polypeptide chain now consists of six amino acids; the sixth amino acid corresponds to codon 6. As in earlier figures, the hydrogen bonds between the bases are shown as orange dashed lines. (Met, Pro, Ala, Val, Gly and Lys are the abbreviations for the first six amino acids in this polypeptide: methionine, proline, alanine, valine glycine and lysine.) Note that the different components shown are not drawn to scale.

ribosome for the short time necessary for a peptide bond to form between the two amino acids that they carry.

The next stage in the process (as shown in Figure 11.8c) would be the departure of the left-hand tRNA from the ribosome. Since only two tRNA molecules can be bound at a ribosome at any one time; a vacant 'slot' has now been created. The ribosome then moves one codon along the mRNA, so that this vacant 'slot' is shifted to the right of the remaining bound tRNA. Another tRNA can now bind to the mRNA in this vacant slot.

Figure 11.9 Binding of mRNA and tRNA at a ribosome. Each ribosome binds up to two tRNA molecules at a time. Here two tRNA molecules have bound, and a peptide bond has just formed between the two amino acids they carry.

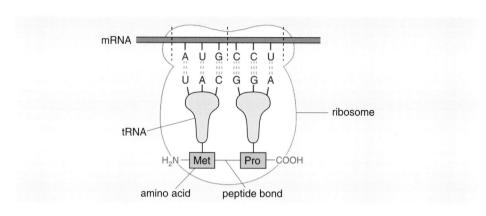

In this way, the ribosome moves stepwise along the mRNA chain, moving from left to right of the mRNA molecule in Figure 11.8 until it reaches the 'stop' codon. However, a number of ribosomes can bind simultaneously to the same mRNA molecule. Figure 11.10 shows this; a string of ribosomes is synthesizing molecules of the same polypeptide and each one is at a different stage in the process. This string of ribosomes on an mRNA chain is termed a polyribosome — more usually abbreviated to **polysome**; each polysome is a string of ribosomes with growing polypeptide chains at different stages of completion. The polypeptide folds up as it is being synthesized to give the protein product with its own characteristic shape (Figure 11.10). When a protein chain is complete, both it and the ribosome are released from the mRNA. The ribosome can bind to either the same or a different mRNA molecule, and so begin the synthesis of another molecule of polypeptide.

Figure 11.10 Synthesis of a polypeptide by ribosomes attached to an mRNA chain. A ribosome binds first at a precise 'start' codon and shifts along the mRNA until it reaches the 'stop' codon when polypeptide synthesis terminates. On the mRNA there is a string of ribosomes with growing polypeptide chains at different stages of completion. This string of ribosomes is called a polysome.

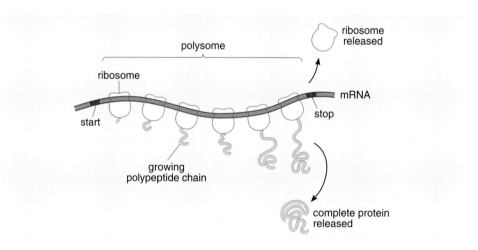

Question 11.3   Fill in the blanks in each of the following sentences about RNA and protein synthesis. (In some cases more than one word is required to fill a blank.)

(a) The enzyme _____ copies a stretch of DNA into RNA in a process known as _____ .

(b) Only the _____ strand of DNA is 'read' in the process of RNA synthesis; the other DNA strand is known as the _____ strand.

(c) There are three different types of RNA molecules: _____ , _____ and _____ .

(d) The transfer of information from the mRNA base sequence to the amino acid sequence of a polypeptide is known as _____ .

(e) The mRNA sequence has a triplet code, and each triplet is known as a _____ .

(f) Reading of the mRNA base sequence begins at a _____ and finishes at a _____ .

(g) _____ binds both an amino acid and mRNA; it attaches to the latter via its three-base _____ .

(h) A ribosome has three RNA binding sites: one for _____ and two for tRNA.

(i) A ribosome moves along an mRNA chain, and there are several ribosomes attached to a particular mRNA at any one time; such a string of ribosomes along an mRNA chain is termed a _____ . ◄

Activity 11.1 The flow of information from DNA to RNA to polypeptide

In this activity you will consolidate your understanding of the processes of transcription and translation. ◄

Activity 11.2 A foretaste of the genetic code

This activity introduces the genetic code, which is explained in the following section. ◄

11.5 The genetic code

The description of the mechanism of translation in Section 11.4 has revealed that there is a code carried within the base sequence of mRNA and of the corresponding DNA. For each triplet mRNA codon that is read, one specific amino acid is inserted into the growing polypeptide chain. The specific relationship between base triplets in DNA or RNA and amino acids is known as the **genetic code**, which we introduced in Section 11.4, but which is examined here in greater detail.

The DNA and corresponding mRNA codons form the basis of the genetic code, whereby each triplet of three bases specifies a particular amino acid.

● Look back at Figure 11.8b and write out the sequence of bases in the mRNA that codes for the amino acid methionine (Met), i.e. the codon for Met.

○ AUG.

● Similarly, look at Figure 11.8d and find the codon for lysine (Lys).

○ AAG.

Note that these are the sequences of the three bases — the codons — in the mRNA (shown at the top of the diagrams). These codons are complementary to the sequences of three bases — the anticodons — of the tRNA molecules.

Figure 11.8 shows the codons for a mere six amino acids, but as you know there are 20 commonly occurring amino acids in proteins. There are also four different bases in RNA, but only three are included in any one codon. These four bases can be arranged in 64 different combinations of a three-letter codon, i.e. $4 \times 4 \times 4 = 4^3 = 64$, since there are four possibilities for the first base of a triplet, four possibilities for the second, and four for the third.

● There are 64 possible mRNA codons but only 20 amino acids. What does this tell you?

○ One possible conclusion is that there are several codons for each amino acid. An alternative possibility is that many codons do not code for amino acids.

Both answers are in fact correct to a certain extent. Actually, 61 codons code for particular amino acids, and the other three are stop codons.

● What is the role of a stop codon?

○ It signals termination of translation and the release of the completed polypeptide and the ribosome from the mRNA molecule (look back to Figure 11.10).

A considerable amount of work from the mid-1950s till the mid-1960s was required before the full genetic code was deciphered. It is shown in Table 11.2. Here the 64 different codons are arranged in terms of the order of the three bases. Let us consider one example: the codon UUU, in the top left-hand corner of the table. This is the sequence coding for the amino acid phenylalanine, abbreviated to Phe. (The abbreviations for all the amino acids are given below the table.) The table shows that for most of the 20 amino acids found in proteins there are several codons.

● Looking at Table 11.2, which amino acids have the largest number of codons?

○ Leu (leucine), Ser (serine) and Arg (arginine) each have six codons.

● Which amino acids have the fewest codons?

○ Both Met (methionine) and Trp (tryptophan) have only one each. {Interestingly, methionine and tryptophan are the least abundant amino acids found in proteins.}

The other amino acids each have a number of codons somewhere between these extremes. The fact that most amino acids have several codons has led to the description of the code as being a *degenerate* genetic code. A consequence of this is that it is not as precise as might be expected, as explained in the following discussion.

● Table 11.2 shows that 61 mRNA codons code for the 20 amino acids. How many different tRNA molecules would you expect to find as a consequence of this?

○ If there are 61 mRNA codons, one would expect 61 complementary tRNA anticodons and hence 61 different tRNA molecules.

In fact, far fewer than 61 different tRNA molecules are found in a given cell. This is because, in many (but not all) cases, accurate base-pairing between codon and anticodon occurs at only the first two of the three bases and a mismatch (or *wobble*) can be tolerated at the third base.

Table 11.2 mRNA codons. (Note that AUG, the codon for Met, is also the start codon.)

first base	second base				third base
	U	**C**	**A**	**G**	
U	UUU ⎱ Phe UUC ⎰ UUA ⎱ Leu UUG ⎰	UCU ⎱ UCC ⎰ Ser UCA ⎰ UCG ⎰	UAU ⎱ Tyr UAC ⎰ UAA stop UAG stop	UGU ⎱ Cys UGC ⎰ UGA stop UGG Trp	U C A G
C	CUU ⎱ CUC ⎰ Leu CUA ⎰ CUG ⎰	CCU ⎱ CCC ⎰ Pro CCA ⎰ CCG ⎰	CAU ⎱ His CAC ⎰ CAA ⎱ Gln CAG ⎰	CGU ⎱ CGC ⎰ Arg CGA ⎰ CGG ⎰	U C A G
A	AUU ⎱ AUC ⎰ Ile AUA ⎰ AUG Met	ACU ⎱ ACC ⎰ Thr ACA ⎰ ACG ⎰	AAU ⎱ Asn AAC ⎰ AAA ⎱ Lys AAG ⎰	AGU ⎱ Ser AGC ⎰ AGA ⎱ Arg AGG ⎰	U C A G
G	GUU ⎱ GUC ⎰ Val GUA ⎰ GUG ⎰	GCU ⎱ GCC ⎰ Ala GCA ⎰ GCG ⎰	GAU ⎱ Asp GAC ⎰ GAA ⎱ Glu GAG ⎰	GGU ⎱ GGC ⎰ Gly GGA ⎰ GGG ⎰	U C A G

The abbreviated names of the 20 amino acids are as follows: Ala = alanine, Arg = arginine, Asn = asparagine, Asp = aspartate, Cys = cysteine, Gln = glutamine, Glu = glutamate, Gly = glycine, His = histidine, Ile = isoleucine, Leu = leucine, Lys = lysine, Met = methionine, Phe = phenylalanine, Pro = proline, Ser = serine, Thr = threonine, Trp = tryptophan, Tyr = tyrosine, Val = valine. You do not need to remember these abbreviations, nor which codons correspond to which amino acids.

⬤ Look at Table 11.2 and identify the codons for alanine (Ala). How do these codons compare?

◯ There are four codons: GCU, GCC, GCA and GCG, and the first two bases are identical for each of them.

This wobble makes it possible to fit 20 amino acids to the 61 mRNA codons with fewer than 61 tRNA molecules. For Ala, for example, there is usually a single tRNA in a cell, with an anticodon that can bind to the mRNA codon GC–, where the third base can be any one of U, C, A or G. Although this wobble is tolerated for many codons, it is not tolerated for all; for example, as noted above, methionine (Met) and tryptophan (Trp) each have just one codon.

Table 11.2 shows that the codon AUG codes for the amino acid methionine. As described in Section 11.4.3, the codon AUG is also the start codon for initiating the translation of all polypeptides. Methionine can therefore appear both at the beginning and within a polypeptide. Every newly completed polypeptide chain released from polysomes has methionine at the N-terminal position. However, this methionine is removed after the polypeptide chain leaves the ribosome.

The final aspect of the genetic code to be considered is its *universal* nature. What this means is that the mRNA codons shown in Table 11.2 apply in virtually all organisms where the code has been examined. This observation provides strong evidence that all cells, or at least the nuclear component of them (leaving the mitochondria and chloroplasts aside), have evolved from a common ancestor.

In fact, the processes of information storage in DNA, replication, transcription and translation are fundamentally similar in all organisms. This demonstrates, most powerfully, the evolutionary continuity between organisms.

Activity 11.2 (continued)

If you did not successfully complete this activity before you studied Section 11.5, try it again now that you have been introduced to the full genetic code.◀

Activity 11.3   The genetic code

In this activity you will examine the relationship between base sequences of DNA and mRNA, and the amino acid sequence coded for by these polynucleotides. ◀

Activity 11.4   Information flow in cells

In this activity you will study a video sequence which shows the structure of DNA and the processes of information transfer: replication, transcription and translation. Thus it illustrates and reinforces the key points of both Sections 10 and 11.◀

11.6 Mutation revisited

You saw in Section 10 that genes are composed of DNA, and that the DNA base sequence of these genes determines the structure of polypeptides via mRNA as the intermediary. The genetic code is the key to understanding this information flow from DNA to RNA to polypeptide. Sequences of three bases (codons) in DNA relate directly to mRNA codons, which in turn provide the template on which a precise sequence of amino acids is joined together to form a polypeptide.

In Section 10.3, however, you saw that the machinery of DNA replication does not always produce a faithful copy of the template strand. In other words, mistakes can occur, in which incorrect bases are inserted into the growing polynucleotide chain. If the errors are not detected and removed, then these become mutations. These errors will then be replicated each time the DNA molecule is replicated.

- If the DNA replication machinery makes such an error so that a base is 'misread' and the 'wrong' base inserted, consider what will happen at transcription. How will the mRNA be affected?

- The error in the template strand of DNA is transferred to the mRNA, so that a 'faulty' message will be produced.

- What effect will this 'faulty' message have on the amino acid sequence of the polypeptide produced at translation?

- An incorrect codon could result in a completely different amino acid being inserted into the growing polypeptide chain.

So, modifications to a DNA sequence can lead ultimately to changes in the amino acid sequence of a polypeptide. It requires only a very small change in a DNA sequence to produce a change at the level of the functional protein.

Let us consider a straightforward example.

● Look back at Figure 11.8. What is the second codon in the short mRNA sequence shown there and for which amino acid does it code?

○ The codon is CCU and the corresponding amino acid is proline (Pro).

Consider an error in DNA replication that resulted in this mRNA codon being CAU instead of CCU, i.e. the second base, C, has been replaced by A.

● From Table 11.2, which amino acid would then be inserted into the polypeptide chain?

○ CAU is a codon for the amino acid histidine (His).

As you learned in Section 10, there are different types of mutations; as well as producing changes in individual bases, sometimes bases can be deleted or additional bases inserted, as demonstrated in the following activity.

Activity 11.5   Mutation and the polypeptide sequence

In this activity you will investigate the effects of mutations at the level of small changes in the DNA sequence and their consequent effect on the amino acid sequence of a polypeptide. ◀

The answer to this activity shows that if a base is deleted or an additional base inserted, all subsequent codons in the mRNA following this error would be changed. In turn, the sequence of amino acids in the polypeptide would also be changed. The effect on the function of the protein will depend on the position of the changed amino acid in the polypeptide chain. For example, in an enzyme some positions can be filled by alternative amino acids, and at least partial function is maintained. But at other positions in the chain the normal amino acid must be present for the enzyme to be fully active.

● Thinking back to the structure and function of enzymes (Sections 3.3.1 and 4.3), which parts of an enzyme are most likely to be affected by a change of amino acid sequence?

○ The parts of the enzyme molecule that contribute to the active site, either directly, or indirectly by helping to maintain the precise shape of the active site.

Very rarely, mutations can be advantageous, producing a protein with 'enhanced' qualities, conferring advantages on the host organism in a particular environment. Such mutations may be replicated and spread throughout the population. (Examples of these mutations are discussed in Section 13.)

Some mutations are deleterious; for instance, those that are responsible for genetic diseases in humans. Here we will consider just one such mutation and the disease resulting from it. Our example is cystic fibrosis, since a lot is known about the gene involved and the protein for which it codes. In cystic fibrosis, individuals are usually affected by lung disease, although other tissues and organs, such as the pancreas (which produces digestive enzymes that are released into the intestine), may be affected too. It is a relatively common genetic disease, affecting 1 in 2 500 babies born in the UK.

In Section 8 we introduced the idea of alleles for alternative forms of a character, e.g. grain colour in maize. But sometimes a gene can only be identified when it is

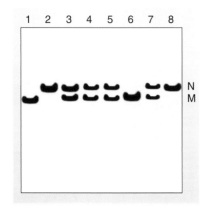

Figure 11.11 Visualizing pieces of DNA that contain a specific gene — in this example, the cystic fibrosis gene. In this procedure, DNA is extracted from cells (usually white blood cells, in the case of humans) and it is cut into fragments using enzymes. These fragments are loaded at one end of a gel (jelly-like substance) and separated according to their size. Since the DNA fragments have a negative charge, when an electric voltage is applied they move across the gel towards the positive electrode; large fragments move with difficulty, but smaller pieces move more easily. Once separated, specific sequences of DNA — genes or parts of genes — can then be visualized in the gel. Thus it is possible to tell whether a gene is present and whether it is normal in structure. Here the DNA has been extracted from cells of eight individuals (numbered 1–8) and two bands have been identified: band N corresponds to the normal allele and band M corresponds to the mutant (cystic fibrosis) allele.

associated with a disease phenotype, as in the case of cystic fibrosis. Here, we talk of the 'cystic fibrosis gene' and the alleles are referred to as the cystic fibrosis, or mutant, allele and the normal allele of the cystic fibrosis gene.

In about 70% of cases of cystic fibrosis, the disease results from a single mutation on chromosome 7 (see Figure 8.2) in which three consecutive base pairs are lost from the cystic fibrosis gene. Consequently, there are two alleles of this gene: the normal allele which includes these three base pairs, and the mutant allele which lacks them. The exact position of the gene on chromosome 7 was mapped in 1989. Using sophisticated molecular techniques, it is now possible to extract and identify the DNA of this gene, as shown in Figure 11.11.

What can we learn from the picture shown in Figure 11.11? The first point is that there is gene variation amongst the eight individuals. For each person there are either one or two bands. There are two band types, one corresponding to the normal allele (N) and the other corresponding to the mutant (cystic fibrosis) allele (M). The individuals can be grouped into three categories in terms of the bands each has. Look at the bands for individuals 1, 2 and 3. Person 1 has just a single band, which corresponds to the mutant allele. So, person 1 has only the mutant allele for this gene. Person 2 has also just a single band, but here it corresponds to the normal allele. In contrast, person 3 has both bands and hence has both alleles.

● Using Figure 11.11, group the eight people into three groups (I–III) in terms of the bands and hence alleles that each has: group I, mutant allele only; group II, normal allele only; group III, both alleles.

○ Group I: individuals 1 and 6 have only the band for the mutant allele.

Group II: individuals 2 and 8 have only the band for the normal allele.

Group III: individuals 3, 4, 5 and 7 have both bands, and hence both alleles.

The people in group III have been identified as having two different alleles of the cystic fibrosis gene.

● What is the term used to describe this genotype, in contrast to that of individuals in groups I and II?

○ Group III individuals are said to be heterozygous, in contrast to members of groups I and II, who are homozygous.

A further significant point is that the mutant allele is recessive.

● Which individuals will exhibit the disease symptoms, and why?

○ Individuals 1 and 6 would be expected to exhibit disease symptoms, because they have only the mutant allele.

We can explore further this question of which individuals will exhibit the disease, and why, by relating the genetics of cystic fibrosis to events at the level of the polypeptide coded for by the gene, and consider how the normal and mutant alleles of the gene and their protein products are operating. The cystic fibrosis gene codes for a protein that is involved in transport of chloride ions across cellular membranes. The normal allele codes for a fully functional protein, whereas the mutant allele codes for a defective protein with greatly reduced chloride transport activity.

Individuals 1 and 6 have only the mutant allele and consequently their cells are able to synthesize only the defective protein. The transport function of the protein in their cells is significantly reduced. In contrast, individuals in group II have just the normal allele, and hence synthesize the non-mutant protein, which functions normally.

Individuals in group III, however, have both alleles, normal and mutant. In these individuals both forms of the protein are synthesized, and yet these people do not exhibit the disease symptoms. The key to understanding this is that the cells of these individuals synthesize sufficient normally-functioning protein to ensure transport of chloride ions, so that disease symptoms are not expressed in the phenotype.

This example shows that the terms 'dominant' and 'recessive' can be better understood at the level of the functioning protein, rather than at the level of the gene. In the cystic fibrosis example, the dominant normal phenotype represents the presence of a fully-functioning protein and the recessive phenotype represents the protein with significantly reduced chloride transport activity. The heterozygote makes both proteins, yet the individual has the phenotype associated with the fully-functioning protein; the mutant protein is not expressed at the level of the whole organism.

Finally, examples like cystic fibrosis tell the story of how information in genes becomes realized in the phenotype. This is illustrated in Figure 11.12. This figure summarizes the sequence of events from the normal allele of the cystic fibrosis gene to the development of the normal phenotype, and, for comparison, shows the sequence of events from the mutation in the cystic fibrosis gene to the development of the disease phenotype.

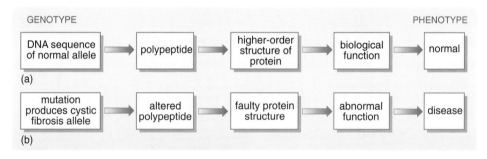

Figure 11.12   The sequence of events from genotype to phenotype, illustrated for the cystic fibrosis gene. (a) From the normal allele to the normal phenotype. (b) From the mutant allele to the disease phenotype.

This section has considered the flow of information from DNA to RNA to polypeptide. However, as well as the DNA that codes for the tRNAs and rRNAs, there are other DNA sequences that do not code for polypeptides, as you will discover in the next section.

11.7 Summary of Section 11

The colinearity of sequences between a gene and a polypeptide is known as the 'one gene — one polypeptide' hypothesis. The flow of information is: DNA makes RNA makes polypeptide.

Transcription is the process of RNA synthesis, in which information coded in one of the strands of DNA becomes coded in mRNA. RNA polymerase adds RNA nucleotides one at a time and the base-pairing rules apply: G of DNA binds C of RNA, and vice versa; T of DNA binds A of RNA, but A of DNA binds U of RNA.

In the process of translation, the four-character language of mRNA is translated into the 20-character language of proteins. A triplet codon of mRNA binds a triplet anticodon of a tRNA molecule, to which is attached a specific amino acid.

The ribosome binds mRNA and up to two tRNA molecules. The first tRNA binds to a particular sequence known as the start codon, which codes for methionine. A second tRNA also binds to the ribosome, and a peptide bond forms between the two amino acids. The first tRNA molecule then leaves the ribosome. The ribosome moves, so that a vacant site is available for another tRNA molecule. In this way, the ribosome moves along the mRNA and the polypeptide chain gets longer. Once the ribosome reaches the stop codon, translation comes to an end. A string of ribosomes attached to a single mRNA molecule is known as a polysome.

The genetic code is degenerate in that some amino acids are specified by more than one codon. It consists of 64 triplet codons, each of which codes for a specific amino acid or is a stop codon. This is a universal genetic code, which applies to virtually all organisms. The processes of information storage in DNA, replication, transcription and translation are fundamentally similar in all organisms.

A mutation in the DNA code can be transcribed into mRNA and subsequently translated into a protein. For example, a single base change in DNA can result in a faulty protein product. In humans, such defects can result in heritable diseases such as cystic fibrosis.

Looking at genomes

A cell's total complement of genetic material is called the **genome**. Genome studies consider the molecular organization and structure of the genetic material, and have given rise to the very new science of genomics. This often involves comparing the genomes of organisms from widely different taxonomic groups, in a search for similar sequences and gene structures. For eukaryotes, the term genome can also be applied to the genetic material of an organelle, as distinct from that in the nucleus: for example, the mitochondrial or chloroplast genome. This is because both these organelles contain DNA, in addition to the bulk of the DNA found in the nucleus. Genomes usually consist of only DNA, but some viruses have RNA instead of DNA as their genetic material, as in the case of HIV (human immunodeficiency virus), the virus responsible for AIDS.

Not all the DNA in an organism's genome is transcribed into RNA, and this section broadens to examine these non-transcribed sequences. In the discussion of DNA replication and polypeptide synthesis (Sections 10 and 11), prokaryotes (bacteria), and eukaryotes were, implicitly, lumped together, but there are important differences between them as far as their genomes are concerned. We begin by looking at the relative simplicity of bacteria, where most of the DNA codes for protein. Then we move on to look at the more complex eukaryotes where a lot of the DNA is non-coding. Some of these non-protein-coding sequences have well defined roles, whereas others do not. We end this section with a look at current projects that are aimed at investigating the sequences of some of these genomes, notably that of the human, and examine some of the important applications of this work.

12.1 Bacterial genomes

Bacterial genomes are relatively small — just a few million base pairs — as against, for example, the few *billion* base pairs of the human genome. There are three important features of the bacterial genome to appreciate. First, the genome consists of a single DNA molecule, and hence, the bacterial cell is haploid. Second, unlike eukaryote chromosomes, bacterial DNA is essentially naked, in that it is not associated with proteins that help condense the DNA into chromosomes. Third, there is great 'gene density' in the bacterial genome, such that virtually all the DNA codes for protein products (apart from those genes that code for rRNA and tRNA).

⬤ Can you recall from Section 2 the two principal structural differences between a prokaryote cell and a eukaryote cell?

◯ In a prokaryote cell, the DNA is not separated from the cytosol by a nuclear membrane, and there are no organelles such as mitochondria and chloroplasts.

Compared to eukaryote cells, therefore, bacterial cells are relatively simple; they are the simplest of known cells. The absence of a nuclear membrane in a bacterial cell has an important consequence for the location of transcription and translation. It means that the synthesis of RNA and protein occur together in the cytosol. In fact, a newly synthesized mRNA molecule is translated into polypeptide molecules whilst being transcribed. Thus the two processes of transcription and translation occur more or less simultaneously and in close proximity to each other in the cell. This is shown in a very diagrammatic way in Figure 12.1. This shows that whilst the mRNA is being synthesized on the DNA template, the 'older' part of this molecule has been released from the DNA. Ribosomes have attached themselves and polypeptide synthesis has started on the mRNA molecule (from the left-hand end of Figure 12.1). Several such ribosomes are attached, so forming a polysome. Moving from left to right, the growing polypeptide chains are getting increasingly longer and more complete.

Figure 12.1 The synthesis of mRNA and protein in a bacterial cell. The dashed lines indicate that the DNA strands are longer than shown here.

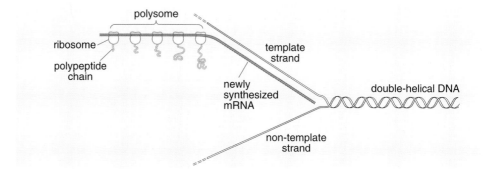

Since most of the DNA of the bacterial genome consists of protein-coding sequences, the straightforward story we have told of the flow of information from DNA to RNA to polypeptide requires no qualification.

12.2 Gene complexity in eukaryotes

Although the simple story of the flow of information from DNA to polypeptide is largely true for bacteria, important complexities exist in eukaryotes. Eukaryotes have far more DNA than is apparently needed to code for all their proteins (and for transcription into tRNA and rRNA). We look at this 'extra' DNA in this section, some of which has identifiable roles, but there are other DNA sequences that have no known roles.

12.2.1 Split genes and RNA processing

In Section 11 we examined the precise linear relationship between the base sequence of DNA in a gene and the linear sequence of amino acids in a polypeptide. In eukaryotes, unlike in prokaryotes, the information for making polypeptides in most genes is *not* an uninterrupted sequence of bases. Rather, most eukaryote genes are 'split' into separate parts along the length of a DNA molecule, by intervening non-coding sequences.

● Consider a protein with a sequence of 300 amino acids. Approximately how many mRNA bases and hence how many DNA base pairs would you expect to code for this protein?

○ Each mRNA codon is a triplet of three bases, so 900 mRNA bases and hence 900 DNA base pairs would be expected to code for this protein.

You may be surprised to learn that for many proteins of average length of around 300–400 amino acids, each gene contains a staggering 100 000 base pairs — about 100 times the number that is apparently needed! Some eukaryote genes coding for proteins of this size even contain as many as two million base pairs. What then is the relationship between all these extra DNA base pairs and the final protein sequence?

The rules we have learnt so far apply in that, for example, 900 DNA bases would be needed to code for a sequence of 300 amino acids. However, only a relatively small number of DNA bases within such a gene actually code for amino acids in the fully-functioning protein: such protein-coding DNA sequences are termed **exons**. Within the DNA sequence of a gene the exons are interspersed with non-protein-coding regions termed **introns**. For a gene of 100 000 base pairs, a large proportion of the base pairs of the gene comprises introns, the sequences of which do not 'appear' in the final protein product of the gene. Such a gene, with exons and introns is described as a **split gene**, a simple sketch of which is shown in Figure 12.2. As this figure shows, usually there are relatively long intron regions interspersed with relatively short exon regions.

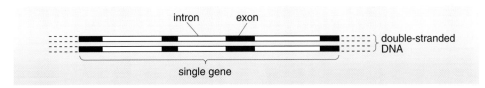

Figure 12.2   A sketch of a hypothetical split gene, consisting of four short exons (protein-coding regions) and three larger, intervening introns (non-protein-coding regions).

The split gene shown in Figure 12.2 is a very simple, indeed hypothetical, example with only four exons. Many genes which have actually been identified and characterized are much more complicated than this. For example, the cystic fibrosis gene is large, comprising 250 000 base pairs including 26 introns.

If a large amount of the DNA in a gene comprises introns, then somehow there must be a series of events between transcription of DNA and protein synthesis (translation), in which these intervening sequences are removed. This series of events is called *RNA processing* and is illustrated in Figure 12.3.

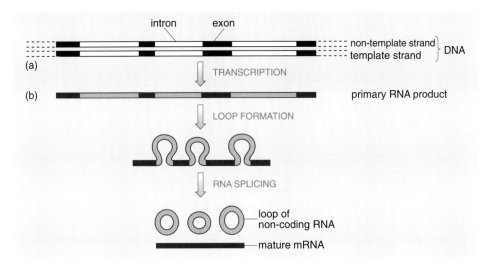

Figure 12.3   A hypothetical example of RNA processing. (a) DNA is first transcribed into a long molecule including exons (protein-coding regions) and introns (non-protein-coding regions), and called the primary RNA product. (b) RNA splicing reactions remove the introns and join the exons to produce the mature mRNA.

As Figure 12.3 shows, the DNA sequence of the entire split gene is transcribed, and the **primary RNA product** includes the non-protein-coding introns as well as the protein-coding exons.

How many bases would you expect to find in the primary RNA product?

Since this contains both exons and introns, the primary RNA product should have the same number of bases as there are base pairs in the DNA template on which it was produced. This follows from the base-pairing rules of transcription.

133

Indeed, the primary product of transcription is a very large RNA molecule.

○ What must happen to this primary RNA product, in terms of its length, before protein synthesis takes place?

○ After transcription, this RNA must be shortened in some way.

The existence of introns means that the primary RNA product must be processed before translation can occur. This processing involves **RNA splicing**, i.e. removal of the introns and joining of the exons to produce a continuous mRNA ready for translation. This is the **mature mRNA** molecule. As shown in Figure 12.3, the RNA regions that do not code for amino acid sequences of the protein form loops which are cut out of the molecule.

○ What is the relationship, in terms of size, between the primary RNA product and the mature mRNA?

○ The mature mRNA is much smaller than the primary RNA product. Its length corresponds to the total length of all of the exon sequences.

The next step is that the mature mRNA leaves the nucleus and translation occurs in the cytosol. This represents a significant difference between eukaryote and bacterial protein synthesis. From Figure 12.1 you saw that in bacteria, transcription and translation occur in close proximity to the DNA. In contrast, in eukaryotes, transcription and translation are separated both in space within the cell and in time, in that one happens after the other, as summarized in Figure 12.4.

Figure 12.4 Summary of events showing the flow of information in a eukaryote cell from DNA to polypeptide via primary RNA product and mature mRNA. The processes involved, namely transcription, RNA splicing and translation, are also indicated.

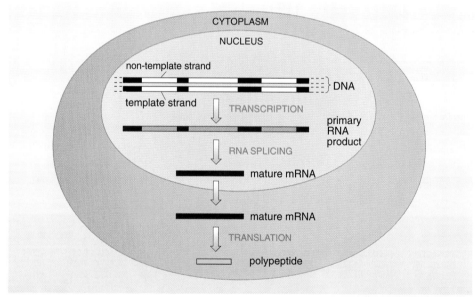

Figure 12.4 shows that, in a eukaryote cell with a nucleus bounded by a nuclear membrane, transcription occurs within the nucleus to produce a primary RNA product. RNA splicing then removes the non-protein-coding introns to produce the mature mRNA. The mRNA then leaves the cell nucleus and passes out into the cytosol, where the final stage of protein synthesis occurs, namely translation.

○ On what structures does translation occur?

○ mRNA binds to the ribosomes, where it is translated into a polypeptide chain.

Many genes in eukaryotes, such as the cystic fibrosis gene, consist of introns and exons, with the sequences comprising the introns being removed during RNA processing. Thus there is not a continuous relationship between the base sequence of a DNA molecule and the sequence of amino acids in the polypeptide. Given this information, we will revisit the one gene — one polypeptide hypothesis.

Question 12.1   It was stated above that the cystic fibrosis gene has 250 000 base pairs, including 26 introns. Its mRNA, however, is only about 6 500 bases.

(a) How many bases are there in the primary RNA product of the cystic fibrosis gene?

(b) What percentage of this primary RNA product consists of non-protein-coding sequences?

(c) What is the mean size of an intron in the cystic fibrosis gene? ◄

12.2.2 The one gene — one polypeptide hypothesis revisited

In this section we take a more detailed look at the one gene — one polypeptide hypothesis, introduced in Section 11.1, and which provided the first insight into how the gene works as a unit of function. This hypothesis states that a given gene has a precise linear sequence which codes for the linear sequence of amino acids in one polypeptide molecule. This colinearity of sequences has been found to be true for prokaryotes (Section 12.1). As more information has been gained about the molecular structure and organization of genes in eukaryotes, the one gene — one polypeptide hypothesis has been found no longer to hold true. The discovery of split genes (Section 12.2.1), which are not colinear with the corresponding mature mRNA, shattered this hypothesis. The structure of split genes has yet further implications for the cell, for during RNA splicing sometimes several *exons* as well as the introns are removed from the primary RNA product, as illustrated in Question 12.2.

Question 12.2   Figure 12.5 represents a hypothetical primary RNA product synthesized in a eukaryote cell.

(a) This RNA molecule can be spliced to give two different mature mRNA products: one (called mRNA X) consisting of exons 1–5 and 11–15, the other (mRNA Y) consisting of exons 1–10 and 15. Which mRNA, X or Y, would produce the longer polypeptide after translation? Assume that each exon contains the same number of bases. (This is unlikely to be the case in reality.)

(b) Which non-protein-coding sequences would be removed from the primary RNA product to produce (i) mRNA X and (ii) mRNA Y? ◄

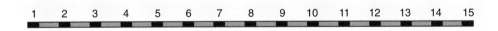

Figure 12.5   A hypothetical primary RNA product synthesized in a eukaryote cell, shown with 15 exons (dark regions). The lighter regions are introns. For use with Question 12.2.

● Now that you have answered Question 12.2, give another reason why the one gene — one polypeptide hypothesis no longer holds.

○ The hypothetical RNA sequence shown in Figure 12.5 can be spliced in two different ways. This produces two different mRNA molecules, which can be subsequently translated to give two different polypeptide products.

Thus a single DNA sequence can transfer information to two different mRNA molecules (via different routes of RNA splicing), which then provide the information for the synthesis of two different polypeptide molecules (via the process of translation). Effectively, *one* gene, or DNA sequence, has produced *two different* polypeptides, and not just one as stated in the original hypothesis. The finding of more than one polypeptide being produced from different combinations of exons of the same gene is true for many genes that have been analysed in eukaryotes. Nevertheless, the original one gene — one polypeptide hypothesis has been a useful working model and was an impressive step forward in our understanding of gene function.

As mentioned earlier, there are some genes that do not code for proteins; the product of transcription, RNA, is their final product. This is true for the genes that code for both tRNA and rRNA. Both these types of RNA are produced on DNA in the same way as mRNA, in both prokaryotes and eukaryotes. Thus we see that, even for prokaryotes, the one gene — one polypeptide hypothesis is not always valid. However, the fundamental idea that the gene is a *unit of function* still holds and is still widely accepted as a working hypothesis.

Although a great deal is now known about the structure and function of individual genes, relatively little is understood about how genes are organized in whole genomes and this is the topic of the next section.

Question 12.3   Compare and contrast the one gene — one polypeptide hypothesis as it applies to prokaryotes and eukaryotes. You should produce a list of points each of which describes a similarity or a difference between gene function in these two groups. ◀

12.3 Gene organization

So far, DNA has been treated as a collection of consecutive genes, like sentences in a book. In eukaryotes there are, however, DNA sequences between genes which do not code for protein but which have other functions, not all of which are well understood, but some are considered here.

For a long time biologists have been puzzled by the large amount of DNA in eukaryote genomes, but what kind of amounts are we talking about here? For example, a typical mammalian cell such as from a human, has around 800 times the amount of DNA present in the bacterium *E. coli*; here it should be emphasized that we are considering haploid amounts, so as to compare like with like. A human cell is far more complex than a bacterium, but there is not a direct relationship between the complexity of the organism and the (haploid) amount of DNA contained within its cells. The mammalian genome has, in theory, enough DNA to code for perhaps three million average-sized proteins and yet estimates suggest that a typical mammal is constructed from a mere 60 000–80 000 different proteins. Many plant genomes are even larger than mammalian ones.

In the case of split genes, we have already met DNA sequences (introns) that do not code for protein. If you look back at Figure 12.2 you will see that there we are considering a split gene to be the sum of the exons and introns it contains. In addition to the introns, which occur *within* split genes, there are other non-protein-coding sequences that lie *between* genes.

In the human genome this DNA appears to account for about 20% of the total DNA, containing sequences that are repeated many times. Most of these highly repeated DNA sequences have no known function. These **repeat sequences** are of different types: some consist of short sequences of just a few bases, while others consist of long sequences of between 1 000 and 5 000 bases. The same sequence may be found at a number of different sites throughout the genome, and is repeated many times over at each site, with the repeats sitting next to one another. Sometimes a cell may contain millions of copies of a basic repeated sequence, an example of which is shown in Figure 12.6 for the fruit-fly, *D. melanogaster*. So, in eukaryotes, protein-coding genes are embedded in a complex array of DNA sequences repeated in tandem, which have no known function.

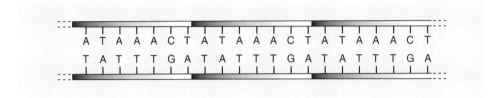

Figure 12.6   A simple repeat sequence from the fruit-fly, *D. melanogaster*. This consists of many serially arranged repeats of a sequence of seven base pairs, which occurs millions of times in the *D. melanogaster* genome.

However, some non-protein-coding DNA sequences between genes have a vital function in controlling the activity of genes. There are *control sequences*, which are stretches of the DNA that facilitate the operation of the protein-coding genes in eukaryotes. These sequences may be located far away from the transcription start site and a number of these may be involved in the control of just one gene. Their function relates to the 'switching on and off' of genes in different tissues. As you learned in Section 2.2, the cells of different tissues of multicellular organisms such as humans are not all the same; there are nerve, muscle and bone cells, to give just three examples. However, the different cell types of an organism all have the same genome. All of these specialized cells have some proteins in common, but each has other proteins that are unique to that particular cell type (Section 3.3). Clearly, therefore, in any particular cell only a certain number of genes are transcribed into RNA, which is subsequently translated into protein. The vast majority of other genes are inactive or 'switched off' and are not transcribed, so that the polypeptides for which they code are not being produced. This control of gene activity in eukaryotes is brought about by the control sequences and these ensure that only the right genes are transcribed in a given cell type.

Activity 12.1   Genomes and gene function

This activity requires you to compare genomes and gene function in prokaryotes and eukaryotes. ◄

12.4 Genome projects

Eukaryote genomes are clearly very complex, especially in comparison with prokaryote ones. In order to understand the degree of complexity, consider the human genome. Here, the base sequence of DNA in the 23 pairs of human chromosomes — some three billion base pairs in total — is equivalent to the number of letters in about two hundred large phone directories. Considering the size of this genome, it is not surprising that at the turn of the century we actually know relatively little about its overall structure and organization. This applies to most other eukaryote genomes. However, research projects are currently in progress which aim to elucidate the sequences of selected eukaryote genomes and thereby determine their organization. Notable ones are those of *Saccharomyces cerevisiae* (the unicellular bakers' or brewers' yeast, which you met in Section 2.2), *Arabidopsis thaliana* (a small plant which often grows as a weed in gardens), as well as that of *Homo sapiens* (humans).

The genome project of *Saccharomyces cerevisiae* reached a scientific milestone in 1996, when the genome had been sequenced completely — the first eukaryote genome to have achieved this status. The reason this yeast was chosen is that it is of major importance in various industrial processes and it is used as a model organism for basic biological research. The aim was to obtain information on this relatively simple organism, which could be applied to more complex eukaryotes. What has been learned from the yeast genome project? In total, it consists of around 12 million base pairs, which include about 6 000 protein-coding genes representing about 64% of the genome. Expressed another way, 6 000 genes are needed to 'construct' this unicellular eukaryote organism.

What role(s) might the remaining 36% of the yeast genome play?

Such non-protein-coding regions might be control sequences or repeat sequences.

Actually, about 22% of the genome consists of control sequences. Overall, the picture that has emerged from the yeast project is of a genome with comparatively few introns and repeat sequences. In contrast, the human genome is of much greater complexity, with many introns and repeat sequences. An important point to realize is that the yeast genome is about 250 times smaller than the human one and it took four and a half years to sequence it. You can thus appreciate the prediction of 15 years to sequence the whole of the human genome in the Human Genome Mapping Project (HGMP). This started in 1990 with the goal to sequence all three billion DNA base pairs by the year 2005.

The HGMP involves hundreds of laboratories in six different countries, the main centres being the USA, Europe and Japan. Such international effort in the HGMP requires cooperation which is promoted through the Human Genome Organization (HUGO). This coordinates the collection of data for constructing gene maps based on DNA sequencing and on other techniques such as traditional mapping as introduced in Section 8.5 (Activity 8.4). It also provides an international forum for considering ethical, legal, and social issues which arise from the project, such as whether any group or individual should be allowed to apply for patent rights on any sequences determined during the course of the project. Sequencing the entire three billion base pairs of the human genome is a mammoth task. The 60 000–80 000 protein-coding genes make up approximately only 5% of the genome. The completed genome sequence is being analysed in order to determine gene function, how genes are controlled and how their function is coordinated, and this is done with the help of computerized databanks.

But why is the HGMP important? Many human diseases, such as cystic fibrosis discussed in Section 11, are inherited; others at least have an heritable component, such as some forms of diabetes. For cystic fibrosis, we are in the fortunate position of knowing precisely where the gene is located on the chromosome, how big it is, and what its protein product is. Arguably, such knowledge of genes opens the way to cure or prevent diseases. For many genetically-based diseases, though, we know little if anything about the genes involved, and indeed many may involve the interaction of many genes (Section 9.3) and their protein products. Having determined where these genes are on the chromosomes, and what their precise base sequences are, the function of each gene can be determined. Therefore, the HGMP will provide the basic information required for the development of improved therapies for — at least some — genetically-based diseases.

12.5 Genome diversity

It is important to appreciate that the HGMP will not provide data on how variable the human genome is, because the DNA from a single individual is being mapped. Let us consider genetic variation within a population by returning briefly to our example of the cystic fibrosis gene. We considered one gene with two different alleles, for which there are three genotypes: homozygous for the normal allele; homozygous for the mutant allele; and heterozygous, where an individual has both alleles. Imagine for a moment how much genetic variation there is within a human population with different alleles for many, many different genes. The number of possible different combinations is really quite staggering. In order to appreciate this, consider an average of, say, 70 000 genes, each with one of three possible genotypes (homozygous recessive, homozygous dominant and heterozygous). The possible combinations for an individual are then $3^{70\,000}$ or over $10^{33\,400}$. So within a population, the chance of any two individuals having the same genotype is infinitesimally small. Furthermore, the variation in base sequences found outside of the protein-coding regions, especially in the repeat sequences, is even greater — so much so, that every individual, apart from identical twins, has a unique DNA profile, as outlined in Box. 12.1, *DNA fingerprinting*.

Box 12.1 *DNA fingerprinting*

The theoretical basis of **DNA fingerprinting** is that each individual in a species (apart from identical twins and clones), whether human or horse-chestnut, has a unique DNA profile. This profile is as unique as the familiar human fingerprint itself, hence the name applied to the technique used in visualizing DNA profiles, six of which are shown in Figure 12.7. The procedure used here is similar to that described earlier for visualizing the cystic fibrosis gene (Figure 11.11). Much variation results from differences between individuals in terms of repeat sequences. We saw in Section 12.3 that short base sequences within a genome can be serially repeated. The number of repeat sequences, however, can vary between individuals of the same species and it is this variation, rather than the variation in protein-coding genes, that contributes most to unique, individual DNA fingerprints.

Comparison of such fingerprints enables examination of a number of features of genomes. First, in the

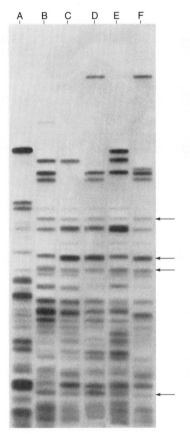

Figure 12.7   DNA fingerprints of six individuals, A–F. The red arrows point to shared bands in individuals B–F which are missing for individual A.

present context, it enables us to 'visualize' the amount of genetic variation within a population. Second, members of a given population can be compared in an attempt to quantify their relatedness. Figure 12.7 shows DNA fingerprints of six individuals (A–F), five of whom belong to the same family, whereas one does not. The first impression you should get from Figure 12.7 is that there is a fair amount of variation in the band pattern of the six individuals, even though five are closely related. In fact, A is unrelated to the other five, whilst B is the mother of C–F. If you look closely at the patterns of bands, you should see that A is somewhat different to the other five. Consider just the patterns of bands in the four rows marked by the red arrows. These bands are common to the DNA fingerprints of individuals B–F, but are missing for individual A. In reality, a superficial, visual comparison like this would be insufficient for an accurate analysis of relatedness, and quantitative methods of comparison are generally used.

The data shown in Figure 12.7 were produced to test the relatedness of one of the offspring (C) to the mother (B) and to siblings D–F; in this case, the father's DNA was not available for comparison. The question was: did individual C have the same mother (B) as individuals D, E and F? The degree of sharing of bands by relatives depends on their degree of relatedness: closer relatives have more bands in common than do more distant relatives. In this particular case, close examination showed that C shared enough bands with B, D, E and F to vindicate the claimed family relatedness. Some of the bands, such as the top one present in fingerprints D and F only, must have been inherited from the father.

DNA fingerprints can be used in other comparative situations, especially involving paternity disputes, and in forensic science, such as in cases of sexual assault or murder. For example, the DNA from very small samples of blood or semen found at sites of crime can be compared with that of potential suspects. It should be noted that there are legal and ethical issues associated with the application of DNA fingerprinting, especially when used in forensic situations. Laboratories carrying out the tests have to be exacting in their procedures. In forensic science it is now more usual to examine the variation in number of *specific* short repeat DNA sequences.

In addition to the genome mapping projects there is a parallel Human Genome Diversity Project (HGDP). Its specific purpose is to study DNA variation within and between populations, so providing an insight into human diversity and evolutionary history. The genetic variation between populations can also be used to trace past population movements.

The HGMP and HGDP will undoubtedly make important contributions to information about the vast amount of genetic variation that exists within human populations. It is the vast reserve of genetic variability on which evolution depends, and this is the subject of the final sections of this block.

12.6 Summary of Section 12

Bacterial genomes are relatively simple, consisting mainly of protein-coding sequences. In contrast, eukaryote genomes are larger and much more complex.

Many eukaryote genes are split genes, containing non-protein-coding introns and protein-coding exons. The primary RNA product, resulting from transcription, is spliced to remove the introns; the resultant mature mRNA molecule is therefore much smaller. After processing, the mRNA leaves the nucleus and moves to the cytosol where translation occurs.

In both prokaryotes and eukaryotes there are sequences that are transcribed into tRNA and rRNA.

Eukaryotes have several types of other non-protein-coding sequences such as short, serially repeated sequences of a small number of bases which have, as yet, no known function. Protein-coding genes are embedded within these repeat sequences. Eukaryotes have control sequences, which regulate the switching on and off of genes and may be located far away from the transcription start site of a gene.

The DNA sequences of selected eukaryote genomes, notably those of yeast and human, are being investigated in genome projects.

The technique of DNA fingerprinting enables genetic variation to be visualized and genetic relatedness to be measured.

Evolution by natural selection revisited

13

Two central points about evolution by natural selection as postulated by Charles Darwin are the existence of variation within species that is heritable, and that certain phenotypes in a population are better able to survive and to reproduce; that is, they have a greater fitness (Block 4). In this section and Section 14, we look again at this topic. Therefore, our focus will not just be on individual organisms but also on populations and species.

In Block 4, natural selection was explained and discussed in much the way that Charles Darwin presented it; that is, the importance of inheritance was emphasized, but no account was taken of the actual mechanisms by which inheritance occurs. A full understanding of evolution must account not only for changes over time in the *phenotypes* of a population of organisms, but also for the corresponding changes over time that must occur in its *genotypes*. Returning to the example of bright coloration in male guppies (Block 4, Section 9.1), we would need to understand what genes and alleles are responsible for male coloration and how the genotype of male guppies changes over successive generations when a population is subject to predation by larger fish. As guppies become more colourful over time in the absence of predators, alleles for bright coloration must become more common in the population. At present, very little is known about the genetics of guppy coloration and so, in this section, we will turn to other examples to illustrate how the genetic make-up of a species changes during evolution.

Evolution depends on the existence of genetic variation in populations, and we begin by considering how much variation there actually is in a species, and where it comes from. This will involve you revising concepts met earlier in this block, such as gene mutation (Sections 9.6 and 10.3) and the recombination of genes (Activity 8.4). We then go on to examine the changes that occur at the genotypic and phenotypic levels in two fairly straightforward examples of evolution in action — colour change in the peppered moth (*Biston betularia*) and a medical condition in humans known as sickle-cell disease.

Activity 13.1   Revision: evolution by natural selection

This activity will help you recall the main features of evolution by natural selection as presented by Charles Darwin, and the biological terms used to describe them. An understanding of these is required for you to follow Sections 13 and 14. ◄

13.1 Genetic variation

Natural selection acts on phenotypes so certain phenotypes are more likely than others to survive to reproductive maturity. But phenotypes are partly determined by the genotype. Understanding evolution in terms of genetic changes as well as phenotypic changes is very important because natural selection can lead to evolutionary change in a particular character only if that character has a genetic basis. Consequently, the direction that evolution takes at any time depends on what genes or alleles are present in the population at that time.

Since genetic variation is important for the process of evolution, we might ask how much of it exists within a species such as humans. One way to look at genetic variation is to begin with an example of phenotypic variation that you have already encountered — the human ABO blood group system (Section 9.2).

Does the ABO system represent an example of continuous or discontinuous variation?

Discontinuous variation, because individuals can be categorized as belonging to one of four *distinct* phenotypes (A, B, AB and O).

A situation like this, in which two or more phenotypes (and genotypes) coexist, is called a **polymorphism**. The ABO blood group system is only one of many polymorphisms that occur in human blood. Another well-known one is the rhesus system, in which there are two phenotypes, called rhesus-negative and rhesus-positive. About a dozen different blood group systems have been identified in humans; in cattle there are over 200!

The relative proportions of the four blood groups in the ABO system vary considerably from one part of the world to another, because of very marked variations in the geographical distribution of the three alleles, as shown in Figure 13.1. In Britain, for example, the alleles *A* and *O* are quite common, but *B* is very rare, whereas in South America, only *O* is common.

Where two or more forms of a particular character exist in a population, it is to be *expected* that one form would have an advantage over the others under natural selection so that, eventually, all but one form would disappear from the population. Therefore, any example of a polymorphism raises important questions about the possible role of natural selection. A common situation in polymorphisms is that each form confers a particular, but different, advantage on individuals, so that each form is favoured by natural selection, though for different reasons. The possible factors that might influence the proportions of the different forms in the ABO blood group system are not known, though there are some clues. For example, people with type O blood have a higher incidence of stomach ulcers than those with the other groups, and those with group A have a higher incidence of stomach cancer. Interestingly, however, both these disorders do not generally occur until after reproductive age. Whilst natural selection can influence how common in a population are alleles that act early in life, it can have no effect on those that cause deterioration or susceptibility to disease late in life, *after* reproductive age. This is because these genes will already have been passed on to the next generation before they exert their deleterious effect. So selection on blood groups arising from stomach ulcers or stomach cancer cannot have any effect on allele frequencies. However, people with blood group A or AB are thought to be more susceptible to smallpox, a disease that has now been eradicated. Since smallpox affected younger people, it may have exerted selection on the frequency of these groups in some parts of the world in the past.

Recall from Block 4 factors other than selection that influence the frequency of phenotypes in populations, such as blood groups in human populations.

Genetic drift and the founder effect. Genetic drift (chance variation in the genetic make-up of a population) plays an important role in the fate of all genetic characters, particularly in small populations. The example of the Dunkers in Pennsylvania (Block 4, Section 10.3) shows how the founder effect may lead to there being small, isolated populations with unusual frequencies of the different ABO phenotypes.

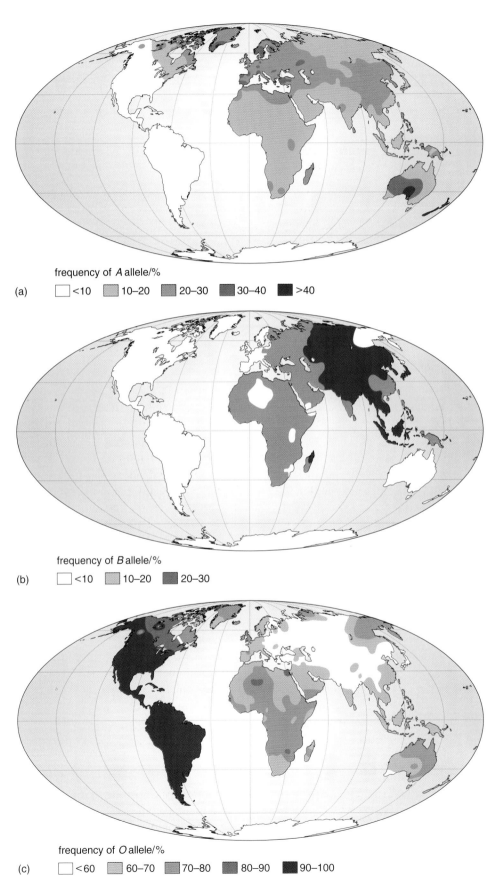

frequency of *A* allele/%

(a)   ☐ <10   ▨ 10–20   ▨ 20–30   ▨ 30–40   ■ >40

frequency of *B* allele/%

(b)   ☐ <10   ▨ 10–20   ▨ 20–30

frequency of *O* allele/%

(c)   ☐ <60   ▨ 60–70   ▨ 70–80   ▨ 80–90   ■ 90–100

Figure 13.1 Geographical distribution of the three alleles underlying the ABO blood group system in humans. The shading denotes the percentage of the population that has the allele *A* in (a), *B* in (b) and *O* in (c). Note that the percentages represented by the shading are different in each map.

The reasons for the geographical distribution of *ABO* blood group alleles shown in Figure 13.1 are not understood, but are likely to be the result of both natural selection and chance factors such as genetic drift or the founder effect, as well as reflecting historical patterns of *migration* in the human population. This distribution also provides a good example of a common feature of organisms: that their genotypes often show geographical variation.

The purpose of looking at the genetics of human blood groups is to give you some idea of how much genetic variation exists within a species. In the ABO blood group example, the three alleles at one locus produce six genotypes and four phenotypes (see Section 9.2). Relative to other characters in humans, this is a low level of variation. For example, a group of 12 genes (called HLA), which determine part of the immune system in humans, has a different number of alleles at each locus; one gene has only two alleles, another has eight, a third has 56 and one has as many as 133 alleles. This gives billions of possible combinations of alleles at these 12 loci. (The immune system, of which the white blood cells form a part, is responsible for protecting the body against invasion by disease-causing organisms, but these particular genes were originally discovered by virtue of their importance in tissue transplantation between unrelated individuals.) It is estimated that the human genome contains 60 000 to 80 000 loci, at many of which there are multiple alleles. Consequently, the number of possible genotypes is effectively infinite, which is why, with the exception of identical twins, every individual in the human population is unique and is genetically distinct from every other individual that has ever lived or will ever live. The term **gene pool** is used to refer to the sum total of all the alleles present at any one time in a population, and so it includes the total genetic variation existing among individuals of a population. Each of us carries a subset of the human gene pool.

Question 13.1 Assume that the current human population in the UK is 6×10^7. What is the total number of copies of the ABO blood group alleles in the gene pool of the UK? ◄

Variation can be observed within and between populations of any species at various levels of phenotype, from external morphology down to the sequence of amino acids in proteins (as described for cystic fibrosis in Section 11.6, for example). Using molecular techniques, it is possible to observe differences in genotype at the level of DNA sequence (as described in Section 12.4 and illustrated in Box 12.1, *Genetic fingerprinting*). Every species of organism ever examined has revealed considerable genetic variation, or polymorphism, within populations, between populations, or both.

13.2 Sources of variation: mutation and recombination

Where does all this genetic variation in populations come from? There are two major sources of genetic variation, both of which have been described in detail in earlier sections: mutation and recombination. We look at each of these in turn, this time at the population level. Recombination by itself produces variation only if the parents have different alleles of the genes. Ultimately, the source of all genetic variation must be mutation.

13.2.1 Mutation

Mutations occur both as changes in the sequence of base pairs in DNA (Section 10.3) and as major structural changes in the chromosomes (Section 9.6.2). When the theory of natural selection first began to gain acceptance, it was thought that mutation was the source of new phenotypes that were more suited to the environment; such phenotypes are said to be *adaptive*. So most mutations were believed to be advantageous. Because the genotype of an organism is so complex and produces a phenotype that is well adapted to its environment, it is nowadays accepted that most mutations that affect the phenotype have a deleterious effect on an individual's survival and that favourable mutations are very rare.

However, there are in eukaryotes large portions of the genome that are not expressed in the phenotype (Section 12).

●   Which DNA sequences are these?

○   The stretches of DNA within genes that form introns, and control sequences and repeat sequences between the genes. None of these are protein-coding.

Mutations in apparently functionless DNA, such as repeat sequences, are unlikely to affect survival or reproductive success (i.e. fitness) and so are categorized as being *neutral* in their effects. It appears that much of the variation that exists in the genomes of organisms is the product of such *neutral mutations*, accumulated over many generations. What is not known is how important these neutral mutations are to evolutionary change, but it is clear that their frequencies would be influenced by genetic drift, rather than by natural selection.

Mutations occur at random. This does not mean that all genes mutate at the same rate, nor that all possible mutations are equally likely. Nor does it mean that mutations are entirely spontaneous; as described earlier (Section 10.3), a variety of environmental agents, such as certain chemicals and ultraviolet light, increase mutation rates. What it does mean is that the chance that a particular mutation will occur is not affected by how 'useful' that mutation might be to the organism. Consequently, natural selection has to 'use' whatever mutations are available to it at any given time. This means that:

> Natural selection acts upon the variation generated by mutation but cannot in any way direct or control which mutations will arise.

The rate at which mutations occur is variable between species, and varies from one locus to another within a species. Mutation rates are commonly expressed as the chance that a mutation will occur at a specific locus in a given number of cells or gametes, and known values range from about one in 10^5 to one in 10^6 gametes. This suggests that mutations are very rare. Individually, they are; but when you consider how many loci there are in each gamete, and how many gametes are produced (a single human ejaculate contains between 3×10^8 and 5×10^8 sperm), you can see that reproduction generates a great many mutations. Then consider how many people there are in the world and you can appreciate that there are very many new mutations present among the world population of humans. The same is true for other species.

13.2.2 Recombination

As described in Section 8, at meiosis, the recombination process generates new combinations of chromosomes or parts of chromosomes, and new combinations of the genes and alleles they contain. The process of fertilization also generates new gene or chromosomal combinations and so is also a form of recombination in the general sense of the term.

Thus recombination arises from three distinct processes, all of which occur at some stage during sexual reproduction:

1   During gamete production, there is independent assortment of maternal and paternal chromosomes from each chromosome pair.

2   During gamete production, crossing over between homologous chromosomes occurs.

3   When gametes combine at fertilization, they bring together novel combinations of alleles.

Recombination is, therefore, a process in which all the alleles in the genome of each individual are 'shuffled' together with alleles from another individual, to generate an almost infinite number of possible new combinations of alleles. Comparing different modes of reproduction (introduced in Block 4, Section 6) will reveal the contribution that recombination makes to genetic variation of a species that reproduces sexually. Before we do this, try Activity 13.2.

Activity 13.2   Revision: genetic recombination

The purpose of this activity is to help you recall how recombination is brought about, as described earlier in Activity 8.4. ◀

Not all organisms reproduce sexually; indeed, there is a rich variety of modes of reproduction. In asexual reproduction, a parent produces progeny by budding (as in strawberry and *Hydra*, Block 4, Section 6.1) or by producing a reproductive cell by *mitosis* which then develops into a new individual without requiring fertilization.

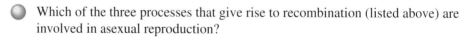

Which of the three processes that give rise to recombination (listed above) are involved in asexual reproduction?

Asexual reproduction involves *none* of processes 1–3 above, and so produces offspring that are genetically identical to their parents (except for any mutations that might arise).

In parthenogenesis (meaning 'virgin birth') a parent produces, by *meiosis*, a reproductive cell that develops without fusing with a sperm. Here the first meiotic division occurs and the chromosome number is halved, but there is no second meiotic division so the chromatids do not segregate to different poles of the cell. Instead, the two chromatids of each chromosome separate from each other but remain in the same cell. Therefore the diploid number of chromosomes is maintained without involving a male gamete. Processes 1 and 2, but not 3, are involved in parthenogenesis and so offspring that are slightly different from their parent are produced. Parthenogenesis is the mode of reproduction used by greenfly (often called aphids) and water fleas (*Daphnia*, Figure 13.2) for much of the year .

Some organisms, particularly among plants, are sexual but self-fertilizing.

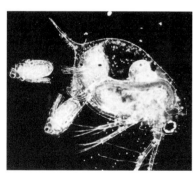

Figure 13.2   Parthenogenesis in the water flea, *Daphnia* (magnification × 15). This individual is giving birth to two offspring, which have developed directly from unfertilized ova.

● Which of the three processes that give rise to recombination are involved in sexual reproduction with self-fertilization?

○ Self-fertilization involves all three processes, but fusion of gametes (process 3) does not produce as much genetic variation among the offspring as does full sexual reproduction in which gametes from different parents are brought together. (This is because the amount of genetic variation within one individual is less than it is among two different individuals.)

The largest reservoir of genetic variability resulting from recombination is found in populations of organisms that have complete sexual reproduction with cross-fertilization, as described in Section 8 for maize or humans, for example. There is thus a great deal of diversity among organisms in their mode of reproduction, a consequence of which is that there is much variation between species in the contribution that recombination makes to genetic variation.

A major topic of interest among evolutionary biologists today is to account for this diversity in mode of reproduction in terms of natural selection. In other words, why is sexual reproduction adaptive for some species, asexual reproduction for others, parthenogenesis for others? A clue to the answer to these questions is given in Box 13.1, *Mode of reproduction and environmental change*.

Box 13.1 *Mode of reproduction and environmental change*

Figure 13.3 compares the genotypes of offspring that are produced by asexual and sexual reproduction, and illustrates the genetic 'shuffling' effect of recombination by independent assortment during sexual reproduction. The figure shows two genes, each of which has two alleles (*Q* and *q*, and *R* and *r*). Study the figure, and suppose first that alleles *Q* and *R* are both deleterious. Whereas the asexual parents inevitably pass these alleles on to their respective progeny, the sexual parents produce some progeny that lack both of them. Thus, an important consequence of sexual reproduction, resulting from independent assortment, is that it can eliminate deleterious alleles in a way that asexual reproduction cannot. Now suppose that alleles *Q* and *R* are both advantageous.

● Looking at Figure 13.3, in what way might the genetic consequences of sexual reproduction be better than those of asexual reproduction?

○ Sexual reproduction produces some progeny that carry both advantageous alleles. (Note, however, that it also produces some that *lack* both.)

Thus, a consequence of sexual reproduction is that it can create new combinations of favourable alleles.

● Could progeny carrying both alleles *Q* and *R* occur in the species with asexual reproduction shown in Figure 13.3? If so, how might this arise?

○ Yes, but not by recombination. Individuals carrying both alleles *Q* and *R* can occur only by mutation, for example, by *R* arising by mutation of *r* in a population of *Q* individuals. (This, as we have seen, would be a relatively rare event.)

In general terms, then, sexual reproduction seems to have an advantage over asexual reproduction in two ways: it eliminates deleterious alleles and it generates novel combinations of favourable alleles. Why, then, do not all organisms reproduce sexually? The full answer to this question is complex, but a part of the answer concerns what is called the *cost* of recombination. As shown in Figure 13.3, sexual reproduction produces some progeny that are 'better' than their parents, in terms of carrying new combinations of favourable alleles, but it also produces progeny that are 'worse', in that they lack either favourable allele. Sexual reproduction is thus, as a result of recombination, very wasteful, in that it produces many progeny that are less well-adapted than their parents. Conversely, asexual reproduction *conserves* adaptations. An individual in an asexual species that survives to reproduce then faithfully replicates the genotype that has enabled it to do so.

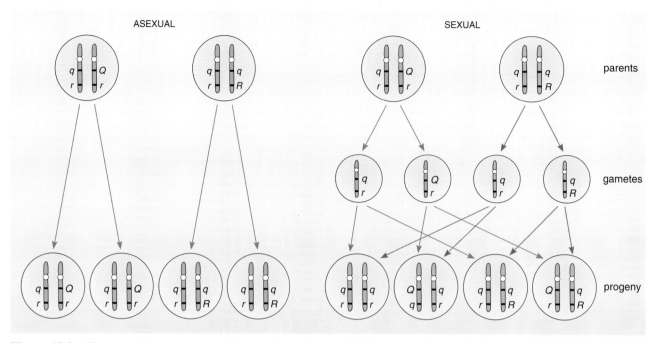

Figure 13.3 The genetic consequences of asexual reproduction (left) and sexual reproduction (right). Asexual reproduction produces progeny that are exact replicas of their parents, carrying the same alleles of the genes Q and q, and R and r. Sexual reproduction produces genetically variable progeny that carry different combinations of parental alleles.

Thus mode of reproduction — asexual, sexual, etc. — is in itself an adaptation. Which mode of reproduction is the more adaptive depends on how much the environment changes from one generation to the next. If an organism is living in a totally stable environment, the best thing to do is to replicate faithfully its successful genotype by asexual reproduction. If, however, the environment is changing, even very slightly, from one generation to the next, then it is better to have progeny that differ from one another. Thus asexual reproduction is more adaptive where the environment is relatively stable, and sexual reproduction, with the attendant recombination, is more adaptive where the environment fluctuates.

Recombination can be thought of as the sum total of all the processes that 'stir up' the gene pool, so that different individuals have different combinations of alleles, each combination conferring upon the owner its unique array of advantages and disadvantages. It is important, however, not to lose sight of the primary source of new genes upon which recombination depends, the process of mutation. This feeds mutant alleles into the gene pool. Genetic diversity, accompanied by corresponding phenotypic diversity, lies at the heart of evolution. Natural selection is dependent on genetic variation, as the next section shows.

13.3 Genes and evolution in action

During evolution by natural selection, a population changes in its phenotypic characters, as demonstrated by the coloration of guppies. This does not mean that the phenotypic character of every individual in the population is different from all individuals in the ancestral population, although this does happen in the course of large-scale evolutionary changes, such as the evolution of separate species (discussed later in Section 14.3). Instead, on a smaller scale, an evolutionary change in a population involves the change of *proportions* of phenotypes present in a population.

However, phenotypes are influenced by genes. Evolutionary change, therefore, has to be considered at two levels. At one level it consists of changes in phenotypes in populations over time. At another level it consists of changes of proportions of alleles in the gene pool, that is changes in genotype. In this section, we examine two examples in which genetic variation, and the associated phenotypic variation, within populations has been associated with natural selection.

13.3.1 The peppered moth in Britain

The peppered moth (*Biston betularia*) is quite common in Britain. It flies around at night and rests on the trunks of trees by day, and it is polymorphic, existing in two distinct forms, as shown in the photos on the title page. Prior to 1848, the peppered moth apparently occurred only in the pale, speckled grey (typical) form, but in that year a completely black individual was reported from Manchester. This darker form, called the *carbonaria* form, rapidly increased in relative abundance until, by 1900, it formed 95% of populations in industrial areas of Britain, while it remained rare in most rural areas. The spread of the dark form, from almost zero to 95% in about 50 generations, illustrates how rapid evolutionary changes can be under certain circumstances.

Differences in the relative abundance of the two forms in different areas were attributed to how well they were camouflaged during the day. In industrial areas, sulphur dioxide pollution kills the pale lichens that grow on tree trunks, making them black in comparison with lichen-covered tree trunks in unpolluted rural areas. Viewed against a background of bark of a tree from a rural area, the pale form of the moth is rather difficult to see, whereas the dark form is very obvious (see title page). On the other hand, when viewed against the bark of a tree from an industrialized area, exactly the reverse is true; the pale form stands out, and the *carbonaria* form is nearly invisible (see title page). It was hypothesized that birds, hunting for food by day, would find the dark form much more easily than the pale form in rural areas, and the pale form more easily than the dark form in urban areas. This hypothesis was tested by the English entomologist H. B. Kettlewell, who caught, marked and released a large number of peppered moths and then recorded how many he recaptured alive in moth traps. Moths that were caught in traps were thus those that had escaped predation by birds. The results are shown in Table 13.1.

○ Do the data presented in Table 13.1 support the hypothesis that there is differential survival of the two forms in the two localities?

○ Yes, they do. A smaller proportion of the pale form was recaptured in the urban area, and a smaller proportion of the dark form in rural areas.

The results of Kettlewell's experiment are consistent with the hypothesis that birds selectively eat the more conspicuous form of peppered moth in each area, but do not confirm it, as his experiment did not include direct observations of the foraging behaviour of birds. Subsequent observations have confirmed the predation hypothesis, but have also suggested that it is not the only factor involved in maintaining high frequencies of the dark form in industrial areas. For instance, there are certain rural areas of Britain (for example, Norfolk) where the dark form is found at quite high frequencies, for reasons that are not understood.

Table 13.1   The proportions of dark (*carbonaria*) and pale (typical) peppered moths, marked and released into the wild, that were subsequently recaptured in moth traps in two localities, one urban, the other rural.

Locality	Dark form/%	Pale form/%
Birmingham (urban area)	53.2	25.0
Dorset (rural area)	6.3	12.5

What does such a change in the proportions of phenotypic forms in a population involve genetically? Such changes reflect changes in the frequency of different alleles in the population. **Allele frequency** is a measure of the commonness of an allele in a population; it is the proportion of a specific type of allele among all the alleles of a particular gene in the population. The genetic basis of colour polymorphism in *Biston betularia* is simple and well understood. There are two alleles at a single locus (T and t), with the allele for dark colour (T) being dominant to that for pale colour (t). In the first part of the 19th century, the peppered moth gene pool for body colour would have been relatively constant, generation by generation, containing an overwhelming proportion of the t allele. The genotype of almost all individuals would have been tt. Here and there, mutation would have produced a T allele, so a few moths would have been Tt.

 What colour would heterozygotes be?

They would be dark, because the dark-colour allele is dominant.

At the phenotypic level, these dark moths would have been disadvantaged through bird predation; almost all peppered moths would have been the pale typical form. The dark form caught in Manchester would have been the result of a mutation.

However, as the Industrial Revolution proceeded and the environment became dirtier, the dark *carbonaria* form would have gained a survival advantage and the proportion of dark moths would have increased. This means that the proportion of alleles for the dark form in the population would also have increased, and the proportion of alleles for the light form would have decreased. Putting it another way, there would have been an increase in the frequency of alleles for the dark form.

> At the genetic level, evolution is expressed as change over time in the frequencies of alleles in a population.

Such change cannot proceed without the presence of genetic variation; in this case, there are alleles for the dark form and alleles for the light form, and one or other allele is favoured as the environment (presence or absence of sulphur dioxide pollution) changes. Thus the gene pool of the peppered moths in 1900 would have been very different from that of the population in, say, 1840, because in 1900 it would have contained a high proportion of T alleles. What was important for the course of evolution was the existence, albeit at a very low level, of the T allele in the gene pool in the 1840s.

The dark *carbonaria* form of the peppered moth is fitter than the pale form in a polluted environment. This illustrates that natural selection acts upon phenotypes. If one phenotype is less fit than another, fewer of its descendants will survive to reproductive maturity, and hence the allele responsible for the less-fit phenotype will be less common in the offspring generation. This can be summarized:

> Differences in fitness among phenotypes lead to changes in the allele frequencies in the gene pool of a population.

In Britain, industrial pollution is now controlled by legislation and, by the early 1970s, levels of sulphur dioxide in the environment had fallen substantially. The impact of this change on peppered moths has been monitored by Open University students taking an earlier version of this course. By 1985, they had collected a total of 1 825 peppered moths from 190 localities in Britain. This long-term survey revealed a steady decline in the frequency of the *carbonaria* form across much of Britain so that, by 1985, it existed at very high frequency only in the extreme north-east of England, having largely disappeared from the Midlands. The OU study looked at the whole of the UK; other studies looked in more detail at particular localities.

○ How would the gene pool of the peppered moth in the UK in 1960 have differed from the peppered moth gene pool of today?

○ The proportion of *T* alleles would have been much higher in 1960 than it is today, and the proportion of *t* alleles much lower.

This example of change in allele frequencies in *B. betularia* shows a number of important points about natural selection. It clearly demonstrates that natural selection is dependent on genetic variation. It also shows how, when a favourable allele arises in a population, it can spread very rapidly under the influence of natural selection. In less than 50 years, the *carbonaria* form had become the predominant form in polluted areas. However, natural selection did not favour the dark form throughout the *range* of the species (i.e. the area over which it is found) and the pale form remained predominant in rural areas. This illustrates how natural selection can have quite different effects on gene frequencies in different parts of a species' range. In other words, natural selection, as well as acting upon genetic variation within a population, can also *maintain* such variation, by acting differently on certain alleles in different parts of a species' range. Finally, the example of *B. betularia* shows that natural selection acts on *individuals* (not on the population), but that evolutionary changes that result from natural selection are seen in the *population* (and not in the individual).

Question 13.2 Which of the following statements about *B. betularia* are true and which are false? Give reasons for your answers.

(a) The increase in the *carbonaria* form between 1850 and 1900 in the UK was due to an increase in mutation rate.

(b) The moths are adversely affected by sulphur dioxide pollution.

(c) The fitness of the *carbonaria* form in urban areas increased over the decades between 1850 and 1900.

(d) As the environment changed between 1970 and 1980, allele frequencies of the colour gene in the Midlands would have changed simply by chance.

(e) The differences in fitness among the two colour phenotypes in the Midlands between 1970 and 1980 would have led to changes in the gene pool. ◀

13.3.2 Sickle-cell disease

Another example of genes and evolution in action is sickle-cell disease (also called sickle-cell anaemia). This is a disease that afflicts people particularly in tropical regions of the world and accounts for between 100 000 and 250 000 deaths per year. People who suffer from sickle-cell disease have an abnormality in their blood. The body of an average human adult contains about a kilogram of a protein called haemoglobin, packed into millions of red blood cells. Normal red blood cells are disc-shaped, and the haemoglobin contained within them carries oxygen from the lungs to the tissues and cells where it is needed. (Haemoglobin has a similar function to myoglobin, which you met in Section 3.) People with normal blood contain a type of haemoglobin called haemoglobin A. Those with sickle-cell disease, however, have an unusual type, called haemoglobin S; the capacity of this to carry oxygen is normal but it tends to crystallize when levels of oxygen in the blood become low. Once crystallized, the haemoglobin is no longer able to transport oxygen. In addition, it causes the red blood cells to assume the 'sickle' shape that gives the disease its name. To appreciate this difference in shape compare the normal red blood cells in Figure 2.9a with those from a person with sickle-cell disease, in Figure 13.4. Sickle cells are more fragile than normal red blood cells. They split open readily and consequently are rapidly destroyed — hence the anaemia. (Anaemia is a deficiency in the quantity and quality of red blood cells.)

Figure 13.4 Red blood cells of a person with sickle-cell disease, at various stages of sickling.

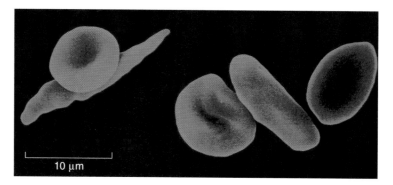

The sickle-cell condition is caused by a mutation involving a single base change in a gene so that one of the mRNA codons is changed from GAG to GUG (see Table 11.2). GAG codes for glutamate and GUG codes for valine. Thus the mutation causes the amino acid glutamate to be substituted by valine at a specific position in the haemoglobin A protein molecule; this results in the mutant protein haemoglobin S. This tiny change in the protein produces a cascade of effects, of which anaemia is only one symptom. The anaemia causes heart failure and physical weakness. Furthermore, the abnormal sickled cells, unable to squeeze through narrow blood vessels, cause failure in blood supply and hence oxygen delivery, which in turn can lead to brain damage and kidney failure.

The genetics of sickle-cell disease are as follows. The gene that codes for haemoglobin is designated *Hb* (note the *two*-letter symbol here). A person with normal haemoglobin A is homozygous for the allele Hb^A and so has the genotype $Hb^A Hb^A$, and a person with sickle-cell disease is homozygous for the mutant allele Hb^S and so has the genotype $Hb^S Hb^S$.

The fact that many people in the world die each year from sickle-cell disease, most of them in childhood, means that there is very strong selection that should ensure that the frequency of the Hb^S allele is kept low. The Hb^S allele remains common, however, and in some parts of the world, such as East Africa, it is present at a frequency of 20%. (In other words, 20 out of every 100 haemoglobin alleles in the population are Hb^S instead of Hb^A.) Why is the Hb^S allele so common if it has such a devastating effect on fitness? Why has it not been eliminated by natural selection? The answer to this puzzle becomes clear when we look at individuals who are heterozygous.

⬤ What is the genotype of people who are heterozygous for sickle-cell disease?

⚪ $Hb^A Hb^S$.

The alleles *Hb^A* and *Hb^S* do not show a simple dominant/recessive pattern; rather, both are said to show *incomplete dominance*, which is similar to the codominance shown by the genes determining the ABO blood groups (Section 9.2). The result of this is that the heterozygous phenotype is *intermediate* between the two homozygous phenotypes. Heterozygotes are described as having the sickle-cell trait. These *Hb^A* *Hb^S* individuals are anaemic, but only slightly, because only a proportion of their red blood cells become sickled. This, of itself, is not sufficient to explain the high frequency of the *Hb^S* allele in human populations, however. Of much greater significance is the fact that heterozygotes have a major advantage over *both* kinds of homozygous individuals; they are better able to withstand malaria. There are several lines of evidence to support this conclusion. Here we will consider two. One line of evidence comes from comparing the geographical distribution of the *Hb^S* allele with that of a particularly severe form of malaria. Look at Figure 13.5.

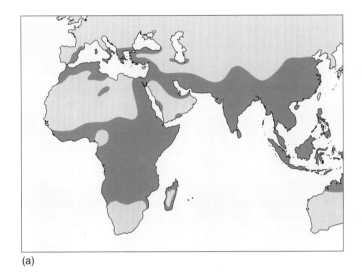

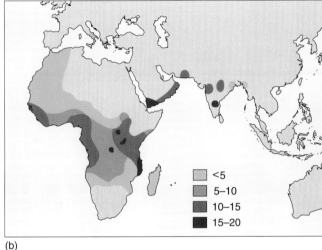

	<5
	5–10
	10–15
	15–20

(a)   (b)

What is the relationship between the two distributions?

They are similar. Most of the areas that have a high incidence of the sickle-cell allele are areas where there is malignant malaria, such as India and tropical Africa.

People who are heterozygous for the sickle-cell allele are less susceptible to malaria than normal homozygotes. Consequently, natural selection actually favours the heterozygotes in those areas of the world where malaria is prevalent. This phenomenon, in which the fitness of heterozygotes exceeds that of either type of homozygote, is called **heterozygous advantage**. It is thought that this effect may account for many other examples where lethal or deleterious alleles persist in populations at unexpectedly high frequencies.

The second line of evidence for the association between malaria and sickle-cell disease comes from a detailed look at the parasite responsible for malaria, a protoctist called *Plasmodium falciparum*. This single-celled organism lives in the blood, within the red blood cells, and is not able to survive and reproduce as well in sickled red blood cells as it does in normal ones. When red blood cells collapse because they contain haemoglobin S, they no longer provide a home for the parasites, which are released into the blood fluid where they are engulfed and destroyed by white blood cells.

Figure 13.5 (a) The distribution of malignant malaria (a particularly severe form of malaria caused by the parasite *Plasmodium falciparum*) in Africa and southern Asia. (b) The distribution, or frequency, of the *Hb^S* allele (per cent within the human population), which causes sickle-cell disease in the homozygous condition.

153

Thus, in regions of the world where there is a high incidence of malaria, heterozygotes ($Hb^A Hb^S$) suffer from mild anaemia, but this adverse influence on their fitness is more than offset by their greater resistance to malaria, in comparison to $Hb^A Hb^A$ homozygotes. This means that many more of them survive to reproductive age, have children, and so pass both Hb^A and Hb^S alleles on to the next generation. This explains why the Hb^S allele is not lost from the population, but is present at an unexpectedly high frequency. Some of the Hb^S alleles will be 'drained off' from the gene pool through the early death of the $Hb^S Hb^S$ homozygotes, but this is offset by the 'topping up' of Hb^S alleles in the gene pool through the success of the $Hb^A Hb^S$ heterozygotes.

This example makes a very important point about the process of natural selection. It is often said that natural selection favours or acts against the spread of a particular allele. This is a short-hand way of viewing natural selection, however, and it can be misleading. Natural selection does not operate directly on alleles, but on individual organisms; that is, it acts on phenotypes, which are the expression of alleles acting together. Thus, whether or not a particular allele is favoured by selection depends not only on the effects of that allele in isolation, but also on how it interacts with other alleles. The sickle-cell allele is lethal in one genetic context ($Hb^S Hb^S$), but advantageous in another ($Hb^A Hb^S$). Its frequency in a population is thus the result of the combined influence of these two effects.

The two alleles Hb^A and Hb^S can combine to give three distinct phenotypes, and corresponding genotypes, which coexist in the human population, a situation described as a polymorphism. Sickle-cell disease is an example of a particular kind of polymorphism, however. Where malaria is prevalent, the heterozygote has a greater fitness than either homozygote. Since selection opposes the elimination of either the Hb^A allele or the Hb^S allele, this situation is called a **balanced polymorphism**. The balance is maintained by the relative costs and benefits incurred by the various genotypes. Persons homozygous for Hb^A do not suffer from anaemia but are susceptible to malaria; those that are homozygous for Hb^S die young from severe anaemia; those that are heterozygous have only mild anaemia, but enjoy resistance to malaria. The relative strengths of these costs and benefits determine the relative frequencies of the Hb^A and Hb^S alleles that are maintained by natural selection, and thus the relative frequencies of the three phenotypes in a population. In the case of sickle-cell disease, natural selection *conserves genetic diversity* rather than favouring or acting against the spread of a particular allele.

Question 13.3   Summarize the evidence supporting the hypothesis that heterozygous $Hb^A Hb^S$ individuals are better able to withstand malaria than are homozygous $Hb^A Hb^A$ individuals. ◄

In this section we have seen that mutation provides the raw materials on which natural selection and genetic drift can act. Natural selection can have no effect on neutral mutations, but genetic drift may cause the frequencies of neutral alleles to increase or decrease slowly. In general, selection will result in the spread of beneficial mutations and reduce the frequency of the harmful ones. The examples of colour form in the peppered moth and sickle-cell disease in humans show how changes of allele frequencies can occur through the natural selection of a 'favoured' genotype in a population of a species. The action and direction of selection depends upon the fitness of the different genotypes at a locus. In the next section we examine natural selection at the level of a species.

Question 13.4   Using both sickle-cell disease and colour form in *Biston betularia* as examples, explain how natural selection can maintain genetic diversity in a population. ◀

Activity 13.3   Sickle-cell disease: a lethal advantage

This activity requires you to view the TV programme, 'Sickle-cell disease: a lethal advantage', which broadens the discussion of sickle-cell disease by putting it into a social context. ◀

Activity 13.4   Sickle-cell disease: an integrative account

In this activity you will plan and write a long account which integrates information from more than one place in this block. ◀

13.4 Summary of Section 13

Mutation is a continuous source of new alleles. The relative importance of neutral mutations for evolution is unknown, but their frequencies will be influenced by genetic drift. Natural selection acts on beneficial or deleterious mutations but cannot control which mutations will arise.

During reproduction, recombination shuffles parental alleles to produce novel combinations of alleles and thus generates genetic variation. Because there is a very large number of genes in the gene pool of a species, mutation and recombination together produce a huge range of unique genotypes.

Different modes of reproduction vary in terms of how much genetic variation they generate; sexual reproduction generates the most.

Natural selection alters the characteristics of species over time as a consequence of different phenotypes having different fitness. Differences in fitness among phenotypes lead to changes in the gene pool. Evolutionary change is detected at the genetic level as changes in the frequencies of alleles that are responsible for different phenotypes.

Studies of the changing frequency of the *carbonaria* (dark) form of the peppered moth in Britain show how the frequency of individual alleles in a population changes under the influence of natural selection. This example shows that natural selection acts on *individuals* but that evolutionary change resulting from natural selection occurs in the *population*.

The example of sickle-cell disease shows how the frequency of a particular allele in a population is influenced not only by natural selection, but also by how that allele interacts with other alleles. Several phenotypes coexist in a population where malaria is present, because each phenotype confers a different balance of fitness costs and benefits. The sickle-cell allele is maintained at a high frequency because it confers a fitness advantage in the heterozygous condition. This example also shows that natural selection can perpetuate genetic variation by maintaining polymorphisms.

14 Natural selection and speciation

Having looked at how natural selection influences the frequency of alleles in a population, we now consider how natural selection operating on *individuals* affects the species as a whole. Like individual organisms, species are entities that have a distinct identity; they also have a history. During evolution, as we saw in Block 4, an incalculable number of species have appeared on Earth, persisted for a while and then become extinct. We begin this section by looking at the role of natural selection in this process of extinction.

The fitness of an individual is a function of its interaction with the physical environment in which it lives, and also of its interaction with other species. We examine both these interactions and how they drive evolutionary change within a species. Finally, we look at another aspect of evolution: the emergence of new species. How does evolution lead to the divergence and separation of organisms into different species?

14.1 Extinction

It is the fate of most species to become extinct. At some stage in their existence, their mortality rate exceeds their reproductive rate and then, inevitably, they die out. As discussed in Block 4 (Section 5.1), estimating the total number of species living today is fraught with uncertainty; estimating the total number of species that has ever existed is even more problematic. It is clear, however, that the species surviving today represent only a minute proportion of all the species that have ever existed on the Earth. For example, there are currently about 9 000 species of birds, a group with a comparatively recent history and a reasonable fossil record, but estimates for the total number of bird species that have ever existed range from 1.5×10^5 to over 1.5×10^6. There has clearly been, over the course of the evolution of life on Earth, an enormous turnover among species, with new species continually replacing existing ones. This seems, at first sight, to pose a problem for the theory of natural selection. The history of life on Earth forces us to ask: if natural selection produces well-adapted organisms, why do the vast majority become extinct?

Humans have witnessed a great many extinctions during the course of recorded history (Figure 14.1). Of course, humans, through their destructive effects on the environment, are the direct or indirect cause of most, if not all, recent extinctions. The data in Figure 14.1a might suggest that 'the worst is over' and that the extinction rate for animals is now declining. This is a very misleading impression, however, for several reasons. First, these data show only those species that have actually become extinct and do not reflect the very much greater number whose populations are in decline. Second, they are based on a very incomplete picture of biodiversity. As discussed in Block 4, we have a good knowledge of only a small proportion of the world's species and therefore many extinctions have certainly occurred, and are now occurring, unnoticed. Third, the extinction rate may apparently be declining for some groups, but may be increasing for others.

○ Looking at the data in Figure 14.1b for the last 100 years, for which classes of vertebrates is extinction rate apparently declining and for which classes is it apparently increasing?

○ Extinction rate is declining in birds and mammals (and possibly reptiles), but is increasing for fishes and amphibians.

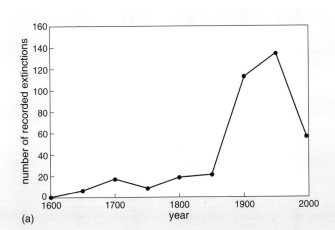

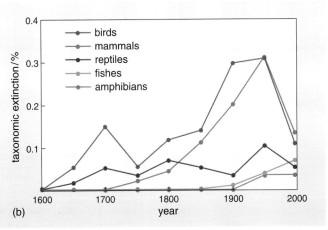

In recorded time, extinctions can often be attributed to specific causes. The great auk (*Alca impennis*, Figure 14.2), for example, was exterminated in about 1852 by a combination of hunting and egg collecting. The Stephens Island wren (*Xenicus lyalli*) lived only on one tiny island off New Zealand, and was totally exterminated in 1894 when a lighthouse keeper on the island acquired a cat. Examples such as these suggest that extinctions are just 'bad luck'. Certain species happened to be subjected to adverse conditions at particular times. However, most extinctions cannot be explained in this way. Rather, it seems that natural selection does not always have the capacity to prevent extinction occurring because the appropriate alleles are not present in a species' gene pool. Consider, for example, what might have been the fate of the peppered moth during the Industrial Revolution if the mutant allele for the dark *carbonaria* form had not arisen.

Figure 14.1 Graphs showing rates of recorded animal extinctions since 1600. (a) *Number* of extinctions among all animals. (b) *Percentage* of species becoming extinct in each class of vertebrates.

Figure 14.2 Great auks diving for fish. The great auk (*Alca impennis*), extinct since the mid-19th century, was an inhabitant of the North Atlantic Ocean. It possessed many adaptations for life in the sea that are similar to those seen in living penguins, which inhabit the southern oceans.

14.2 Interactions with the environment and other species

Short-term fluctuations and long-term changes in the environment mean that organisms have to adapt continually to new conditions. Even if the Earth were not subject to physical and climatic changes, the environment in which organisms live would not be constant. This is because species live and interact with each other. There is probably no species on Earth that suffers neither predation nor parasitism (Block 4, Section 7). Top predators of food chains may suffer only the problem of parasites, but individuals of most species are probably affected by both evils. Thus any evolutionary change in one species alters the environment for other species, which in turn have to adapt. Such interactions between an organism and its physical environment, and between one species and another, *drive* adaptation and maintain much of the genetic variation on which selection acts.

These continual evolutionary battles are commonly referred to as the **Red Queen effect**. In Lewis Carroll's *Through the Looking Glass*, the Red Queen was famous for telling Alice: 'Now here, you see, it takes all the running you can do, to keep in the same place'. In other words, it is necessary for organisms to constantly change just in order to survive. In this section we explore the Red Queen effect and look at how fluctuations in the physical environment and interactions between species drive evolutionary change.

14.2.1 Interaction with the environment

If the environment in which organisms live were stable, one could envisage that natural selection could produce organisms that were perfectly adapted and so did not become extinct. However, the physical environment is far from stable, and changes in two principal ways:

Short-term fluctuations We know from personal experience that the weather changes from year to year. We may get a warm, sunny summer one year, a lousy, wet one the next. Climatic fluctuations are the cause of numerous biological fluctuations; for example, changes can occur in the time of the year that plants flower, which will affect any organisms that are dependent on them for food, such as insects that feed on the nectar and herbivores that consume the fruits and seeds they bear.

Long-term trends The Earth's climate keeps changing in the long-term. Over geological time, the Earth has gone through a succession of glacial periods, separated by warmer interglacial periods. As discussed in Block 2, evidence suggests that the effects of human activities on the Earth's atmosphere are currently causing global warming, which may result in major changes in both the abundance and geographical distribution of numerous species.

Both short-term fluctuations and relatively long-term trends are shown in Figure 14.3, which you first met in Block 2.

If we view natural selection as a process that causes animals to approach perfect adaptation, it is as if the goalposts keep moving, so that perfect adaptation can never be achieved. This is where the Red Queen effect comes into play. The discussion of the evolution of clutch size in birds (Block 4, Section 9.3) illustrates this effect very well. In any given year, there is an optimal clutch size, determined by the food supply available during the nestling stage. Only some birds will lay a clutch of that size. In years of very unusual conditions, the optimal clutch size may be very different from

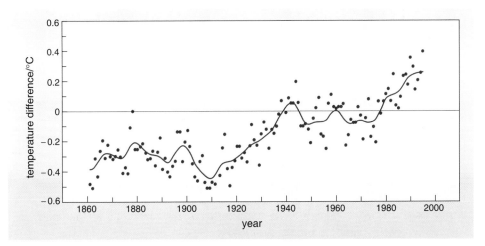

Figure 14.3 Variations in the global mean surface temperature of the Earth in recent years. Note that temperature fluctuates from year to year and that there is an underlying upward trend. (The 1961–1990 GMST is indicated by the horizontal line and represents 15 °C.)

the mean clutch size, so that only a few birds get even close to it. Natural selection will favour those individuals whose clutch size is closest to the optimum, so that alleles for clutch sizes near the optimum value will increase in frequency in the next generation. The next year, however, will typically bring different conditions; there will be a different optimal clutch size and different alleles will be favoured.

It is important to appreciate that, while natural selection favours an increase in the frequency of alleles that confer fitness advantages, at the same time it reduces the frequency, and may eliminate altogether, alleles that do not. In Block 4, attention was drawn to the very high mortality that occurs among many organisms. This mortality involves the loss of a huge amount of the genetic variation that exists in natural populations. Suppose that a population of great tits (*Parus major*) experiences, alternately, a succession of warm springs and a succession of cold springs. During the mild years, alleles for larger clutch size will increase in frequency and those for smaller clutches will decline. When cold springs return, selection favouring an increase in alleles for smaller clutches will only be effective if natural selection has failed to eliminate all the 'small-clutch' alleles in the population. If natural selection has eliminated them during warmer years, clutch size will remain high and the great tit population may go into sharp decline as a result. Reduced population size exacerbates this effect and makes extinction more likely, because there is obviously less genetic variation in a small population than there is in a large one.

The effect of small population size is illustrated by the recent history of the northern elephant seal (*Mirounga angustirostris*), a species that lives in the Pacific and breeds on the west coast of North America (Figure 14.4). At one time, elephant seals were ruthlessly hunted (for the oil they contained) and very nearly became extinct. Hunting has now been banned and their numbers are increasing rapidly. Genetic studies of elephant seals have revealed that they show very little genetic variation between individuals; in other words, the gene pool of the species is very small. Elephant seals are said to have gone through a **genetic bottleneck**. When their population was reduced to a very small size, it also reduced the amount of genetic variation in the population. Even though the population is now increasing again, the amount of genetic variation has not yet increased to previous levels. In Africa, the cheetah (*Acinonyx jubatus*) seems also to have gone through a genetic bottleneck and, in this instance, the resultant loss of genetic variation has had a harmful effect. Cheetahs are very susceptible to a leukaemia-like disease and it is thought that a reduction in their numbers has eliminated alleles that previously conferred some resistance to this disease.

○ In which other context have you come across a link between small population size and reduced genetic variation?

○ In the founder effect, where a small population that is formed from a large one contains less genetic variation than the larger population (Block 4, Section 10.3).

Thus, the Red Queen effect means that organisms can never be optimally adapted to their environment because it is constantly changing. As a result of natural selection, a species may keep up with environmental fluctuations for a time but, eventually, changes may be such that a population becomes greatly reduced in size. Small populations are especially subject to extinction, in part because of their reduced levels of genetic variation.

Question 14.1 Earlier (in Section 13.2.2) we compared the genetic consequences of sexual and asexual reproduction. Explain why, in a constantly changing environment, species that reproduce sexually are more likely to persist than asexual species. (Assume that the rate of mutation is similar in both types.) ◀

14.2.2 Interactions among species

Even if the Earth were not subject to physical and climatic changes, the environment in which organisms evolve would not be constant. Species do not live and evolve in isolation but interact with one another in many different ways, so that any evolutionary change in one species alters the environment for other species. Consider a predator and its prey, for example. The most important cause of mortality in African lions (*Panthera leo*) is starvation among their cubs; many prides of lions cannot catch enough prey to keep their cubs adequately fed. Consequently, natural selection will favour any adaptation in lions that makes them more effective hunters. Such adaptations would, however, impose selection on wildebeest (*Connochaetes taurinus*) and other species on which lions prey, favouring the evolution of better defences against predators. Thus any relationship between species in which one species exploits the other is inherently unstable and contributes to the overall environmental instability that creates the Red Queen effect.

Even more important than predator–prey relationships as a cause of environmental instability are *pathogens* (disease-causing organisms), which include parasites of all sizes, such as tapeworms, and microscopic pathogens, such as bacteria and viruses. Such is the specificity and intimacy of the relationship between pathogens and their hosts that it is clear that each has become adapted in many ways to the other — an example of what is called **coevolution**. Coevolution refers to specific, reciprocal adaptations between two, or a few, species that have evolved through prolonged, intricate interaction with one another. In the coevolution of a host and a pathogen, the pathogen has a huge advantage. Pathogens typically have a very short generation time and a very high reproductive rate; a bacterium in the human gut can generate several dozen generations in a single day. Although pathogens typically reproduce asexually, their genotypes are subject to mutation, so there is some genetic variation on which natural selection can act. Some viruses, such as HIV and the influenza virus, have very high mutation rates and so generate many, slightly different varieties. As a result, pathogens can evolve, becoming better adapted to the defences of their host, within the host's lifetime.

Any new mutation arising either in the host and causing it to be more resistant to a pathogen, or in the pathogen and causing it to be more damaging to its host, alters the relationship between them and leads to evolutionary changes in the partner. If the pathogen becomes more damaging, the host must evolve greater resistance or die out; if the host evolves a more effective immune response, the parasite evolves counter-measures. For this reason, pathogen–host relationships are evolutionarily unstable and are subject to change over time, favouring one partner or the other at different times.

Coevolution between host and pathogen, one or both of which has a harmful effect on the other, is often likened to the human arms race, because any adaptation by one side that increases its effectiveness tends to lead to counter-adaptations by the other side. This analogy is a poor one, however, because, in the natural world, coevolution commonly leads to adaptations by each organism that reduce, rather than increase its harmful effects on the other. This means that pathogen–host relationships tend to evolve towards a situation in which both organisms can coexist without the host being affected as severely as it once was. Is this due to evolutionary changes in the host, the pathogen or both? The history of the disease myxomatosis provides some answers to this question.

The *Myxoma* virus is indigenous to South America and rabbits there are prone to myxomatosis (a form of fibrous skin cancer) but do not usually die from the disease. The virus was unknown in other parts of the world until it was deliberately introduced into Australia in 1950 in an attempt to control the rabbit population, which threatened the livelihood of sheep farmers. Rabbits (*Oryctolagus cuniculus*) had themselves been introduced to Australia from Europe in the 19th century and had undergone a population explosion. Carried by mosquitoes, the *Myxoma* virus caused an epidemic that killed 99.8% of all rabbits; a second epidemic killed 90% of the generation that resulted from those that survived the first. A third epidemic, however, killed only 50% of the remaining rabbits. This rapid decline in the virulence of myxomatosis was due both to the rabbits evolving resistance to the virus and to the virus evolving reduced virulence. The rapid speed of evolution here is also striking.

● Why do you suppose that reduced virulence might be adaptive for the *Myxoma* virus?

○ A pathogen that does not kill its host has greater opportunity itself to survive, reproduce and infect new hosts than one that kills its host quickly. At the point when it had reduced the host population by 99.8%, the *Myxoma* virus must itself have been at some risk of becoming extinct.

● At the point when the rabbit population was reduced to 0.2% of its original size, what process do you suppose the gene pool of rabbits went through?

○ A genetic bottleneck.

The myxomatosis story illustrates the potentially devastating effect that pathogens can have on other organisms. It also illustrates natural selection at its most powerful. Evolutionary biologists have come to regard pathogens as one of the most potent forces in the course of evolution.

The above examples of interactions between species not only reveal how complex these can be, but also show that evolution can occur even in the absence of changes in the physical environment. Both types of interaction, between organism and environment and between species and species, drive change over time within individual species.

Question 14.2   Earlier (in Section 13.2.2) we compared the genetic consequences of sexual and asexual reproduction. Suggest reasons to support the hypothesis that sexual reproduction (of a potential host) is an adaptation against pathogenic parasites. ◀

Question 14.3   Which of the factors (a)–(f) below would tend to promote genetic diversity and which would lead to its reduction?

(a) Founder effect; (b) Red Queen effect; (c) a constant environment; (d) recombination; (e) a genetic bottleneck; (f) mutations. ◀

Activity 14.1   Galapagos: adaptation and evolution on islands (Parts 2 and 3)

In this CD-ROM activity, you will explore variation, natural selection and the evolution of new species in the Galapagos Islands. ◀

14.3 From variation to species

There is more to evolution than the changes that take place over time within a single species; evolution can also lead to the splitting of one species into two or more different species. (The definition of a species is discussed in Block 4, Section 4.1.) In this section, we examine this process of splitting that gives rise to new species.

In Section 14.2 and Activity 14.1, you have seen how species evolve in response to changes both in their physical environment and in their interaction with other species. These changes take place over time within a species. However, throughout the history of life, new species have continually emerged, while existing ones have continually become extinct. Even if there are as many as 30 million species living today (Block 4), this is only a small proportion of the thousands of millions that have probably existed over the whole of evolutionary time. In other words, the vast majority of all the species that have ever existed are now extinct (see Section 14.1)!

How do we explain the emergence of a new species? It can only happen by the splitting of one species into two or more different species, a process called **speciation**. Without speciation, the world would contain just one species of living organism, descended from the first form of life that ever existed. Some of the species living today have diverged from each other only recently, but others have followed separate evolutionary pathways for millions of years or more.

Many mechanisms have been proposed to account for how speciation might occur, but argument still rages among evolutionary biologists as to which mechanisms could and could not work, and which are likely to be the most common. In Activity 14.1, you have seen how speciation might have taken place in the Galapagos finches after the original population of birds became separated on different islands. In such allopatric (geographically separated) populations, interbreeding is reduced because of the distance between them. If interbreeding is reduced sufficiently, and for long enough, genetic recombination between the two populations will be at such a low level that each population will be able to evolve in a different direction without being swamped by alleles from the other population. When interbreeding between two groups of organisms is reduced sufficiently to allow them to diverge, they are said to be **reproductively isolated** (this does not mean that no interbreeding takes place at all, just that it is reduced to a very low level).

It is generally accepted that this kind of **allopatric** (literally 'other country') **speciation**, the divergence of two or more populations into separate species after they have become separated geographically, has occurred commonly. However, most suggested mechanisms for **sympatric** ('same country') **speciation**, the formation of two or more species without any geographical separation between the diverging populations, remain controversial. We will consider these two types of speciation in more detail.

14.3.1 Allopatric speciation

In the Galapagos Islands, the finches on different islands are separated by sea, but populations can be separated geographically by all kinds of barriers.

Geographical barriers need not be on a grand scale — a tiny stream can be just as great a barrier for a land snail as the English Channel is for a land mammal. Differences in habitat can also be important — a woodland species may be unable to cross a grassy field to reach the next wood, and a population of fish adapted to living by a rocky coastline may be separated from another population by a stretch of sandy sea-bed. During evolutionary history, new geographical barriers have arisen constantly, separating populations and creating conditions suitable for allopatric speciation to take place. Land masses have moved apart as a result of plate tectonic motion (Block 3); mountain ranges have been formed; large lakes have divided into a collection of smaller pools as water levels declined and have reformed millennia later as water levels rose again; rivers have changed their course; and lava flows from volcanic eruptions or ice flows during glacial periods (Block 2) have cut off one population from another.

Question 14.4 Make a list of possible geographical barriers that could separate populations. In addition to the ideas introduced in Activity 14.1 and this section, try to think of some of your own. ◄

14.3.2 Sympatric speciation

For sympatric speciation to occur, two groups of organisms within the same species must diverge from each other without there being any geographical barrier to separate them. Divergence can take place between two sympatric forms (the ancestral type and a novel type) without total geographical separation, as long as they are reproductively isolated.

● Recall the term used to describe two or more distinct forms of the same species that occur sympatrically (i.e. in the same geographical area).

○ Polymorphisms.

There are a number of ways in which sympatric forms can be reproductively isolated. The two forms may fail to interbreed because, for example, they occupy different habitats within the same area and so do not meet, or they show differences in sexual behaviour, or they become sexually active at different times of year.

The American haw-fly *(Rhagoletis pomonella)*, for example, has very specific host-plant preferences. Females lay their eggs only inside fallen fruit either from the hawthorn *(Crataegus* spp., i.e. several species within the genus *Crataegus)* or the apple tree *(Malus pumila)*. The larvae develop in the fruit and, when the adult insects emerge, they normally mate on the same food plant and usually lay their eggs on the same food plant. There are thus two sympatric forms of this fly: one that lives and breeds only on hawthorn and one that lives and breeds only on apple.

● What will be the likelihood of interbreeding between individuals of the hawthorn form and the apple form?

○ The two forms will very rarely interbreed because mating usually takes place on the food plant.

Haw-flies prefer the plant in which they hatched and their offspring are adapted to it. Analysis of proteins in the two sympatric forms has also shown that there are marked genetic differences between them. However, apple trees were introduced into the USA only in the late 18th century and, previous to that, only the hawthorn form of the fly existed. Thus, within the last 100 years or so, a single species of fly has split into two sympatric forms with very little interbreeding between them. Eventually the two forms may become completely separate species.

Insects frequently have very specific habitat preferences, e.g. parasites that have only a single host species, herbivores that feed on only one species of plant, and predators that have only one type of prey. Insects also often show a tendency to mate and lay their eggs in their preferred habitat. So it is not surprising that some biologists think that many insect species evolved by this kind of sympatric speciation. Others believe that **gene flow** (the spread of alleles from one population to another) will usually remain too high to allow speciation to occur in this way.

Probably the only mechanism of sympatric speciation that is widely accepted by biologists is **polyploidy**. This involves the multiplication of whole sets of chromosomes (each set being the haploid number, n). For example, a tetraploid has $4n$ chromosomes and a hexaploid has $6n$ chromosomes instead of the usual diploid number of $2n$. The chromosome numbers of related plant species are often multiples of some common basic number and some estimates suggest that as many as 80% of flowering plants may have originated as polyploids. Polyploids also occur in some groups of animals, such as earthworms.

Polyploidy usually happens as a result of *hybridization* (cross-fertilization) between two different species, followed by the accidental duplication during cell division of every chromosome present in one of the cells of the offspring. If this cell happens to be a gamete, or a cell involved in asexual reproduction, then a polyploid individual may arise in the next generation. Polyploids are new species: they have a different karyotype from that of either of the parent species and so are rarely able to interbreed with either parent successfully. Most strikingly, these new species can emerge extremely rapidly — sometimes in just one or two generations.

Polyploids often have a different phenotype from the parent species too. For example, they often have larger cells than diploids.

○ Why might polyploids have larger cells than diploids?

○ Because the nucleus has to contain at least twice as many chromosomes and is therefore larger.

Polyploid plants may also have thicker, fleshier leaves and larger flowers and fruits. These are very desirable features in plants cultivated for food, so it is not surprising that many of our common food plants are polyploids. Wheat provides a good example (Figure 14.5). The wheat grown for bread (*Triticum aestivum*) is a hexaploid species ($6n$). Notice how much larger it is than durum wheat (*T. durum*), grown for pasta, which is tetraploid ($4n$). In turn, both these species are larger than the diploid ($2n$) einkorn wheat (*T. monococcum*). The latter was the first wheat grown by humans and still grows wild in south-eastern Europe.

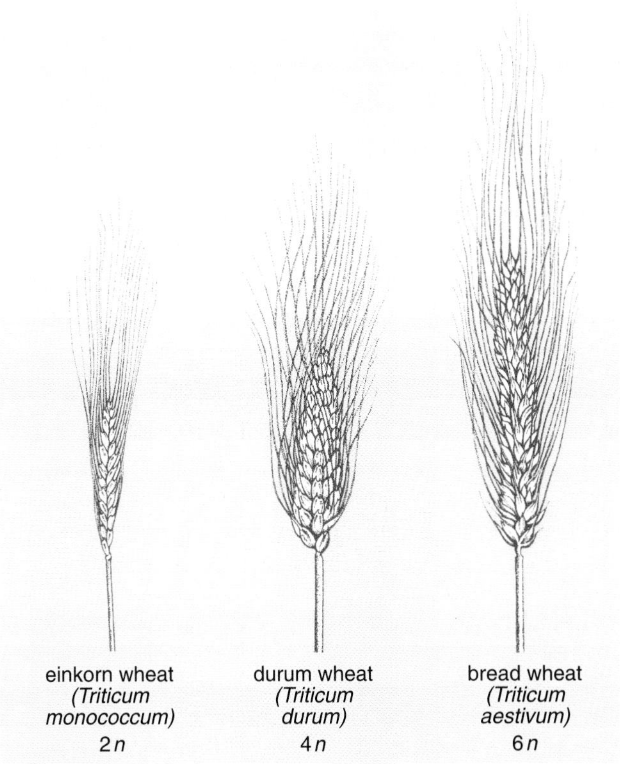

Figure 14.5 Polyploidy in three species of wheat (genus *Triticum*).

einkorn wheat
(Triticum
monococcum)
$2n$

durum wheat
(Triticum
durum)
$4n$

bread wheat
(Triticum
aestivum)
$6n$

Question 14.5 (a) Why has polyploidy been important in evolution? (b) Give one reason why polyploidy is important to humans. ◄

14.3.3 Genetic and phenotypic differences between species

Non-interbreeding populations, whether separated allopatrically or sympatrically, are affected by natural selection in different ways, experience different chance fluctuations in allele frequencies, and are unlikely to develop exactly the same mutations as each other. As a result, the longer two populations are reproductively separated, the more different they are likely to become, both genetically and phenotypically. Differences in allele frequencies between populations or between species can therefore be used to estimate the length of time they have been separated. Closely related species have not been separated as long as less closely related species and the number of genetic differences between them should be smaller. By analysing DNA from different populations or different species, and comparing allele frequencies, taxonomists can work out the *phylogeny*, or evolutionary history, of a group of organisms. This method has allowed taxonomists to work out the phylogenies of many groups of organisms that have traditionally been difficult to classify on morphological grounds alone.

However, there is not always a strict relationship between the amount of difference between genotypes and the amount of difference between the corresponding phenotypes. Some species may look almost identical but be very different genetically, while others may look very different yet be very similar genetically.

○ Think about frogs compared with mammals. Which group shows the greater variation in morphology?

○ Mammals.

There are thousands of species of frog living today but they all look very similar, even though their genomes may differ substantially. Mammals, on the other hand, show enormous variation in morphology — just think about bats, whales, horses and cats! Yet the genomes of two mammalian species, e.g. a bat and a whale, may show relatively few differences.

14.3.4 Speciation past and present

Speciation is not something that just happened in the past. It is going on all around us. We just don't notice it, because the process is generally very slow. There is often quite a lot of variation between populations within a single species, both in genotype and phenotype. A species in a particular geographical area may be polymorphic, like the peppered moth with its light and dark forms (Section 13.3.1). Where polymorphisms exist, the different sympatric forms may interbreed freely or be reproductively isolated to a greater or lesser extent. If a particular species has a wide range, it is also quite common for individuals in one part of the range to differ in one or more characteristics from those in another part of the range — they might be larger, for example, or have different coloration.

○ What familiar animal species varies in coloration in different parts of its range?

○ Humans (*Homo sapiens*) vary in eye colour, hair colour and skin colour in different parts of the world.

Depending on the degree of difference between them, distinct forms of a species in different geographical areas are designated as *races* (slight differences) or *subspecies* (greater differences). Subspecies are recognized by adding a third part to the Latin name for the species. In Activity 14.1, you have seen that many of the species of

Darwin's finch are divided into a number of subspecies, each found on a different island or island group within the Galapagos. Another example is the crow, *Corvus corone*, which is divided into two subspecies: the carrion crow, *C. corone corone*, and the hooded crow, *C. corone cornix*. The all-black carrion crow is found in western Europe, including southern Scotland and eastern Ireland. The hooded crow is grey with a black head, wings and tail, and is found in central and eastern Europe, northern Scotland and western Ireland. Figure 4.16 shows the area of overlap, where the two subspecies interbreed.

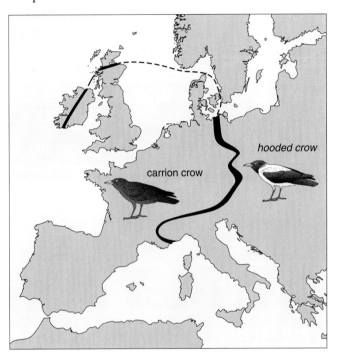

Figure 14.6 Map of part of Europe to show the range of the hooded crow and of the carrion crow. The solid black band denotes the area of overlap betwen the two subspecies.

The various degrees of difference between geographically separated populations or between sympatric forms can be thought of as a 'snapshot' of the speciation process. The process takes place over many generations as differences accumulate. As long as there is little or no interbreeding between diverging populations or between sympatric forms, they will continue to evolve in different directions and will eventually become so different that they are recognizable as completely separate species. The two populations or two forms may become reproductively incompatible at some stage because of a specific change in one of them, or the accumulated differences between them may cause a gradual increase in the degree of reproductive isolation. However, the evolution of reproductive incompatibility is not inevitable. Different species of frogs, for example, with very different genotypes (as determined by analysis of DNA base sequences or of amino acid sequences of proteins) often can and do hybridize easily.

At any one point in time, some geographically separated populations will be just starting to diverge from each other, some will have diverged further into different races, while others will have become subspecies so different that they are almost separate species. Sympatric forms will go through a similar process of gradual divergence, as long as interbreeding between them is sufficiently reduced. The populations or forms that have completed the process are the separate species we recognize today. The ones that haven't are seen as examples of within-species variation. This is why is it not always easy for biologists to decide whether a particular group of organisms should be classified as one species or as several.

This doesn't mean to say that speciation is inevitable. If gene flow between two races or subspecies, or between two sympatric forms, remains high enough, the speciation process will never be completed. Depending on the amount of gene flow and the different selection pressures operating on the two types, either the two types will merge and the species will become uniform throughout its range, or a 'balance' will be maintained with each type occupying a different area or a different habitat but hybridizing relatively freely with the other.

Question 14.6   Which of factors (a)–(g) would tend to hinder speciation and which would tend to promote it?

(a) Large numbers of individuals migrating between two diverging populations.

(b) A genetic bottleneck in which a geographically separate population is reduced to a very small size.

(c) The intense selection operating on a population in a newly colonized, novel environment.

(d) Hybridization between two diverging populations.

(e) The presence of a polymorphism in a population, such that there are two types of female and two types of male; one type of female prefers to mate with one type of male while the other type of female prefers to mate with the other type of male.

(f) Reduced fertility of hybrids between two populations.

(g) A greater than average number of offspring produced by hybrids between two populations. ◀

14.4 Summary of Section 14

Short-term environmental fluctuations and long-term environmental changes mean that organisms have to adapt constantly to new conditions. In addition, species interact in different ways, so that any evolutionary change in one species alters the environment for other species. The most intimate forms of interaction exist between pathogens and their hosts, and it is clear that each has become adapted in many ways to the other in coevolution. Interactions with both the physical environment and other species drive evolutionary change and maintain genetic diversity.

Species with greater amounts of genetic variation are more likely to persist over a long period, because they can adapt to changes both in the physical environment and in their interactions with other species. Natural selection cannot always prevent extinctions occurring, because the alleles necessary for adaptation to new conditions may not be present in the gene pool.

Speciation occurs as the result of a reduction in gene flow between two populations, which can be brought about by various means. For example, the populations become separated by a geographical barrier, as in allopatric speciation; or they occupy different habitats within the same area or show differences in sexual behaviour, as in sympatric speciation. This is followed by adaptation to local conditions, resulting in the two populations diverging even further. Finally, the two populations become so different that they can be defined as separate species.

Darwin's finches evolved from the birds that originally colonized the Galapagos Islands, mainly by a process of allopatric speciation.

Polyploidy, which involves the multiplication of whole sets of chromosomes, is a common mechanism of speciation in plants and is the only means of sympatric speciation that is widely accepted by biologists.

The longer two species have been separated from each other, the greater the number of genetic differences between them tends to be.

Speciation is a continuous process and polymorphisms, races and subspecies can be seen as representing different stages of that process. Speciation is not inevitable and the process can go into reverse.

15 Levels of explanation reviewed

The story of sickle-cell disease (Section 13.2.2) contains much biological information. Most obviously it is a disease that dramatically affects the health and viability of the people who have it. We can examine the disease at a number of different levels of explanation, and in so doing revise some of the important points of this block. The first three of these levels are illustrated in Figure 15.1.

First, a look at the molecular level (level 1 in Figure 15.1) reveals how a change in the DNA — a single base change — can affect the polypeptide product. Of the 150 amino acids known to make up a haemoglobin chain, a substitution of glutamate by valine at just one point in the chain is all that is needed to produce the defective haemoglobin. This emphasizes the close relationship between structure and function of the protein; the precise structure of haemoglobin is essential for its normal functioning.

An examination of the disease at the cellular level (level 2 in Figure 15.1) shows that the changed protein structure in turn affects the cellular phenotype, causing the red blood cells that contain the haemoglobin to adopt a sickle shape and be more fragile. This illustrates that structure and function at the cellular level, and hence cellular phenotype, depend on proteins with a precise structure.

This altered cellular phenotype of damaged red blood cells in turn affects the phenotype of the whole organism (level 3 in Figure 15.1). An individual suffering from the disease may show a number of symptoms. The haemoglobin from the ruptured red blood cells leaks into the blood fluid and is no longer able to transport oxygen. This leads to a rapid rate of destruction of red blood cells and eventually to anaemia. The misshapen red cells cannot squeeze in single file through the narrow blood vessels (capillaries) that supply oxygen to tissues, thereby blocking blood flow and causing local failures in blood supply, which results in a great deal of pain. In any one affected individual, different tissues in the body can be deprived of oxygen in this way. So, at the whole-organism level, sickle-cell disease is a genetic disease that affects a number of characters (Section 9.3). This emphasizes that the phenotype of the individual depends ultimately on the molecular composition and the chemical processes that take place inside him or her.

Finally, at the population level, sickle-cell disease illustrates natural selection in action. Natural selection results from differences in survival and fertility among individuals in a population when these differences have a genetic basis.

⬤ Summarize the differences in survival and fertility between the genotypes $Hb^S Hb^S$, $Hb^A Hb^S$ and $Hb^A Hb^A$, for a population living in regions of Africa where there is a high incidence of malaria.

◯ Homozygotes with sickle-cell disease ($Hb^S Hb^S$) have severe anaemia and survival is low. Heterozygotes ($Hb^A Hb^S$) have a greater chance of surviving to reproduce than normal homozygotes ($Hb^A Hb^A$), because the presence of haemoglobin S offers some protection from malaria.

Sickle-cell disease also clearly illustrates the relationship of fitness to environment. In the 18th century, 150 million black Africans were transported to the Americas as slaves, taking the disease with them. Hence, this group of people were geographically separated from those left behind in Africa. The frequency of the Hb^S allele has

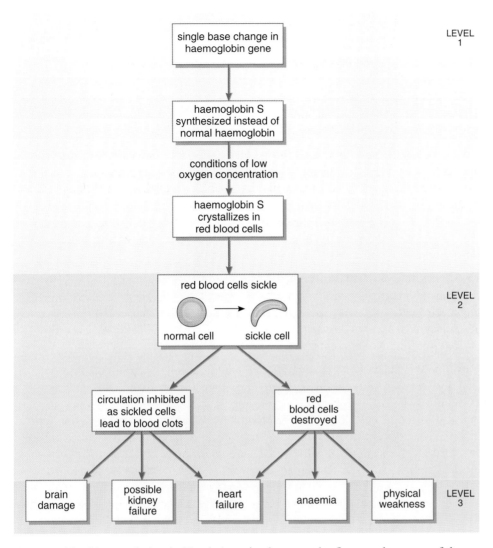

Figure 15.1   Some of the effects of the mutation that causes sickle-cell disease. Levels 1, 2 and 3 are explained in the text.

decreased in this population in North America because the fitness advantage of the heterozygote over both homozygotes is lost where malaria is absent.

A description of this disease at different levels of explanation — the molecular, cellular, whole organism and population levels — reveals the interrelationships between these levels. Sickle-cell disease amply illustrates how these four levels provide a different perspective on the same biological phenomenon and, furthermore, shows that knowledge of each individual level of explanation enhances our understanding of all the other levels.

Sickle-cell disease is a story about one gene. Organisms have thousands of genes, many of which are polymorphic. It is this genetic diversity upon which evolution can work and which leads to change over time. Evidence for more dramatic change over time is provided by the fossil record, and it is to an examination of the changes in life on Earth through time that we turn in Block 10.

Activity 15.1   (a) Reviewing your study of Block 9: learning to be a good judge; (b) reflecting on revision

In this activity you will explore further the criteria used to judge the quality of a piece of writing in science, and consider methods that you have used to revise. ◀

Questions: answers and comments

Comments on the answers are given in curly brackets {...}.

Question 2.1 (a) See Table 2.2.

Table 2.2 Completed version of Table 2.1, Comparison of three basic cell types.

Cell feature	Cell type		
	animal	plant	prokaryote
cell membrane	✔	✔	✔
cell wall	✗	✔	✔
chloroplasts	✗	✔	✗
cytoplasm	✔	✔	✔*
cytosol	✔	✔	✔
mitochondria	✔	✔	✗
nucleus	✔	✔	✗
nuclear membrane	✔	✔	✗
organelles	✔	✔	✗
ribosomes	✔	✔	✔
rough endoplasmic reticulum	✔	✔	✗
large vacuole	✗	✔	✗

* In the case of prokaryotes, the cytoplasm is everything contained within the cell membrane, i.e. cytosol and subcellular structures, including the DNA.

(b) From Table 2.2 you will see that all the cell features listed are found in plant cells, whereas some are absent from either animal or prokaryote cells. Consequently, plant cells are the most varied in terms of the range of cell features present.

Question 2.2 The following eukaryote cell features are composed of, or are bounded by, membranes:

1   The *cell* itself has a cell membrane.

2   The *nucleus* has a nuclear membrane.

3   *Mitochondria* are bounded by a membrane, and have an internal membrane too.

4   *Chloroplasts* are bounded by a membrane, and have internal membranes too.

5   *Vacuoles* are bounded by a membrane.

6   *Rough endoplasmic reticulum* is composed of membranes.

Question 2.3 (a) This is a eukaryote cell, because it contains a nucleus and other membrane-bound organelles.

(b) Structures labelled A are mitochondria; they resemble the mitochondria shown in Figure 2.2. There is an outer membrane, and an internal convoluted membrane too.

(c) Since this is a eukaryote cell, the organism is not a bacterium. There is no evidence of chloroplasts, so it is unlikely to be a plant. Cell wall material is labelled in the figure, which precludes the organism from being an animal since animal cells lack cell walls. It is probably not a protoctist, for the same reason (although a few protoctists *do* have cell walls). By a process of elimination, therefore, the organism shown in Figure 2.10 is a fungus. {It is actually a unicellular yeast (*Saccharomyces cerevisiae*), which is producing a new progeny cell by the process of budding. Figure 2.10, which is an electron micrograph, shows more detail than does the drawing from a light micrograph of *S. cerevisiae* (Figure 2.7a).}

Question 3.1 The answer is shown in Figure 3.19.

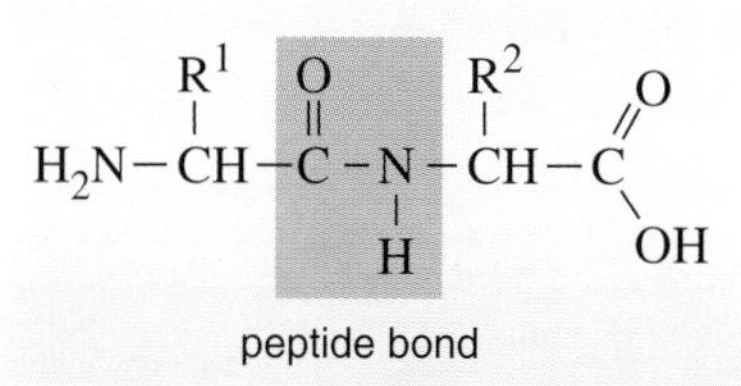

Figure 3.19 The result of the condensation reaction between two amino acids; a molecule of water is eliminated and a peptide bond is formed.

Remember that in a condensation reaction, a molecule of water is removed in the formation of a covalent bond between two molecules (an OH group is lost from one molecule and an H atom from the other).

Question 3.2 Collagen is a protein that forms a triple helix in which three long polymer chains are intertwined (see Figure 3.3a). It functions as an extracellular support material. {Keratin is made up of *pairs* of intertwined helices; myosin, which is also mentioned in Section 3, has a more complex structure than collagen and keratin.}

Question 3.3 (a) Protein X is most likely to be a receptor protein.

(b) A change in the amino acid sequence, that is the primary structure, of protein X may change its higher-order structure. If this change occurs in or near the adrenalin binding site, the binding of this hormone will be impaired. So the cells of these individuals will respond to adrenalin less readily than those with normal protein X.

Question 3.4 (a) True. Proteins are polymers of amino acids so they all yield amino acids on hydrolysis.

(b) False. A given protein does not necessarily contain all 20 amino acids.

(c) False. When 100 amino acids condense, the protein thus formed has 100 monomers joined by 99 peptide bonds.

Question 3.5 (a) True. A trisaccharide consists of three monosaccharide monomers joined by two glycosidic linkages and a water molecule is released when each of these linkages is formed.

(b) False. *Cellulose* is the principal polysaccharide of plant cell walls and consists of *glucose* monomers joined by glycosidic linkages. Collagen is a structural *protein* in *animals* and is made up of *amino acid* monomers.

(c) True. Sucrose is a disaccharide made up of one molecule of glucose and one of fructose.

(d) False. Starch is the main energy-storage polysaccharide of *plants*. In animals *glycogen* serves as the polysaccharide energy store.

Question 3.6 Proteins, polysaccharides and nucleic acids all have the following properties:

1 They are large molecules.
2 They consist of chains of monomers.
3 Their constituent monomers are covalently linked.
4 Weak bonds are important for their higher-order structure.

Question 3.7 (a) L-1 is a phospholipid since it contains a phosphate group, and L-2 is a TAG since it contains three fatty acid groups.

(b) L-1 would be located in all the cell membranes, and L-2 would be located inside a vacuole in the cytosol.

(c) L-1 forms membranes which define the cellular boundary and the boundary of organelles (see Section 2), separating the different cellular functions and acting as barriers, whereas L-2 acts as an energy store.

(d) Both L-1 and L-2 have long hydrocarbon fatty acid chains which avoid water. This property causes TAGs to aggregate into globules inside the cells in which they are stored and causes phospholipids to form a bilayer with the hydrophobic fatty acid groups on the inside and the hydrophilic phosphorus-containing groups in contact with the water on the outside.

Question 3.8 (a) Myoglobin is a protein that stores oxygen, and the monomers from which proteins are synthesized are amino acids; alanine (i) and lysine (v) are both amino acids.

(b) TAGs are made from glycerol (iii) and fatty acids; the latter are present in the cell predominantly as ions, such as palmitate (vi).

(c) Glycogen is a polysaccharide made from monomers of the monosaccharide glucose (i). (Fructose (iv) is also a monosaccharide but is not the monomer unit of glycogen.)

Question 3.9 (a) Fibrous *proteins* (e.g. collagen) and fibrous *polysaccharides* (e.g. cellulose) both provide support.

(b) *Polysaccharides*, such as starch and glycogen, and *TAGs* serve as energy stores.

(c) Globular *proteins* called enzymes have catalytic activity.

(d) *Nucleic acids* carry genetic information.

(e) Membranes separate the cell into compartments (both surrounding and within organelles, such as those making up the mitochondria), and *phospholipids* and *proteins* are the main molecular components of cellular membranes.

Question 4.1 (a) True. The ending '-ase' in amylase tell you that it is an enzyme, and all enzymes are proteins.

(b) True. The basic metabolism of all living things is the same. The metabolic reactions involved can only occur at the rate they do because of enzymes, so life depends on the activities of enzymes.

(c) False. Receptor proteins and antibodies (described in Section 3.3.1) are not enzymes.

(d) True. Specificity is a crucial feature of enzymes.

Question 4.2 (a) NAD is reduced to NAD.2H. The two hydrogen atoms are transferred from BH_2 to NAD.

(b) The enzyme involved has an active site tailored to bind both BH_2 and NAD. Presumably it is able to bind JH_2 less well than BH_2 because the 'lock and key' fit is less precise, i.e. the enzyme is very specific for the substrate BH_2.

Question 4.3   The oxygen concentration would fall and the carbon dioxide concentration would rise due to the respiration taking place in the bacterial cells.

Question 4.4   There would be little or no change. ATP levels will remain roughly constant, but there will be a greater rate of both ATP synthesis and ATP breakdown, i.e. ATP turnover, as the $ATP \rightleftharpoons ADP + P_i$ system is coupled to the energy-requiring activity of working muscles and the energy-releasing process of glucose oxidation in muscle cells.

Question 4.5   (a) False. The conversion of $ADP + P_i$ to ATP is coupled to energy-*releasing* reactions.

(b) True. ATP is a carrier of chemical energy in that it transfers energy between energy-releasing and energy-requiring reactions.

(c) False. ATP is used in many processes other than biosynthesis, such as muscle contraction and the transport of ions and molecules across membranes.

(d) True. ATP is a short-lived energy store, typically being converted to ADP within a minute.

Question 5.1   The fate of the glucose molecule is summarized in the following sequence of steps.

(1) The glucose is converted to starch — the form in which it is stored in the plant; (2) the plant is eaten by an animal; (3) the starch is digested to glucose in the animal's gut; (4) the glucose is transported from gut to cells throughout the body; (5) it enters the cell with the help of glucose transport proteins present in the cell membrane (see Section 3.6.3).

Question 5.2   All four statements apply to glycolysis. Only statement (d) applies to both. None of the statements apply only to the link reaction.

Question 5.3   (a) False. Carbon dioxide is not produced in glycolysis; each molecule of glucose (6C) is converted to two molecules of pyruvate (3C), so no carbon atoms are lost.

(b) False. The 4C TCA cycle intermediate (oxaloacetate) combines with acetyl groups from acetyl CoA (2C) to give a 6C compound (citrate).

(c) False. With each turn of the TCA cycle, citrate (6C) is converted back to oxaloacetate (4C) and the two carbon atoms shed in this process appear as *two* molecules of carbon dioxide.

(d) True. All the carbon dioxide produced in glucose oxidation (and also in the respiration of other energy sources) is produced in the link reaction (pyruvate $\rightarrow$

acetyl $+ CO_2$) and the TCA cycle (acetyl $\rightarrow 2CO_2$). Both of these stages occur within the mitochondrial matrix.

Question 5.4   (a) (iii): NAD.2H is converted to NAD in the electron transport chain.

(b) (i) and (ii): this is glycolysis, in which a 6C molecule is split into two 3C molecules and NAD is converted to NAD.2H.

(c) (i) and (ii): this is the link reaction, in which a 3C molecule (pyruvate) is split into a 2C fragment (acetyl) and a 1C molecule (carbon dioxide), with the transfer of of two hydrogen atoms to NAD.

(d) (i) and (ii): this is the overall reaction of the TCA cycle, in which a 6C intermediate is split to a 5C compound ($+ CO_2$) and a 5C intermediate is split to a 4C compound ($+ CO_2$) and quantities of NAD.2H are made.

Question 5.5   (a) In Stage 4, NAD.2H molecules, produced by reduction of NAD, are oxidized back to NAD, and (b) ADP is phosphorylated to form ATP.

Question 5.6   (a) Protons are pumped from the matrix, through the inner mitochondrial membrane and accumulate in the intermembrane space. Thus the proton concentration here is higher than that in the matrix, i.e. a proton concentration gradient is established.

(b) 2,4-DNP damages the inner mitochondrial membrane, thereby uncoupling electron transport from oxidative phosphorylation; NAD.2H is converted to NAD as electron transport proceeds, but there is no net change in the distribution of protons because protons would leak back into the matrix, and so no ATP is produced in the process.

(c) In the presence of carbon monoxide, the final carrier, cytochrome oxidase, cannot pass electrons on to oxygen because the binding site for oxygen is blocked. Hence electron transport cannot occur, so there is no energy made available for pumping protons and so no proton gradient is produced.

Question 5.7   (a) True. This is shown in Figure 4.9.

(b) False. The first step in amino acid catabolism is removal of the amino (NH_2) group.

(c) True. This is explained in Box 5.2.

(d) True. This is shown in Figure 5.10.

Question 6.1   Photosynthesis is essential for life because: (1) it converts solar energy into chemical energy of sugars, which can be used to fuel all the energy-requiring processes of life; and (2) it releases oxygen, which is required for respiration.

Question 6.2 The dark reactions (i.e. the reactions in which carbon dioxide is reduced to sugar) are driven by the products of the light reactions, namely ATP (as a source of energy) and NADP.2H (for the reducing power).

Question 6.3 M, consisting of the chloroplast membranes, contains the chlorophyll (a) and all the components that carry out the light reactions which produce oxygen from water (c).

S, consisting of the solution between the chloroplast membranes, contains the enzymes required for the dark reactions which convert carbon dioxide to sugars (b).

Question 6.4 The processes of oxidative phosphorylation and photophosphorylation are compared below.

Similarities

1 ATP is synthesized from ADP + P$_i$.
2 The energy required is harnessed from the flow of electrons along an electron transport chain.
3 Electron transport drives proton pumping, so creating a proton concentration gradient.
4 The discharge of the proton gradient through a proton channel protein, which is also an ATP synthase, directly fuels ATP synthesis.

Differences

1 Oxidative phosphorylation takes place in mitochondria; photophosphorylation occurs in chloroplasts.
2 The energy source for oxidative phosphorylation is glucose (and other fuel molecules); photophosphorylation is fuelled by solar energy.
3 For the process of oxidative phosphorylation to occur, NAD.2H must be oxidized to NAD; while photophosphorylation is occurring, NADP is being reduced to NADP.2H.
4 During oxidative phosphorylation, oxygen is consumed and water is produced; during photophosphorylation, water is split and oxygen is released.

Question 8.1 The missing terms are: (a) homologous; (b) karyotype; (c) meiosis; (d) fertilization.

Question 8.2 (a) The karyotype is the number, size and shape of all the chromosomes and is characteristic of a species. Members of a species have the same karyotype, although there may be slight differences between males and females because of the sex chromosomes.

(b) The term genotype can mean either the full complement of genes or the copies of a gene for a particular character, present in an individual. The former will vary between individuals of the same species (unless they are identical twins or clones), while the latter may or may not vary.

(c) Likewise, for the phenotype — meaning either the sum total of all characters, or a particular character, of an individual. The former will vary between individuals of the same species, while the latter may or may not vary.

Question 8.3 The matches between the terms and the descriptions are as follows: (a) (iii); (b) (ii); (c) (iv); (d) (vi); (e) (i); (f) (v); (g) (vii).

Question 8.4 The results of Experiment 1 differ from those we have described for maize because in this experiment the character that *vanishes* in the first offspring generation is the one that reappears in about three-quarters of the individuals in the second generation. This is the other way round from the results in the maize breeding experiments, where it was the character that *persisted* in the F$_1$ generation that appeared in about three-quarters of the F$_2$ generation.

The results of Experiment 2 differ from the maize results because the colour of the first generation of offspring is intermediate between those of the parents. In the corresponding maize cross, one parental character persisted and the other vanished. {This outcome is possible in some situations; it is described as incomplete dominance, an example of which is given in Section 13.3.2.}

The results of Experiment 3 contrast with those for maize in that the outcome was different depending upon which plant provided the ovules and which the pollen. With maize, the outcome of the breeding experiment was the same, irrespective of which parental phenotypes provided the ovules and which provided the pollen.

Question 8.5 There are four possible outcomes: $G\,G$; two $g\,G$; and $g\,g$. Since three of the four possible fertilizations contain at least one g allele, the probability that the offspring will contain at least one g allele is $\frac{3}{4}$.

Question 8.6 The completed Figure 8.11 is shown in Figure 8.14. The ratio of the genotypes of the offspring will be $1\,G\,g : 1\,g\,g$, and the phenotypic ratio will be 1 purple : 1 white.

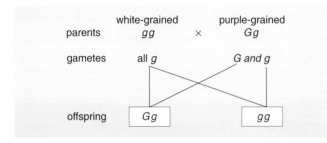

Figure 8.14 Completed Figure 8.11, showing a cross between a pure-breeding white-grained maize and a heterozygous purple-grained variety.

Question 8.7 The mating diagram for this cross is shown in Figure 8.15.

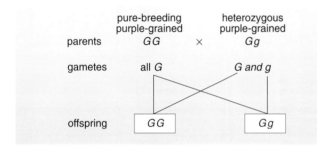

Figure 8.15 Mating diagram for Question 8.7.

The genotypic ratio of the offspring is $1\,G\,G : 1\,G\,g$; the phenotype of all the offspring is purple-grained, since they all carry at least one, dominant, G allele.

Question 8.8 Brown-eyed parents must be pure-breeding in all cases, since their genotype must be homozygous recessive.

(a) The red-eyed parents must have been pure-breeding; had they not been pure-breeding, then two different phenotypes would have been observed in the offspring. The situation is analogous to the maize example shown in Figure 8.7.

(b) This experiment cannot have involved pure-breeding red-eyed parents. If the red-eyed parents had been pure-breeding, all of the offspring would have been red-eyed.

(c) The crosses between the brown-eyed flies produce brown-eyed offspring, and this is the result you would expect to find if the parental lines are homozygous recessive.

Question 8.9 (a) The F_2 phenotypic ratio for seed colour is 3.01 : 1 (*yellow* : green) and that for pod colour is 2.82 : 1 (*green* : yellow).

(b) The deviations from a 3 : 1 ratio are due to chance. However, we do *expect* larger variations with smaller samples. This is what we observe in Mendel's results. In the experiment in which Mendel counted a large number of seeds, he obtained a ratio very close to 3 : 1. In the experiment in which he counted a much smaller sample of pods, he obtained a ratio that showed a greater deviation from a 3 : 1 ratio. {You may also have observed that in the phenotype for seed colour, yellow is dominant to green, but in the phenotype for pod colour, green is dominant to yellow! So one should not make assumptions about which phenotype is dominant and which is recessive.}

Question 8.10 In the first plant, the genes are on different pairs of homologous chromosomes — E and e on one pair and T and t on another pair, as shown in Figure 8.16a. This means that at gamete formation the genes assort independently from each other to give the four different gamete genotypes in equal proportions.

In the second plant, the genes must be linked on the same chromosome, as shown in Figure 8.16b. This means that at gamete formation E and Q, and e and q, will stay together more often than they separate. Only when the linkage is broken by crossing over will the gametes of genotypes $E\,q$ and $e\,Q$ be produced. As this is a relatively rare event, most of the gametes will be $E\,Q$ and $e\,q$, with only a small proportion of $E\,q$ and $e\,Q$; hence the $8\,E\,Q : 8\,e\,q : 1\,E\,q : 1\,e\,Q$ ratio.

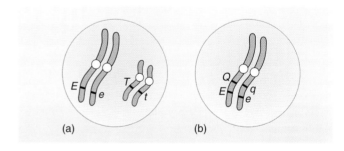

Figure 8.16 (a) The arrangement of genes and alleles $E\,e$ and $T\,t$ on the chromosomes of the first plant. (b) The arrangement of genes and alleles $E\,e$ and $Q\,q$ on the chromosomes of the second plant.

Question 8.11 Genes that are in the same linkage group are on the same chromosome, so you would expect to find (a) five chromosomes in each gamete and (b) ten chromosomes in each fertilized ovum.

Question 9.1   Figure 9.8 is the completed diagram.

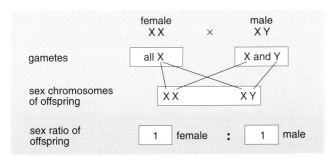

Figure 9.8   Completed version of the mating diagram given in Figure 9.2.

Question 9.2   The X chromosomes carry the genes responsible for sex-linked characters. A son inherits the Y chromosome from his father and an X chromosome from his mother. The X chromosome of the father will be transmitted only to daughters and not to sons.

Question 9.3   (a) (ii). Both plants are presumably heterozygous and one-quarter of the offspring inherited two recessive wrinkled-grain alleles, one from each parent. This is a similar situation to the second cross of the maize experiment (Figures 8.8 and 8.9) which gave a phenotypic ratio in the offspring of three with the dominant phenotype : one with the recessive phenotype (or three-quarters : one-quarter).

(b) (iii). The variation in cob lengths appears to be continuous, which suggests that several genes are involved in this phenotype, and probably environmental factors, such as soil nutrition, as well.

(c) (i). Since purple grain colour is dominant and neither parent has this phenotype, a new mutation in a gamete of one of the parents must be involved.

(d) (v). Only two alternative phenotypes (green and virtually white) are described, suggesting that leaf colour shows discontinuous variation; however, many genes affect the development of the green pigment, chlorophyll (Section 6), and if *any* one mutates, chlorophyll will not be produced.

Question 10.1   (a) 100 bases would form 50 complementary base pairs.

(b) The number of nucleotides is the same as the number of bases, i.e. 100.

(c) Again, the number of deoxyribose molecules is equal to the number of bases, i.e. 100.

(d) Since C always pairs with G, the number of guanine (G) bases is the same as the number of cytosine (C) bases, i.e. 30.

(e) and (f) Sixty of the 100 bases are either C or G, so the remaining 40 are either thymine (T) or adenine (A). As A always pairs with T, then half this number, i.e. 20, are T and 20 are A.

(g) Each C–G pair forms *three* hydrogen bonds, giving a total of $3 \times 30 = 90$ for the 30 C–G pairs present; each A–T pair forms two hydrogen bonds giving a total of $2 \times 20 = 40$ for the 20 A–T pairs; therefore the total number of hydrogen bonds in the DNA fragment is $90 + 40 = 130$.

Question 10.2   (a) Figure 10.11 is the completed version of Figure 10.10. Note that sequences must be the same in the two daughter strands, so these can be deduced from the limited information provided in Figure 10.10. Here is one example. One member of the base pair at the bottom right is C. Since C always pairs with G, the missing base must be G. Because the two daughter strands are identical, the missing base pair at the bottom left must also be C–G.

(b) Since the DNA shown in Figure 10.10 is replicating, the cell must be at interphase. This is the stage between two nuclear divisions during which the DNA, and hence the chromosome, becomes replicated, and two double helices, and hence the two chromatids, are produced.

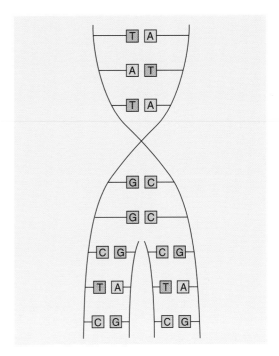

Figure 10.11   Completed Figure 10.10, showing base-pairing in part of a double-stranded DNA molecule during replication.

Question 11.1   The three important differences between the structures of DNA and RNA are listed below.

(a) DNA contains the sugar deoxyribose; RNA contains ribose instead.

(b) DNA contains the base thymine (T); RNA contains uracil (U) instead.

(c) DNA is double-stranded, i.e. it consists of two polynucleotide chains wound around one another to form a double helix; RNA is mostly single-stranded.

Question 11.2   (a) Descriptions (i) and (x) apply to both DNA and RNA. With reference to (i), RNA is a single polynucleotide chain and DNA is made up of two polynucleotide chains.

(b) Descriptions (iii), (v), (vi) and (ix) apply to DNA but not to RNA.

(c) Descriptions (ii), (iv) and (viii) apply to RNA but not to DNA.

(d) Only description (vii) applies to neither DNA nor RNA.

Question 11.3   The completed sentences are as follows (missing words shown in italics).

(a) The enzyme *RNA polymerase* copies a stretch of DNA into RNA in a process known as *transcription*.

(b) Only the *template* strand of DNA is 'read' in the process of RNA synthesis; the other DNA strand is known as the *non-template* strand.

(c) There are three different types of RNA molecules: *rRNA*, *mRNA* and *tRNA*.

(d) The transfer of information from the mRNA base sequence to the amino acid sequence of a polypeptide is known as *translation*.

(e) The mRNA sequence has a triplet code, and each triplet is known as a *codon*.

(f) Reading of the RNA base sequence begins at a *start codon* and finishes at a *stop codon*.

(g) *tRNA* binds both an amino acid and mRNA; it attaches to the latter via its three-base *anticodon*.

(h) A ribosome has three RNA binding sites: one for *mRNA* and two for tRNA.

(i) A ribosome moves along an mRNA chain, and there are several ribosomes attached to a particular mRNA at any one time; such a string of ribosomes along an mRNA chain is termed a *polysome*.

Question 12.1   (a) The DNA of the cystic fibrosis gene contains 250 000 base pairs, so the template strand has 250 000 bases. Transcription of this would, therefore, produce a primary RNA product with 250 000 bases.

(b) Of these 250 000 bases, only 6 500 remain in the mature mRNA. Therefore, the number of non-protein-coding bases is 250 000 − 6 500 = 243 500. Thus the percentage of the primary RNA product that consists of non-protein-coding sequences is:

$$\frac{243\,500}{250\,000} \times 100\% = 97\% \text{ (to two sig figs)}$$

So 97% of the primary RNA product consists of non-protein-coding sequences (introns) which are removed during RNA splicing to produce mRNA.

(c) 243 500 base pairs in the cystic fibrosis gene are non-protein-coding (i.e. form introns). The gene contains 26 introns. Therefore

$$\text{mean size of an intron} = \frac{243\,500}{26} = 9\,400 \text{ base pairs}$$

(to two sig figs)

Question 12.2   (a) mRNA Y is larger than mRNA X, because it is made up of 11 exons rather than 10, and would therefore code for more amino acids and hence give a longer polypeptide after translation.

(b) (i) mRNA X has exons 1–5 and 11–15; therefore, for this mRNA exons 6–10 *in addition to the introns* are non-protein-coding and would be removed in splicing. (ii) mRNA Y has exons 1–10 and 15; therefore, for this mRNA exons 11–14 and the introns are non-protein-coding and would be removed in splicing.

{Notice that an exon is not always an exon, that is, not always protein-coding! Consider region 6 as an example. In the processing of RNA, this is removed to produce mRNA X, so here it is non-protein-coding. However, this sequence is not removed in the production of mRNA Y; here it is a protein-coding sequence. Consequently, a sequence of RNA (and the corresponding DNA) can sometimes be non-protein-coding and in another situation can be a coding sequence.}

Question 12.3   You should have included the following three points in your answer.

1   Both prokaryotes and eukaryotes have genes that code for tRNA and rRNA (which are not translated into polypeptides).

2   The one gene — one polypeptide hypothesis is basically true for prokaryote cells (other than for tRNA and rRNA). Each gene sequence is colinear with the polypeptide sequence for which it codes. The gene sequence is transcribed into an mRNA molecule, which is subsequently translated into a polypeptide. In contrast, many eukaryote genes include introns, which are non-protein-coding sequences. Introns are transcribed into the primary RNA product along with the exons. The introns are, however, removed during RNA splicing. The mature mRNA product, which is translated into protein, is smaller than the primary RNA product. In eukaryote genes, therefore, there are large sequences of DNA within genes that do not code for protein.

3   In eukaryotes different combinations of exons within a gene may be transcribed to produce different polypeptides from the same gene.

Question 13.1   Each person has two alleles at the ABO blood group locus. Since there are 6×10^7 humans, the answer is therefore $2 \times (6 \times 10^7) = 1.2 \times 10^8$.

Question 13.2   (a) False. No evidence was presented in the text that the rate of mutation changed; if there had been some increase, it is unlikely to have been high enough to explain the dramatic increase in the *carbonaria* form from almost zero to 95% in urban areas.

(b) False. There is no evidence to suggest that moths died because of the direct effect of sulphur dioxide pollution.

(c) True. Recall that fitness is defined as the relative ability of an organism to survive and leave offspring that themselves survive and leave offspring. We know that the frequency of *carbonaria* moths increased in industrial areas of Britain from almost zero to 95% during this time.

(d) False. It is highly unlikely that the changes were due simply to chance. Since the environment was changing and since colour form is adaptive, differential reproduction of genotypes would have occurred within the population — and this, by definition, is natural selection!

(e) True. Between 1970 and 1980 the number of the typical form was increasing and the number of the *carbonaria* form was decreasing; hence the gene pool must have changed.

Question 13.3   There are two main lines of evidence. One is the similarity of the distribution in the world of the Hb^S allele that causes sickle-cell disease and of malaria. The other is the observation that the protoctist responsible for malaria (*Plasmodium falciparum*) is not able to survive and reproduce as well in sickle-shaped cells as it does it normal red blood cells. Thus $Hb^A\,Hb^S$ individuals have a greater resistance to malaria than do $Hb^A\,Hb^A$ individuals.

Question 13.4   In the case of sickle-cell disease, both alleles remain in the population in regions of the world where malaria is common, because of heterozygous advantage, i.e. the heterozygote is fitter than either homozygote, leading to a balanced polymorphism. In the case of *Biston betularia*, both alleles for colour form were maintained because natural selection acts differently on the two phenotypes in different parts of the species' range, i.e. where the environmental factors — presence or absence of sulphur dioxide pollution — were different.

Question 14.1   Sexual reproduction generates much more genetic variation than asexual reproduction. In a constantly changing environment, species that reproduce sexually are more likely to persist than asexual species, because the former have a higher level of genetic variation upon which natural selection can act. {The distribution of asexual species among animals provides some support for this theory. Asexual species occur in all animal groups, with the exception of birds and mammals, but are not nearly as abundant as sexual species. A strong possibility is that asexual species have arisen repeatedly in most groups during evolution, but that they do not persist for as long as sexual species, because of their limited capacity to adapt to changing environmental conditions. This argument is supported by the observation that many asexual species, among reptiles for example, have smaller geographical ranges than sexual species. Asexual species typically lack the genetic variation that enables sexual species to adapt to local conditions and thus have a wide range.}

Question 14.2   Because pathogens have a short generation time and produce lots of progeny, they are able to undergo rapid evolution. This gives the pathogen the opportunity to become better adapted to the host. If the host reproduces asexually, it produces offspring genetically identical to itself and for which there is, therefore, a population of pathogens that are already adapted to infect it. However, no such population of ideal hosts is formed if the host produces genetically variable young by sexual reproduction. {Sexual reproduction ensures that at least some progeny are produced that are genetically different, and thus likely to be less susceptible to attack by those pathogenic parasites that have evolved during the lifetime of their parents (Box 13.1). The advantage of sexual reproduction — a higher level of genetic variation (see also answer to Question 14.1) — means that sexually reproducing organisms are likely to persist for longer than those that reproduce asexually; however, this is only an incidental consequence.}

Question 14.3   Factors (b), (d) and (f) would tend to promote genetic diversity. The Red Queen effect (b) means that organisms have to change just in order to survive because their physical environment and/or their interaction with other species are constantly changing, and this in turn promotes genetic diversity. Recombination during meiosis (d) is a process in which the genes and alleles in the genome of an individual are shuffled, and this, together with the combining of gametes at fertilization, generates an enormous number of combinations of genes and alleles. Mutations (f) are the ultimate source of all variation.

Factors (a), (c) and (e) would lead to a reduction in genetic diversity. In the founder effect (a), a small population that is formed from a larger one contains less genetic variation than the larger one. A constant environment (c) would lead to all members of a species becoming adapted to it by selection of similar phenotypes with correspondingly similar genotypes. A genetic bottleneck (e) occurs when a population is reduced to a very few individuals, in which case the amount of genetic variation in the population may be much reduced, even if population numbers build up again later.

Question 14.4   You may have thought of some of the following examples of geographical barriers: populations on different islands or continents separated by sea; fish in different lakes or rivers separated by land; populations on areas of land separated by rivers or streams; populations living on a rocky coastline separated by areas of sandy shore; populations living on a sandy coastline separated by areas of rocky shore; lowland populations separated by mountains; alpine populations separated by valleys; rural populations separated by bands of urban development; woodland populations separated by open fields; areas of vegetation on a volcanic island separated by new lava flows; areas of vegetation separated by areas covered in ice.

Question 14.5   (a) Polyploidy has played an important role in evolution because it is probably the most common mechanism by which speciation in flowering plants has occurred.

(b) It is important to humans because many of our food plants are polyploids.

Question 14.6   Factors (a), (d) and (g) will tend to hinder speciation. Speciation is prevented when there is sufficient gene flow between two populations; (a) migration and (d) hybridization both transfer alleles from one population to another. (g) A greater than average number of offspring produced by hybrids between two populations, assuming the offspring survive and are themselves fertile, will also lead to a greater proportion of individuals carrying a mixture of alleles from both populations, i.e. to greater gene flow.

Factors (b), (c), (e) and (f) will tend to promote speciation. Speciation is promoted when gene flow between two populations is reduced. A genetic bottleneck (b) will greatly reduce the genetic variability of the population, with some alleles disappearing completely, and make the population more different from other populations of that species, than it was before. In a novel environment, intense selection (c) can cause the colonizing population to evolve adaptations to the new environment very quickly, and become different from other populations of that species in the process. If there are two types of female in a population, each of which prefers to mate with a different type of male (e), then this will tend to lead to two subgroups within the population, with mating mostly taking place within each subgroup, so that gene flow between them is reduced. Reduced fertility of hybrids between two populations (f) will mean that hybrids will tend to have lower reproductive success than other members of each population so that individuals carrying a mixture of alleles from the two populations will become less common, i.e. gene flow is reduced.

Acknowledgements

Grateful acknowledgement is made to the following sources for permission to reproduce material in this block:

Figures

Figures 2.1a, 2.1b, 2.9b, 2.9c: Mike Stewart; *Figures 2.2a, 2.3a, 2.5b*: Heather Davies; *Figure 2.4*: Courtesy of I. D. J. Burdett; *Figure 2.9a*: Andrew Syred/Science Photo Library; *Figure 2.9d*: Alberts, B. *et al.* 1989, *Molecular Biology of the Cell*, 2nd edition, Garland Publishing Inc.; *Figure 2.10*: Courtesy of L. Booth and H. S. Vishniac; *Figure 2.11*: Steve Long/University of Massachusetts Photo Service; *Figure 5.6*: Godfrey Argent/Argent Studio; *Figure 6.1*: Shelagh Reardon, Wye College, University of London; *Figures 8.1, 8.2*: Institute of Cancer Studies, University of Birmingham; *Figure 8.10*: Science Photo Library; *Figure 8.12*: From *Flies and Disease*, Vol. 1, 1971, by Bernard Greenberg, published by Princeton University Press, 1971. F. Gregor, artist; *Figure 9.1*: Biophotos Associates; *Figure 9.4*: Marc Henrie — Photographer of Animals; *Figure 9.6a*: Courtesy of Chris and Cathy Gannon; *Figure 12.7*: Reprinted with permission from *Nature* (Jeffreys, A. J., Brookfield, F. Y. and Semeonoff, R. 1985, 'Positive identification of an immigration test-case using human DNA fingerprints', *Nature*, **317**(31), 31 October 1985, pp. 818–819) Copyright 1997 Macmillan Magazines Limited. Image courtesy of Professor Sir Alec J. Jeffreys, Department of Genetics, University of Leicester; *Figure 13.1*: Harris, M. 1997, *Culture, People, Nature. An Introduction to General Anthropology*, 7th edition, Addison Wesley Longman, New York; *Figure 13.2*: Courtesy of Oxford Scientific Films; *Figure 13.4*: Dr Gopal Murti/Science Photo Library; *Figure 14.1*: Reprinted with permission from *Trends in Ecology and Evolution*, **8**(10), Smith, F. D. M., May, R. M., Pellew, R., Johnson, T. H. and Walter, K. R. 1993, 'How much do we know about the current extinction rate?', p. 376, Copyright © 1993, Elsevier Science Ltd, Oxford, England; *Figure 14.2*: Halliday, T. 1978, *Vanishing Birds*, Sidgwick and Jackson, London; *Figure 14.3*: Parker, D. E. *et al.* 1996, 'Global and regional climate in 1995', *Weather*, **51**(6), Royal Meteorological Society; *Figure 14.4*: Slater, P. J. B. and Halliday, T. R. 1994, *Behaviour and Evolution*, illustrations by Priscilla Barrett, Cambridge University Press; *Figure 14.5*: Patterson, C. 1978, *Evolution*, Routledge, by permission of Natural History Museum, London.

Photos on title page

Top left: Heather Angel; *Bottom right*: John Mason/ARDEA London.

Index

Entries and page numbers in **bold type** refer to key words which are printed in **bold** in the text and which are defined in the Glossary. These are terms that we expect you to be able to explain the meaning of, and use correctly, both during and at the end of the course. An entry followed by ^G indicates a term which is defined in the Glossary but which is not bold in the text. Where the page number is given in *italics*, the indexed information is carried mainly or wholly in an illustration or table. Section summaries and answers to questions are not indexed.